Russell O. Ly day

1932

Selections from
The Papers and Speeches

of

JOHN CHALMERS DaCOSTA, M. D., LL. D.

Samuel D. Gross Professor of Surgery at the Jefferson
Medical College, Philadelphia

Philadelphia and London

W. B. SAUNDERS COMPANY

1931

Copyright, 1931, by
W. B. Saunders Company

THE DEDICATION

This Book is Dedicated by

Dr. JOHN CHALMERS DaCOSTA

TO

Dr. HARVEY CUSHING

THE DISTINGUISHED PROFESSOR OF SURGERY IN HARVARD UNIVERSITY. THE DEDI-
CATION IS FROM ONE OF HIS WARMEST ADMIRERS. HE HAS AIDED ENORMOUSLY
IN THE DEVELOPMENT OF MOST BRANCHES OF SURGERY. HE WAS ONE
OF THE VERY FEW FOUNDERS OF THE SURGERY OF THE BRAIN AND
SPINAL CORD. HE HAS DISCOVERED PRINCIPLES AS WELL AS
FACTS, AND IS ALSO A TEACHER, AUTHOR, BIOGRAPHER,
OPERATOR, AND PHILOSOPHER. HE IS ONE OF THE
GREATEST SURGEONS LIVING. HE HONORS
ME GREATLY BY ALLOWING ME TO
MAKE HIM THE RECIPIENT OF
THIS DEDICATION

" 'The time has come,' the Walrus said,
   'To talk of many things:
  Of shoes—and ships—and sealing wax—
  Of cabbages and kings—
  And why the sea is boiling hot—
  And whether pigs have wings.' "
           —Through the Looking Glass,
               by LEWIS CARROLL.

"When 'Omer smote 'is bloomin' lyre,
  He'd 'eard men sing by land an' sea;
  An' what he thought 'e might require,
  'E went and took—the same as me!"
           —RUDYARD KIPLING.

Some of my papers have not been used in this book. For the explanation look below and see what Mr. Venus said was the reason he could not use the bones of Wegg's leg ("hospital amputation") in making up a skeleton.

"I can't work you into a miscellaneous one, nohow. Do what I will, you can't be got to fit."

CONTENTS

MEDICAL PARIS DURING THE REIGN OF
LOUIS PHILIPPE*

To Paris, in the time of Louis Philippe, came students from all parts of the world. At this period the city contained between 8000 and 9000 students, and nearly 5000 of them were students of medicine. Medical students flocked to Paris from all corners of the earth, and that city was the medical center without a real rival. One who would study obstetrics, toxicology, orthopedic surgery, microscopy, diseases of the skin, venereal diseases, medical diagnosis, pathologic anatomy, human or comparative anatomy, ophthalmology, nervous diseases and insanity, plastic surgery, the higher chemistry, or experimental physiology went there, if able, as a matter of course.

Not only was Paris the medical center. There, also, were the great art schools, the conservatories of music, the theological college, and schools of every branch of science and philosophy. The army of students that went to Paris every year constituted a potent element in the fame and prosperity of the city. But Paris was much more than a great finishing school. In it fashions were inaugurated; the tone was set for social customs; literature flourished; the drama and the opera were sedulously cultivated by great artists; and vices were discovered, cloaked, adorned, and made palatable.

France was then, in truth, the laboratory of civilization in which experiments were made in art, literature, science, govern-

---

*In these rambling remarks I have used various letters, biographies, notices, and books. I am particularly indebted to the "Memoir of J. Mason Warren, M. D.," by Howard Payson Arnold, and to the "Hospitals and Surgeons of Paris," by F. Campbell Stewart, M. D. As a source of names and of some descriptions that entertaining production "An Englishman in Paris" has been found useful. Reprinted from the University of Pennsylvania Medical Bulletin, March, 1904.

ment, and vice; and Paris was a crucible in this laboratory, gleaming with incandescence. There, a few years before, the giant cataclysm of the French Revolution had engulfed the city in sanguinary horror; there the curtain had been rung down on the mighty Napoleonic drama. Thousands were still living that had worn red caps during the terror, or had marched with victorious legions into most of the capitals of Europe. In the alleys and byways of the city herded the bloody, dreadful mob, which still deified the memories of Marat and of Danton; shouted the praises of liberty and equality, and longed for the good old times of the guillotine and the maximum, of the 45,000,000,000 assignats and the worship of reason, of the Committee of General Security and the Committee of Public Safety—the days of the implacable Robespierre, the dreadful golden-haired St. Just, the crippled maniac Couthon, the blood-thirsty Collot, the fanatical Billaud, and the murderous hypocrite (the so-called Anacreon of the Guillotine) Barèr. Still standing were many relics to remind the mob of the days of license. There were prison houses whose walls were spattered with the blood of the victims of the September massacre, and there was the Queen's cell in the Conciergerie, as yet unscorched by fire and unaltered by vandal hands.

The city then was vastly different from what it is now. There were not the well-paved and brilliantly lighted streets (pavements were first laid in 1823), the broad avenues, the enchanting parks and drives, and the "long white colonnades." In construction, Paris was still the city of the Revolution. The heights above it at Montmartre and other places were covered with windmills; cows were tethered in the Bois; most of the streets were dark, crooked, narrow, and ill-paved, and many of them were without sidewalks. The Convent of the Cordeliers, in which the great voice of Danton had thundered, had become the medical school; the Carrousel was surrounded on three sides by squalid tenements; the Parc Monceau, in which Robespierre used to walk with his pet dog, was a private garden belonging to the Orleans family. The column in the Place de la Bastille was then being erected, and this column commemorated not the fall of that fa-

mous prison, but the Revolution of July, 1830. The Obelisk of
Luxor was being put up in the Place de la Concorde, and the
Arc de l'Etoile had just been completed. It was in this reign
that the body of Napoleon was brought from St. Helena and laid
to rest beneath the golden dome of the Invalides, "in the heart
of that people" he had "loved so well." Many historic buildings, since destroyed, were then standing. Among them may be
mentioned the following: the palace of the Tuileries, which was
built of variegated marble. In this building Louis XVI played
the last moves in his poor game of royalty; the Tuileries was
burnt by the Communists in 1870; the prison of the Abbaye,
where Charlotte Corday was incarcerated, and where one of the
most fearful massacres of the Revolution took place; and the
prison of La Force, where the Princesse de Lamballe was imprisoned, tried, and murdered.

The Latin Quarter was still the real Latin Quarter so graphically depicted in *Life in Bohemia*. It had not yet been in-
vaded by the tourist, and was not even touched by the kid-
gloved hand of respectability. Its inhabitants were almost
slighted by the law. It was populated by persons that, in the
words of an observer of that period, had fled to this region to
escape the contaminating touch of civilization. It was the home
of unconventionalism, of idle good-fellowship, of light-hearted
gaiety, of laughter and of song, of wild debauchery, and of pic-
turesque poverty; and in this student's world the grisette presided
as the mistress of the house, and the songs of Beranger constituted the staple music. The Latin Quarter of this time is spoken
of by a former distinguished Professor of Surgery in the University of Pennsylvania, Doctor Gibson,* who says it is a quarter
"where the streets are so narrow and filthy and without pavements or sidewalks as to endanger life at every corner; where the
houses are so high, old-fashioned, and gloomy as to resemble jails
or penitentiaries, and nearly shut out the light of Heaven; where
the Catacombs, those vast depositories of human bones, the accumulated collection of ages, lie beneath the feet, extend unknown

* See the "Memoir of J. Mason Warren," by Howard Payson Arnold.

distances, and seem to respond by hollow groans to the tread of
the foot-passenger and rumble beneath the jar of cumbrous
vehicles and the tramp of clumsy animals that are incessantly
threading the narrow defiles above their desolate, but populous
domains; where innumerable smells of concentrated vigor and
activity and varied odor assail the olfactories from every quarter;
where loud and discordant cries of wandering tribes of vagabonds,
vending their peculiar animal and vegetable productions, fall upon
the sensitive and startled tympanum of the stranger, like strokes
of the sledge-hammer or harsh gratings of the saw-pit; where the
barking of dogs, the screams of parrots, and the chattering of
monkeys are mixed with the gabble of old women and men;
where the bowing and nodding, and scraping and salutations, and
recognitions of street-passengers bobbing against and shoulder-
ing each other, followed by the incessant and everlasting apology . . . afford the most amusing and melancholy mixture of
pleasurable and disagreeable sensations that can possibly be
conceived."

In the *Memoir of J. Mason Warren*, by Howard Payson
Arnold, the Latin Quarter is most entertainingly sketched. Warren
was a student, and he found a constant delight in the bizarre
manners and whimsical customs of the Parisians: "In their petty
domestic economies, narrowed by the practice of ages to the
finest point that human nature could endure and live; in their
supreme vanity and self-satisfaction; in their speaking gestures
that meant everything, and their dramatic language that meant
nothing; in their politeness, unequalled except by their wit and
their selfishness; in their worship of 'l'honneur' and 'la gloire';
in their outer cleanliness and their inner lack thereof; in
their food, transmuted into every form of succulent enticement,
under every alluring name; in their marvellous taste and efful-
gence of the toilet, as revealed by the apparel of either sex."
Arnold continues to say that in this region "life was more or less
a thin tissue of fancy. Birth was a jest; marriage, a convenience;
and death, the last scene in the melodrama, where everything was
done for present effect, and, when done, faded away into the

limbo of vanity and delusion." Doctor Warren found that the students of this period were, as a rule, seditious, coarse, licentious, extravagant, and not overclean; that they were free from the slightest check of public opinion, and could without criticism indulge to the limit in every pleasing vice. Almost to a man they were Radicals, vastly interested in politics as a rule, idle to a degree that made the working student the exception. Doctor Warren, who was a New England Puritan, felt strange and out of place in this society, and viewed his associates with considerable suspicion. For instance, he took the trouble to note down in his journal that on the 29th of December, 1833, one of the worthy students of the School of Medicine stole his umbrella. At a later date, in 1837, his father, Dr. John C. Warren, while visiting Paris, made a record that indicates that the same tendencies were still present. He says that Roux warned him under no circumstances to leave his cloak in any room or ward.

Those interested in the Latin Quarter of Paris about the time referred to should read of the students in Victor Hugo's *Les Miserables;* and should also view the town in Eugène Sue's *Wandering Jew.* At this time a multitude of interesting characters dwelt in Paris. There was Madame Lenormand, the fortune-teller, who had prophesied to Joséphine Beauharnais that she would become Empress, had frequently been consulted by Napoleon, and had been the mistress of the infamous Hébert. Strolling on the boulevards one might see Théophile Gautier, arrayed in his famous scarlet waistcoat and driving his team of ponies. Eugène Sue, that celebrated son of a good doctor, standing, thoughtful, preoccupied and scornful, on the steps of the Jockey Club; George Sand, entering the studio of Eugène Delacroix; Beranger, idling in the sunlight; Guizot or Thiers, going to the Chamber of Deputies; Claude Bernard, hastening to do some work for Magendie in the College of France; Alfred de Musset, musing, bashful, arrayed in faultless attire, glancing at the pretty faces about him; Chopin, dragging gloomily along; Chateaubriand, with bowed head, brooding over an eloquent sentence in defence of religion and despotism; Lamartine, who was to publish in 1847 his delightfully interesting and altogether false *History of the Girondins*, and who had not even dreamed of the great political part that he was so soon to play; Victor Hugo, destined to become what Swinburne calls him, "the greatest exile and, hence, the greatest man of France"; Alfonsine Plessis, soon to be immortalized by the younger Dumas as *La Dame aux Camèlias;* Von Flotow, humming the music of *Martha;* Meyerbeer, anxiously watching the billboards for the announcement of *Robert le Diable;* Auber, taking some recreation and sunlight in the intervals of the composition of *Fra Diavolo;* Saint-Georges, the author of the libretto of the *Bohemian Girl;* Felicien David, who introduced the dreamy East to musicians; Palmerston, the great English statesman, arguing a point with Metternich, the Austrian; Talleyrand, telling a wicked and witty anecdote to old Marshal Soult; Lola Montez, the adventuress, striking and captivating, who was soon to pull down kings and kingdoms into ruin; Paul Delaroche, the artist, who painted the most famous picture of Napoleon, and was later to paint, what never took place, the Last Supper of the Girondins. If one had time to spare, one might go to the Comédie Française and see Regnier or Rachel; to the opera and see Taglioni dance and hear Malibran or Mario sing, or to Bobino and revel in vaudeville. If hungry, one could drop into the Café de Paris, the best restaurant in Europe, where coal and gas were not allowed, where lamps gave the necessary light, and where the cooking was done exclusively over a peculiar and expensive kind of charcoal. In this restaurant one might often meet the great Balzac and hear the titanic laugh of Dumas, the mighty Alexander.*

This was the day of the salon, artistic, literary, fashionable or political; of mad gambling; of fierce duels, which frequently ended in death; and of the contest between Classicism and Romanticism. Classicism had come in with the French Revolution. The idea of most of the leaders in this movement was to create a government founded upon the heroic virtues of Greece and Rome. Their favorite heroes were Greeks and Romans. The speeches in the

* An Englishman in Paris.

Convention literally teemed with classical illusions. Persons dropped their own Christian names and took the names of Roman generals and statesmen, or of Greek philosophers. Like appellations were given to various Sections. The speeches most admired were those of Robespierre, filled with wearying classical similes. It is interesting to note that among the members of the Convention there were practically but three that rarely indulged in this habit. The first was one that we now know to have been incomparably the greatest orator of the period, the celebrated Mirabeau; the second was one of the best educated of them all, the keen, unscrupulous, subtle, and sagacious Talleyrand; and the third was in many respects the most forceful figure of the Revolution, the lion-hearted Danton.

When the Revolutionary Government had been overthrown there was a reaction against this exaggerated worship of antiquity; and, just at the period of which I am now speaking, we find that in the circles of art and literature (especially in the drama) Classicism was fighting a losing battle with the hosts of Romanticism, which were headed, with splendid genius and energy, by Victor Hugo and Alfred de Musset. It was truly a wonderful, a captivating, an entrancing city.

During the reign of Louis Philippe Paris contained the best organized hospitals in the world.* There were 20,000 patients lodged in hospitals and almshouses, and utilized for the instruction of students; and many thousands visited the dispensaries. The hospitals were supported by fixed taxes levied upon the theatres and other places of amusement. The public hospitals numbered thirty-six, and patients went to them freely, for there was no stigma attached to being a hospital patient. All students had access to these hospitals and dispensaries.

The hospitals were governed by the General Medical Council, which was itself appointed by the State. A visiting surgeon was required to be 30 years of age; a visiting physician 35. These officials were paid small salaries (from six hundred to eighteen

---

* The statements which follow are largely from Doctor Stewart's work, which was previously referred to.

hundred francs a year). In 1840 $3,400,000 was expended to maintain the hospitals. The students were obliged to be educated men, and no one could take the medical degree without having already obtained the degree of Bachelor of Arts or of Sciences. The professors received no fees directly from the students, in contrast with the practice in vogue in this country at the same period.

These rules and the patronage of the Government elevated medical science to a high plane of dignity. The medical course lasted four years; and the Government supplied the teachers with costly charts, diagrams, and apparatus. Specialties were assiduously cultivated. The positions of intern and extern were open to competitive examinations; and, although the Government required much of a man that wished to become a physician, after he had once obtained his degree he was protected from the competition of quacks and charlatans.

The great strength of the Paris School consisted in practical anatomy and surgery, for there was a plentiful supply of subjects for dissection and for the teaching of operative surgery. In England, at the same period, dissection was looked upon with absolute horror. The condition of affairs in that country is well exhibited by Lord Macaulay's famous speech on the Anatomy Bill of 1832. This was a bill to legalize dissection and to provide subjects by legitimate methods. Macaulay objected to the statement of the opposition that the law was designed to benefit the rich at the expense of the poor. "What," he said, "are the evils against which we are attempting to make provision? Two, essentially; that is to say, the practice of Burking and bad surgery. Now, to both of these the poor alone are exposed. What man in our rank of life runs the smallest risk of being Burked? That a man has property, that he has connections, that he is likely to be missed and sought for are things which secure him against Burking. It is curious to observe the difference between murders of this kind and other murders. An ordinary murderer hides the body and disposes of the property; Bishop and Williams dig holes to bury the property and expose the body for sale. The more wretched, the more lonely any human being may be, the more desirable prey is he to these wretches. It is the man, the mere naked man, that they pursue." The great historian and orator then discusses the question of bad surgery, and pictures a condition in which dissection could be entirely prevented, in which the English school of anatomy would be destroyed and every student forced to go to the expense of securing a foreign education. He asks on whom would the bad consequences fall. "On the rich? Not at all. So long as there is in France, in Italy, in Germany a single surgeon of eminent skill—a single surgeon who is, to use the phrase of the member from Preston, 'addicted to dissection'—that surgeon will be in attendance whenever an English nobleman is about to undergo a critical operation. The higher orders in England will always be able to procure the best medical assistance. Who suffers by the bad state of the Russian School of Surgery? The Emperor Nicholas? By no means; but the poor dispersed over the country. If the education of a surgeon should become very expensive, if the fees of surgeons should rise, if the supply of regular surgeons should diminish, the sufferers would be not the rich, but the poor in our country villages, who would again be left to mountebanks and barbers and old women, to charms and quack medicines." Macaulay then goes on to recount an historical anecdote, in order to show from what fearful sufferings improved surgical science has rescued the species. He tells how the leg of Leopold, Duke of Austria, was crushed; how the surgeons said it should be amputated, but were unable to do it; and how Leopold laid a hatchet on his thigh and commanded his servant to strike it a blow with a great mallet. The leg was thus removed, but the duke perished of the gush of blood. Macaulay closes by saying: "Why there is not now a bricklayer who falls from a ladder in England who cannot obtain surgical assistance infinitely superior to that which the sovereign of Austria could command in the twelfth century. I think this a bill which tends to the good of the people, and which tends especially to the good of the poor. Therefore I support it. If it is unpopular, I am sorry for it; but I shall cheerfully take my share of its unpopularity; for such, I am convinced, ought to be the conduct of one whose object it is not to flatter the people, but to serve them."

In Paris, at this time, an intern was still a student of medicine; he was obliged to be at least 18 years of age, and to have served at least one year as extern. He served four years as an intern, and received four hundred francs a year, with board and lodging. He was permitted to add to his salary by taking private classes through the wards and by quizzing students in the evening. An extern received no pay. He was allowed to serve four years, and was obliged to go to the hospital twice a day in order to bleed and blister patients and dress wounds. The nurses were usually Sisters of Charity. A walking patient that wished to be admitted to a hospital applied to a Central Bureau, and was sent to a suitable hospital, in which there was a vacant bed. The medical men of the Central Bureau took turns in examining applicants for admission. The surgeons of this bureau were Nélaton, Denonvilliers, Maisonneuve, Chassaignac, Marjolin, and Cullerier. There was a Central Pharmacy, where the medicines for all the hospitals were compounded; a Central Bakery, which used 7,700,000 pounds of flour a year, and cost $300,000 a year to maintain; and a large wine vault, which served out 1,500,000 quarts of wine a year.

The death rate in the hospitals was extremely large, varying from one in fifteen in some of the small hospitals to one in eight in the Hôtel Dieu. The Hôtel Dieu was the largest of the hospitals, and had 1000 beds. It stands on the south of the Pavis Notre Dame. Among its surgeons were Roux, Blandin, Breschet, and Dupuytren. Among the physicians to this institution may be named Rostan, Magendie, Chomel, and Récamier. It was founded in the ninth century. La Charité had 500 beds. Velpeau was one of the surgeons; and among the physicians were Andral and Cruveilhier. This institution is in the rue Jacob, back of the Beaux Arts. It was founded by Marie de Medicis in 1602. La Pitié had 600 beds, and Lisfranc and Berard were on its staff. It is behind the Jardin des Plantes, and was founded by Louis XIII.

Directly opposite the School of Medicine was the Hôpital des Cliniques, which accommodated 150 patients. The professors of the school of medicine were the surgeons and physicians of this institution. Here numbers of obstetric cases were received. About 800 women were delivered each year, and the students of the medical school were permitted to witness the deliveries. When a woman was taken in labor during the night, a single lantern was hung up in the porter's lodge, and the first two students to arrive upon the scene were permitted to assist in the delivery. In this institution the students were obliged to undergo their final examination for a degree, and this examination was practical. The chief surgeon was Cloquet, and the chief accoucheur was Dubois.

The Hôpital Beaujon had 500 beds. Marjolin was the surgeon and Louis the physician. The Hôpital Necker accommodated the same number. Civiale was its surgeon and Trousseau its physician. The St. Louis Hospital received all forms of skin disease, but took care of other cases as well. The surgeons were Jobert and Boyer, the physicians were Alibert, Lugol, and Cazenave. The male venereal hospital was Du Midi, which contained 450 beds and had a dispensary service of 3000 cases. Whereas the nursing in the other hospitals was done by the Sisters, there were, of course, no sisters here. In comparison with others, therefore, this institution was ill-kept, dirty, and unsanitary. Its surgeons were Ricord and Vidal-de-Cassis. On examining the yearly statistics of this institution the remarkable fact is noted that the admissions of shoemakers far exceeded those of persons of any other occupation.

The Lourcine contained 200 beds. It was the venereal hospital for the reception of public women, and was in charge of the Sisters of Compassion. Students were not admitted to this institution, only graduates being allowed to see the service. The surgeon was Huguier. Afflicted women that were not public women were sent to St. Lazare.

The Hospital of Children's Diseases contained 560 beds. Its surgeon was Guérin, its physician Baudelocque. In the Maternity

Hospital were 400 beds. Unless in danger of aborting, women were not admitted to this institution until they had reached the eighth month, and, unless ill, were permitted to remain but nine days after confinement. Any woman that desired could take her child away with her. If she did not wish to take it, it was sent to the Foundlings, being marked for possible future identification. In the Maternity Hospital there was a school of accouchement, where midwives were instructed. The Maison Royale de Santé was a large pay hospital, which was usually called the Hôpice Dubois, because Dubois had been for years connected with it. A similar instance of popular designation may be found in our own city, the Pennsylvania Hospital for the Insane having long been known as Kirkbride's.

Besides these hospitals, Paris contained a hospital for the blind under the care of Alibert; a hospital for blind children, two hospitals for incurables (one for women and one for men and boys), and sixty purely private hospitals. The Charenton Lunatic Asylum was situated in a village four miles from Paris. This institution contained 1200 patients, and had long been managed by the celebrated Esquirol, who was succeeded by Fauville. At the time of which I speak its chief physician was Calmeil. The Salpêtrière, in the Boulevard de l'Hôpital, was and is an almshouse for indigent and lunatic females, idiots, and epileptics. It had 7000 beds. Falret and Trélat were on its staff. The building was originally an arsenal, and was erected in the time of Louis XIII. The Bicêtre was an asylum for males, containing 4200 beds. This institution is situated just behond the old Barrière de Fontainebleau. It was founded by Cardinal Richelieu. Malgaigne was the surgeon, and the physicians were Voisin, Moreau, and Heurteloup. We should also mention the hospital of St. Louis on the rue Bichat, which was founded by Henry IV, and the military hospital of the Val de Grace in the rue Claude Bernard. In this institution are preserved the sleeping rooms of Anne of Austria.

It will be noticed that in the institutions of which I have spoken there were a number of distinguished physicians, surgeons, obstetricians, and specialists. They taught classes of students, but only some of the teachers were members of the Faculty of Medicine of Paris. The Dean of the Faculty of Medicine and the Professor of Toxicology was Orfila. He was one of the greatest men that has adorned this branch of study. It was Orfila who first devised the methods for detecting poison in the stomach and the tissues, and his views upon many subjects are still considered authoritative. He is frequently quoted in text-books upon legal medicine, particularly in reference to postmortem findings in the drowned, the condition of the tongue after strangulation, vesication by burns, the determination of the length of time a person has been dead, and measurements of the skeleton.

The Professor of Anatomy was Breschet, the distinguished surgeon who had recently succeeded Béclard. Breschet was surgeon to the Children's Hospital and to the Hôtel Dieu. He was a master not only of human anatomy, but of comparative anatomy as well, and he was a profound physiologist. Some of his preparations are still to be seen in the Museum Dupuytren, notably his dissections of the middle ear and his preparations of the venous and of the lymphatic system. The picture that is still used in most text-books of anatomy to show the veins of the diploë is from Breschet's preparations.

The Demonstrators of Anatomy were Sappey and Gosselin, each of whom afterward became eminent. The latter is still frequently quoted upon surgical and anatomical matters, and a certain fracture is named after him. Sappey is known to us all, and cuts from his writings—especially pictures of the lymphatics and of certain portions of the brain—are yet regarded as authoritative.

The Professor of Pathologic Anatomy was the great Cruveilhier, and all the world knows of his useful labors. Andral was Professor of General Pathology and Therapeutics; Trousseau, of Therapeutics and Materia Medica; Adélon, of Legal Medicine; Dumas, of Organic Chemistry; Marjolin, of Surgical Pathology; Pellatan, of Medical Physics; Broussais, of the Practice of Medicine; Moreau and Dubois, of Obstetrics; Chomel, Louis, and Rostan, of Clinical

Medicine; and Gay-Lussac, of Chemistry. Blandin taught Operations and Bandaging, and Bérard, Physiology. Medical Natural History was set forth by Richard. Gerdy was the colleague of Marjolin in teaching External Pathology; Internal Pathology was taught by Duméril and Piorry. Fouquier and Bouillaud were also professors of Clinical Medicine; the professors of Clinical Surgery were Roux, Cloquet, Velpeau, and Bérard. Until his death in 1835 Dupuytren was one of the distinguished Professors of Surgery of the Faculty. The great name of Lisfranc does not appear in this list.

These eminent Parisian teachers were by no means harmonious, and the bitterest enmities and the fiercest jealousies existed among them. Each professor won his place after prolonged effort and desperate conflict, in which, perhaps, he had employed arts and denunciations to encompass the defeat of his opponents; and every appointment to a surgeonship or professorship left disappointed and embittered rivals.

These rivals were prone to attack the successful man's character before their students, and the successful one would retort from the arena of the college or the hospital. It will thus be seen that the lectures were not restricted to medical and surgical subjects, but that they frequently contained political reflections, personal denunciations, and vigorous condemnations of men and motives, set forth with flashing wit and biting sarcasm. At no other period have I been able to find so much bitter personal vilifications of colleagues and contemporaries as in some of the Parisian lectures of this period. Dr. John C. Warren wrote from Paris in 1837: "The jealousy and hatred among the medical men in Paris are excessive. It is dangerous to speak of one in the presence of another."

Some particularly bitter invective or especially biting sarcasm, after being furiously applauded by the listening students, would be taken up and disseminated through the Latin Quarter, and would finally reach the ears of the one against whom it had been directed, who would retort in a like manner. In the *Memoirs of J. Mason Warren* we are told: "A lecture by Lisfranc is a flourish of bludgeons and daggers. He lashes Velpeau and Roux, and even stabs Dupuytren in his winding-sheet, but he has as many lashes in return." In a public lecture Lisfranc gracefully alluded to Dupuytren as "le brigand" and as "l'infâme du bord de l'eau." Dupuytren spoke as follows of Lisfranc: "Que sous une enveloppe de ranglier ou portrait parfois un coeur de chien couchant." Victor Hugo tells us that Lisfranc and Récamier once had an argument in the arena of the Medical School concerning the divinity of Christ, and almost came to blows in the presence of the students.

One characteristic of the French surgeon of this period was an effort to be brilliant rather than a desire to be earnest, truthful, and profound. He was apt to perform startling operations that required remarkable dexterity, and to perform them with marvellous speed and precision; but, as I have already shown, the death rate in the hospitals was simply frightful; but a considerable portion of deaths, of course, were in the medical wards. There was a tendency to operate with some other end in view than to cure the patient; that is, to operate as an actor performs— for applause. Hear what Doctor Warren says: "More than two thirds of their patients die after amputation. It seems to be rather an object to study the natural history of disease and to perform an operation beautifully than to save the life of the patient."

Again, Warren thus refers to Dupuytren: "His operations are always brilliant, and his diagnoses sometimes most extraordinary. He is one of the most suspicious persons that I have ever encountered. He is continually seeking to convince us that he is a great man, and that we do not sufficiently value his talents. He likes much to make a show, and generally talks during the whole operation." Doctor Warren again refers to Dupuytren in the following terms: "For brutality I do not think his equal can be found. If his orders are not immediately obeyed, he makes nothing of striking a patient and abusing him harshly. A favorite practice of his is to make a handle of a man's nose, seizing him by it and pulling him down on his knees, where he remains, half in sorrow and half in anger, until he is allowed to rise and describe his symptoms."

Boyer died in 1832. For some years before his death his eyesight was poor, his hands were shaky, his will was uncertain, and his judgment was bad. Nevertheless, he continued to perform all sorts of operations, with disastrous results that might have been anticipated, fiercely denouncing anyone of his associates that even suggested the propriety of his withdrawing.

Sir Astley Cooper, the illustrious English surgeon, informed Dr. John C. Warren in 1838 that a short time before he had been going through the Hôtel des Invalides with Baron Larrey, the surgeon-in-chief of that institution, and that the latter had informed him that he had never in his life lost a case of amputation at the shoulder joint. They soon afterward entered the dead-house, where there was a dead body upon which amputation at the shoulder joint had recently been performed. Sir Astley asked Larrey the cause of the man's death, and the latter calmly, but positively, and without a smile said, "Inflammation of the lungs." Such an answer is not what we would have expected from one so esteemed for truthfulness as Larrey, and we wonder if Sir Astley did not mistake his meaning.

Among all these men there is one conspicuous exception to the prevailing tendency. Velpeau had the courage to oppose unnecessary operations on the mere ground that they were inhuman, and he seems to have done nothing whatever for dramatic effect. He was probably one of the most honest as well as one of the most capable of them all.

In speaking of Roux, Doctor Warren says: "Roux has gone to Italy, having completely quartered an old man of about 70 years, while operating on a tumor of the shoulder joint which Dupuytren had refused to undertake. In general, I decline to criticize the work of great men, who are often most unjustly attacked; but the performances of Roux, which depend entirely on a desire to operate, without the least consideration of the cases, seem to me fair game. This patient died an hour after the operation. Without it he would probably have lived five or six years longer."

It is beyond question that Dupuytren, throughout all his years of distinction and leadership, was most jealous of any young man that showed ability, ferociously attacking all aspiring geniuses in whom he detected the possibility of future rivalry. That he was intensely unpopular with his associates is certain; and it is further-more beyond doubt that they despised him on the ground that he was vain, perfidious, and untruthful. Guérin was accustomed to speak of Dupuytren as being entirely without veracity, and to tell the following incident: Dupuytren was engaged to Boyer's daughter, but on the very evening before the marriage was to have taken place he sent a short, sharp, curt note, in which he informed the family that he had decided not to marry her. Boyer did not recall the wedding invitations, but when the guests ar-rived he arose and read Dupuytren's letter aloud, and then pro-ceeded to hold a celebration in honor of his daughter's escape from the clutches of such a wicked man.*

Dupuytren was exceedingly cool in performing his operations; and during his later years he seems to have become somewhat overconfident. Warren was present at a clinic in which this sur-geon was operating for a strangulated hernia and accidentally slashed into the intestine. This did not at all disturb him, how-ever. He merely said: "Gentlemen, here is the fecal matter," and, without another word, stitched up the wound. He was excessively irritable while operating, and would become very much disturbed by the outcries and protests of the patient; and it must be remembered that these operations were performed before the days of ether. Not unusually he abused his patients violently, sometimes even striking them. He was a wonderful operator, but was not the best of teachers, for if a student failed to understand any point and subsequently asked a question Dupuytren would become furiously angry and refuse to answer. He loved money, and debased his professional reputation in order to obtain it.

* For thirty years Dupuytren accepted blame and never said a word. "On the very morning of the ceremony Mlle. Boyer had written to him confessing that she did not care for him, that she loved another man, and imploring him to prevent the marriage." (Recollections of a Parisian, Docteur Poumies de la Soubitie, 1789–1863.)

For instance, it is said that he permitted an itch salve to be sold with his own great name attached as recommending it. Doctor Warren considered Dupuytren the very best lecturer of the day, because his ideas were set forth with absolute clearness, and the subjects discussed by him were invariably of practical importance.

Doctor Warren describes Dupuytren's personal appearance as follows: "Dupuytren is a very well-formed man, a little inclined to corpulence, with a short, thick neck and an injected face— that of a *bon vivant.*" He was reported to be a heavy gambler, and the students were accustomed to judge from the condition of his temper in the morning as to whether he had won or lost the previous evening. Warren was impressed with the difference between his treatment of hospital and of private patients. With the first he was often as a wild beast; with the second, as a cooing dove.

The house in which Dupuytren lived looks out upon the Seine, and set in its front is a marble tablet stating: "Here lived Dupuytren, the celebrated surgeon." This is an illustration of the French people's valuable custom of preserving the traditions of their great men; for, in spite of his failures of disposition and his blemishes of character, Dupuytren was a great man, who added many things to surgery, and whose name still occupies a high place in the estimation of all students of surgical literature. The Museum Dupuytren of the Medical School is the result of one of his bequests. He founded the Chair of Surgical Pathology in the College, and left 300,000 francs as an endowment for twelve old retired physicians. On the day of his burial the students of the Medical School removed the horses from the hearse and dragged the vehicle to the tomb. Just before his death he sent a message to Lisfranc and to Richerand, his two bitterest enemies, and those three great men are said to have made up their differences. Certain it is that Warren tells us that from the moment of Dupuytren's death Lisfranc spoke more respectfully of him, although he had never previously quoted Dupuytren except to abuse him. After his death, however, Lisfranc frequently alluded

to the investigations and discoveries of Dupuytren, always refer-
ring to him as M. Dupuytren. This remarkable man seems to
have had few if any warm personal friends.

Lisfranc was fully as arbitrary and vain as Dupuytren, and
almost as able. He was always making a public exhibition of his
supposed wrongs, and was accustomed to attack his enemies, real
or imaginary, with ferocity and ability. He was a lover of bleeding, and Dr. Oliver Wendell Holmes says that one morning he
ordered fifteen persons to be bled. He was one of the best surgical anatomists in Paris, and was an operator of magnificent
skill. Warren says: "His amputations of fingers and toes are
very neat and rapid; and all his operations are marked by a kind
of off-hand way, not premeditated, but depending entirely upon
the state of the disease or the extent to which he carries them."
Doctor Warren did not consider Lisfranc so scientific as Velpeau,
but thought him more original—a judgment that posterity has
not confirmed.

Lisfranc used to go to the hospital early in the morning, just
as did Dupuytren, and would pass through the wards arrayed in
a blood-stained white apron, and wearing upon his head a black
skull-cap like that of a hanging judge. He was an extremely
large and powerful man, and is described as wearing a long-
waisted, snuff-colored coat, with a long tail reaching to his heels
and shaped like the tail of a kite. His pantaloons were baggy
about his hips and fluttered in the wind as he walked. His shoes
were always large and ill-fitting, and he used to stride like a
burly, careless giant through the streets of Paris. His voice was
loud and his accents emphatic, and he denounced in unsparing
terms every human being that ventured to differ with him in the
slightest particular. His hand was against every man, and every
man's hand was against him; and he seemed thoroughly to enjoy
the situation. His face gives no indication of this ferocity of
temper, for it is singularly pleasant and genial.

The man whom posterity has come to regard as probably the
greatest of this group is Velpeau. We see him in his old age in
Daudet's *Kings in Exile*, for old Burchereau is drawn from Vel-

peau. He was of humble origin, being the son of a blacksmith, and was born near Tours in 1795. He received but a limited education, being put to work at an early age in the forge, using the bellows. He was a silent, quiet, thoughtful boy. He did not mix with other boys, and spent all his spare hours in perfecting himself in reading. In his father's house were three books: the works of Hippocrates, the *Poor Person's Physician*, and the *Rustic Mason*. Alfred Velpeau, by means of these books and with some occasional assistance from a kind stranger, taught himself to read, and he then began to seek for knowledge in every direction. He could not obtain any new books, so he committed to memory these three old ones; and he also taught himself writing, and became proficient in it.

As a mere child, Velpeau was fond of prescribing for cut fingers, bruises, etc., and was finally looked upon in the village as a veritable authority on all such matters. The curé of the village took an interest in him and helped to teach him. Velpeau, like most persons that are ignorant of medicine, but love to dabble in it, soon got beyond his depth, administering to a young girl a dose of medicine that almost killed her. It became necessary to send for a physician, who arrived and saved the patient's life. On hearing Velpeau's story and obtaining a knowledge of his enthusiasm for medicine, this physician promised to help him, and did so. He subsequently induced a gentleman of the neighborhood to permit the blacksmith's son to take lessons with his own children. Velpeau studied every moment of his time, succeeding, within a few months, in making himself an excellent Latin scholar.

Finally, with all his effects wrapped up in a handkerchief, with a week's supply of food in his pockets, and with the sum of thirty-seven francs in his possession, Velpeau set off for Tours to begin the study of medicine. While studying he lived in a garret on the supply of bread and cheese that his mother sent to him once every week. He passed all the time during the day at the hospital and in the dissecting-room, spending most of the night in hard study. Bretonneau, a distinguished physician, became in-

terested in the young student, and obtained for him a remission
of the usual fee that had to be paid to the hospital. He was soon
afterward appointed intern, and while holding that position secured the post of health-officer, which paid him a small salary.

His friends expected that he would come home to practice
after finishing his course, but he declined to do so and became
assistant to Bretonneau. He continued to study and work, ac-
quiring a certain amount of practice, until he reached the age of
twenty-five years, when a young lady to whom he was engaged to
be married, suddenly and apparently without reason, broke the
engagement; and Velpeau determined to leave his prosperous surroundings in Tours and go to Paris. He borrowed $40 from his
master, packed his clothes, collected $100 which was owed to him,
and went to Paris, carrying a letter of introduction to Cloquet.

Here Velpeau at once began to study in the hospitals. He
lived in the cheapest manner, paying only seven francs a month
rent. After having been in Paris three months he had spent but
one hundred of his four hundred francs. With the aid of Cloquet
he obtained a position in the St. Louis Hospital, which he held
for three years. He gained both the anatomical and the physiologic prize, and made a certain amount of money by delivering
lectures on anatomy and surgery to junior students.

On leaving this hospital he became a private assistant to
M. Bougon. He then began to deliver lectures on surgery and
also on midwifery. He obtained his degree in 1823, and then
became Chief of the Surgical Clinic in the Hospital of the School
of Medicine. In the year 1824 he was appointed Professor Agrégé,
and substituted at times for various teachers. He became surgeon to La Pitié and La Charité. He was the candidate for the
Chair of External Pathology, which was won by Marjolin. He
also ran for the Chair of Physiology and was defeated. In 1830
he became a candidate for Professor of Obstetrics. For this he
was defeated, but he was finally elected to the Chair of Clinical
Surgery, winning the fight against Lisfranc, Sanson, and Blandin.

Velpeau wrote a treatise on *Operative Surgery*, which was considered an authority for many years. Strange to relate, he also

wrote a treatise on *Obstetrics*—for I am not familiar with any other instance of a great surgeon who also excelled as an obstetrician. Velpeau's treatise on *Obstetrics* was translated into English by the late Professor Charles D. Meigs, and had a large sale in America.

Velpeau's enemies were accustomed to attack him on account of his humble origin; but his splendid talents overcame all opposition, and most of those that opposed him were really jealous of his achievements. As a man, he was loved by his friends. He was not a kind man, for his personal demeanor was frequently quite harsh to his patients and violent to his assistants. He was of middle height, and neither very stout nor very thin. He walked somewhat slowly and stiffly and held himself erect. He had a habit of turning his head rapidly from side to side without moving his body. His features were well marked. His eyes were gray and penetrating, and were covered with thick, bushy eyebrows, which, as years advanced, became white. His round face was most carefully shaved, and the students learned that he despised whiskers and mustaches, and that he was quite likely to "throw" a man applying for his degree if the applicant were not well shaved. Velpeau's curly gray hair bristled up from his head. His forehead was noticeably high. He always wore a black dress-coat when not at the hospital; when there, he arrayed himself in a gray morning gown, and in this guise he operated. For many years no one saw him in public without a white tie.

Velpeau had the greatest consulting practice in the city of Paris, but not the greatest operating practice, which was divided between Lisfranc and Roux. As time advanced, Velpeau's disposition mellowed and softened somewhat. Professor Keen, who was once a student of his, invariably speaks of him with the utmost affection.

I regret that time does not permit of the consideration of some other eminent surgeons of this period, to say nothing of the great practitioners of medicine. I would like to speak to you of Nélaton, the pathologist and surgeon, the inventor of the flexible catheter, the one who devised the porcelain-tipped probe as a result of his experience in the case of General Garibaldi—a man who is shown as Doctor Rameau, in Ohnet's novel of that name. Of Amussat, the kindly and suave—the man whose study of the anatomy of the urethra led him to devise an operation for crushing stone in the bladder and thus apparently antedate Civiale; who devised the double saw that is still used to open the spinal canal at postmortem examinations; who stood practically alone in advocating suprapubic lithotomy; who introduced torsion for the arrest of hemorrhage (in 1827); who gave lectures upon *experimental surgery*, and who published a celebrated treatise upon the entrance of air into the blood vessels; of Marjolin, the skilled pathologist, the famous diagnostician, the surgeon, and the best of "good fellows," whose name at the present day is given to a variety of ulcer; of Civiale, one of the most noted men of the century, who, if he did not independently invent at least perfected and made practical the operation of crushing stone in the bladder; who was accustomed to increase his dexterity in crushing stone by walking through the streets with a lithotrite in his hand and endeavoring to grasp objects in his coat-tail pocket; who, in 1824, was honored by a report of the Committee of the Royal Academy of Sciences, giving him the credit of having devised the operation of crushing stone and naming it the operation of Civiale; who so impressed his medical contemporaries that Lisfranc himself submitted to the operation soon after its introduction. Civiale performed this operation upon more than 1000 patients; of Cloquet, Lafayette's warm personal friend, whose views upon hernia are still quoted; and who, on two occasions, performed major amputations under hypnosis; of Guérin, who was one of the first surgeons to devote himself to the study of deformities, and was therefore one of the founders of orthopedic surgery, and who claimed to have devised the operation of subcutaneous tenotomy; of Jobert, who was the first to utilize the principle of Lembert in the human being (Lembert had used inversion sutures upon animals; Jobert employed them upon men); of the elder Larrey, the greatest military surgeon of all time, who had been with Napoleon in twenty-six campaigns; who had operated upon Napoleon, Ney, Lannes, Moncey, Duroc, Soult, and many others of the most celebrated men of the period; a man in whom the Emperor had reposed a trust greater, almost, than in any other; a man who always dared to tell his master the truth; who was never a time-server nor a groveller; who placed military medicine upon the foundation that has never since been disturbed; and whose tomb in Père Lachaise has upon it Napoleon's saying, "He was the most honest man I ever knew"; of Malgaigne, whose work upon fractures and dislocations is still frequently referred to; of Ricord, who was born in Baltimore of French parents; who studied for one year at the University of Pennsylvania; who went to Paris in order to take some specimens to Cuvier; who finished his course in that city; and who became the most distinguished authority on venereal diseases of the time; who was a master-teacher; who was much given to peculiarities of expression and to phrase-making (some of these expressions have lived; for instance, the term used by him to designate the enlarged glands in the groin found in some venereal infections, the "Pleiades," and his state-ment that if a man with secondary syphilis were drowning and a would-be rescuer were to grasp him by the hair of his head his life would not be saved); and who is referred to in the auto-biographical work of Daudet, in which this great French author describes his own early years in Paris; of Roux, who, after the death of Dupuytren, was regarded as sharing with Lisfranc the position of first operative surgeon in France; who, more than any other surgeon, made the operation for cleft palate a practical procedure; who was famous for his operations for cataract; and who not only was Dupuytren's professional rival, but also had aspired to the affections of the lady upon whom Dupuytren had set his heart; of the younger Larrey; of Richerand; of Blandin; of Boyer; of Maisonneuve; of Chassaignac; of Huguier; of Sanson; of Cullerier; of Denonvilliers, and of others.

I must, however, forego the privilege of setting forth the lives of these remarkable men; and I will close this paper with the statement of my belief that never in the records of the human race have so many illustrious surgeons been gathered together at one time in one city as were living in Paris during the time of Louis Philippe.

THE TRIALS AND TRIUMPHS OF THE SURGEON *

MANY years ago the great, the wise, the eccentric, the irascible, the lovable John Abernethy, as he walked into the lecture room in St. Bartholomew's Hospital, looked out upon the crowd of medical students, and said, half in curiosity, half in sorrow, "Good God! what is to become of you all?" The same thought must often arise in the mind of every teacher. What will become of the students? We all know in a general way. All will die sooner or later. All will get more or less happiness and prosperity. Some will become rich. Most will continue poor. Some will remain bachelors. Most will marry and breed children for good or ill. Most will cleave to the profession for life. Many will abandon it. A very few will become eminent, but a majority will not. Some will rise as the soaring eagle, others will mount as the mousing owl. Some will snatch at comets and grasp them. Others will only pick up jelly fish and be stung for their pains. Some will set traps for birds of paradise and catch skunks. Some will dwell upon the muck heap. Others will move among the constellations of profundity, drinking in as mother's milk the glory of the stars.

In 1869 Sir James Paget endeavored to find a more specific answer to Abernethy's question. He traced the careers of 1000 pupils of St. Bartholomew's for fifteen years after their graduation: Only twenty-three achieved distinguished success; sixty-six attained considerable success; 507 attained fair success, that is, made a decent living but worked hard to get it; 124 did very poorly indeed; fifty-six failed utterly; ninety-six abandoned the profession; forty-one died while pupils; eighty-seven died during the first twelve years of practice, and twenty-one of them perished from diseases due to their calling.

* Delivered before the Philadelphia County Medical Society March 10, 1915. Reprinted from the *New York Medical Journal* for April 10, 1915. Copyright, 1915, by A. R. Elliott Publishing Company.

The conclusion is that only 8.5 per cent of a class will attain eminence or achieve considerable success, that 50 per cent will make a decent living, but it will be bought by strenuous effort, that 18 per cent will do very poorly indeed, or will fail utterly, and that nearly 10 per cent will abandon practice. Were the estimate made thirty years after graduation, it would be found that a somewhat larger percentage had attained eminence or considerable success—that a somewhat larger percentage had failed—that a larger percentage had given up practice, and that a greatly larger percentage had died.

According to Paget's figures, almost one third of any class of students made a mistake when they selected medicine for a profession. I am disposed to think that Paget's figures would apply today, that about the same proportion of a class will succeed, about the same proportion will fail, about the same proportion will abandon the profession. Most of them will feel a lack of public understanding, will be denied public appreciation, will pass lives made up of laborious days which know no eight-hour law, and of disturbed nights, each of which may be a continuous performance, will do much good, for which they will obtain small reward and little praise, and will die, worn out, long before the period allotted by the psalmist. In using the term "success" I do not regard it as synonymous with wealth. Some men are so busy making money that they have no time to study, to observe, or to think. A rich man who has not brought honor to his profession is not a real success. He has lost more than can be paid for by wealth. He may be scheduled as a successful man, but he knows better and knows he has failed. "He that maketh haste to be rich shall not be innocent." To quote Captain Cuttle, "In the proverbs of Solomon you will find them 'ere words, and when found, make a note of."

It is discouraging to think of so many failures and so few successes. Some of the failures would have succeeded in another occupation, and when they entered medicine spoiled a good business man, lawyer, broker, or farmer. Some would have failed in anything because of temperamental inaptitudes or futilities, cowardice, stupidity, laziness, mendacity, dishonesty, disloyalty, or jealousy. Many such men began the study as Richard Carstone did in *Bleak House*—because it would do "as well as anything else." Some most worthy men fail because of pure ill luck, and are elbowed out of every opening, and never gain credit for any of the good things they do.

Some years ago, after reading Paget's figures, I undertook an investigation as to why men leave the profession, as so many men do. I found the reasons various. Some complained they got no help from the profession. Such men are like an electric button and won't do any work unless they are pushed. Others groaned that they had no pull, evidently believing that their great abilities would have burst into effervescence had a kindly barkeeper been adjacent to open them up. Others asserted that they were persecuted. As a matter of fact, when a man becomes an embodied grievance there is generally something wrong with him. Some did not reach the top, where there is said to be so much room, because there was no elevator and they were too lazy to climb there. They preferred sitting at the bottom and complaining. Such men work like a sun dial on a dark day and move like a glacier. Some failed because what they did not know about medicine would populate a colossal morgue; some, because they tried to screw up their energies with a corkscrew; some, because they were so busy attending to other people's business they could find no time to work.

Some got too poor to stay in the profession without learning to live on the diet of Lucian's moon men, that is, the odor of a roast frog's leg and air squeezed into goblets. Sir Conan Doyle says he abandoned the profession because the profession abandoned him. Some were too rich to be bothered with practice. Some did not like the work and gave it up for more congenial employment which had regular pay days. Some could not stand the responsibility. Some fell into a big chance out of medicine and took it. The wives of some objected strongly to the profession, and the husbands became meek, as they wished to inherit the earth.

It is interesting to note what men do who give up medicine. History shows that there is great diversity in their choice. Keats gave up being a dresser in Guy's Hospital and wrote the *Ode on a Grecian Urn*. The late Herman Mutgett, alias Mr. Holmes, took up wholesale murder for life insurance. Oliver Wendell Holmes became our greatest literary man. Doctor Garrison went on the Supreme Bench of New Jersey, and Doctor Cook went somewhere (I don't know where) up north. Some go to the devil and some go to Congress. One is a major general and was chief-of-staff of the United States Army. One is the celebrated Sir Conan Doyle. One is Governor of West Virginia. One was a pauper in Blockley Alms House. One is a prisoner in the Eastern Penitentiary of Pennsylvania. One is a railroad conductor on the Pennsylvania Railroad. One became a Philadelphia millionaire. Some sell books, some become life insurance agents, some write for magazines, some travel for drug firms, and a good many adopt matrimony for a profession and settle down in order that they may settle up. Such matrimony may prove eminently successful as a breeder of happiness and it may not. It is usually a life sentence only to be commuted by bad behavior. Most men who take up this calling to obtain an easy life find that they earn their wages. Those who embark on the matrimonial sea for gain and not for love often come to wish they had missed the boat, and ever afterward regard the elder Weller as having been directly inspired when he told his son that if he felt like getting married, to "Pizen yourself first, Samivel, and you will be glad on it arterwards." The lady in the case, too, may sometimes have reason to doubt if she obtained the worth of her money.

It is vastly to the credit of the medical profession that so few leave it to go into quackery; I only know of two or three who did do so. If a regular chooses to apostasize and then turn quack he can often make money rapidly and in quantity, but very few are willing to become pariahs. The old training has left its mark. Certain beliefs are fixed so firmly that they become as intuitions. A man may leave the army of healing, but he seldom joins the enemy. He feels, as did Doctor Holmes, who, though he had abandoned medicine for literature, cried out to the members of the profession, "Claim me, hold me, call me brother still." In holding certain higher ideas in spite of all temptations to abandon them, the medical profession surely stands above the common run of men. Robert Louis Stevenson said: "There are men who stand above the common herd—the soldier, the sailor, and the shepherd infrequently; the artist rarely; rarer still the clergyman; the physician almost as a rule." Failure, disappointment, disenchantment, embitterment, neglect, even actual want very seldom cause a physician to become a quack and thus cease to be a man who stands "above the common herd."

Of all the causes of failure I doubt if any is more potent than vanity. The proper attitude toward all scientific questions is one of humility. When one can no longer wonder at nature, he can no longer progress. When he would settle everything by a formula, he is consigned forever to the compartment of useless odds and ends. Vanity tires out even the most patient colleague, gives a weapon to every opponent, and potential friends quickly weary of the society of the discoverer of everything that is useful and important. Such men obey the command to let their light shine before men, and it shines so strongly and persistently that it resembles a conflagration in a shop of fireworks. It may be added that those about find their nostrils assailed with noisome odors and their ears bombarded with sounds of destruction. Were the walls which bar the way to success like the walls of Jericho, they might be expected to fall from noise, but they do not do so. The man who does the bombarding is of small caliber in spite of being a big bore. Every now and then we see such a man purchase a two-cent stamp as though he were laying the cornerstone of a cathedral. Such a vanity makes one suspicious, critical, resentful, ungrateful, and bombastic. The athletic exercise of throwing bouquets at oneself never strengthens the muscles of the mind. When it is practised for a long time, a man sets as exaggerated an estimate on his own value as though he were suing a railroad company for damages. Such a man can't obtain real success, but he may get rich, because he may persuade the general public to

take him at his own estimate. The public may know he is a great
man, just as Thaddeus Stevens knew that his client was an honest
man. Stevens said: "Your honor, my client is an honest man.
I know he is an honest man because he told me so himself."

The vain man in surgery is a deadly peril. He mistakes his
own half-formed opinions for oracles speaking within him. He is
never conscious of his mistakes and hence keeps on making them.
He misleads others by his positive assertions regarding unproved
views. He clamors insistently for credit. What he aims at is to
attract attention. He would rather be abused than not spoken
about at all. He has noticed the fact that a plain, modest, hard-
working man, doing his duty and serving humanity, attracts no
more real attention than a thermometer on a balmy day. It is a
sad commentary on the world that bowlegs attract more attention than great virtues, and that a red nose causes more comment than a blameless life.

A surgeon is like a postage stamp. He is useless when stuck
on himself. A vain surgeon is like a milking stool; of no use except
when sat upon. I don't see how any real surgeon can be vain.
He is too often near to the inscrutable mystery of death—he
sees too often the weaknesses of men—he too often stands at
cross roads of judgment, knows that one way is the wrong way,
but finds no sign to mark it—he too often has to reproach himself
for mistakes—he too often sees calamity tread on the heels of
calamity—he too often laments, impotent to save, and watches
"Beauty and anguish walking hand and hand, the downward
way to death"—he knows too well that Sophocles spoke the truth
when he said:

> " The power of learning may a while prevail.
>   A time prolong a mortal's fleeting breath,
>   But useless all her arts are to avail
>   To conquer Fate or check the hand of Death."

I don't see how any surgeon can be vain any more than I can
see how an astronomer could be vain—an astronomer who peers
into the depths of infinite space which the hand of Omnipotence
has strewn thick with star dust.

Real success comes only from persistent hard work. No lily handed child of ease is entitled to it or can have it. Its insignia do not come from the general public, but are conferred by the profession itself. Any temperament which keeps a man from sticking at it forbids success. Mere episodes of busy idleness do not constitute work. The loafer is a failure. To loaf in front of a church is just the same as to loaf in front of a saloon. One may loaf in a library, a laboratory, a hospital, as well as on a street corner, in a bar room, or at an afternoon tea. Indolence sterilizes the mind, but work will not create genius. It is an infinitely rare gift to dream the fairy tales of science. Genius alone dreams them, but even genius must work to make them real. I believe that real success can come only from work, but I know that even the hardest work may not command it. "'Tis not in mortals to *command* success." Some work wrong and fail. Some work right and fail. Some work but fail "until they grasp the skirt of happy chance," by which they are dragged to the openings they lacked and the opportunities they despaired of obtaining. No man could dive for pearls on a mountain; no man could become an astronomer in a cave, and it may be impossible to create opportunity.

I know that opportunity was opened to me directly by the kindly act of one great man. I have received recognition and reward, beyond my merits it is true, "but I should have received neither without him. I was breasting the waves of circumstance" and my strength was failing with every stroke. Whenever I tried to grasp the gunwale of a boat, some one hit my knuckles with a boat hook and my hold was loosened. A strong hand reached out, grasped me by the hair, and dragged me, all but drowned, from the waters. It was the hand of my dear old chief and master, Professor W. W. Keen. So, you see, I am forced to believe in the lucky chance.

When we think of how many men fail, we naturally wish there was some infallible method by which we might recognize the unfit when they seek to begin study or at least very early in their student days, so that we might turn them back from medicine.

To do so would be good for medicine and good for the men themselves. Unfortunately such men are not labeled like reserved
seats, or brandy bottles, or boxes of cigars. To make a mistake
and admit the unfit man would wrong medicine and the man.
To make a mistake and exclude the fit man would wrong the man
and medicine. A trouble in handling such men is a trouble in
eugenics, viz., Who is to do the deciding, and, when you select
the judges, what proof is there that they are competent? Certain
it is that mere examination marks can't enable any one to make a
just and reasonable decision. The world has a mania for examination tests. In Philadelphia the city subjects even the scrub
women to examinations. Some of the questions asked by civil
service boards must have been conceived in the incurable ward
of a lunatic asylum. The same is true of medical examinations.
They are not tests of the man. They are only tests of his memory
for facts. They tell us nothing of his judgment, tact, energy,
enthusiasm, idealism, reason, observation, temperament, disposition, honesty, loyalty, courage, truthfulness, or intelligence.
Memory for facts means little. The other things mean nearly all.
The graduate is like a sausage—that is, he is whatever comes out
of the machine. I admit that the purity, flavor, and healthful-
ness of the sausage depend upon what goes into the machine.
Seasoning won't do everything, although some teachers agree
with Sam Weller's friend, the meat pie man, who said it was all
in the seasoning.

It is to be earnestly hoped that some great genius will discover
a method by which the schools can tell if the germs of success are
in a man or if he is hopelessly immune and ordained to failure.
Oh, for some x-ray which would show us in the human the glass
from the diamond, the plate from the gold! Oh, for some test to
show what is presented to be made into the sausage! How many
men out of a class become surgeons? Many men will become occasional operators, practising surgery and internal medicine. Very
few, indeed, will become pure surgical specialists. In Philadelphia,
at the present moment, I can count on my fingers the men who are
pure surgical specialists—count them on my fingers and perhaps

have a finger or two to spare. I suppose the same thing is true in other cities. No man should start out as a pure surgeon. He should be just as unable to do this as Wilkins Micawber, Jr., was unable to proclaim himself a barrister. Every man ought to do several or a number of years' general practice before he limits himself to surgery. He must have the broad training that only general practice can give. Every day he works and studies in surgery, but he studies and practises general medicine as well. He works at surgery in a hospital. He helps an older man in operations. He could not live on surgery alone at this stage. He must make the rent and board from general practice. A training in general medicine broadens a man immensely; increases his diagnostic acumen, his therapeutic skill, his prognostic ability; his knowledge of diet, of hygiene, and of the control and management of patients and their families. It takes years of training to equip a man to follow surgery as a specialty. If a man tries to start out as a surgical authority, he never learns the rudiments throughout all of his days. During the war between the States a number of politicians were made generals. One of these generals made a dreadful failure and was fiercely criticized. General Grant said, "Don't be too hard on the poor fellow—he could not help it. Remember he started life as a brigadier general." A man can't start professional life as a hospital surgeon and a professor of surgery any more safely than he can start military life as a brigadier general. Of course, when a man has become really equipped and desires to follow a surgical career, he ought to abandon general practice. He simply cannot keep himself properly informed in both branches.

Why do men become surgeons? Very few because of an early natural inclination, though some do. Ambroise Paré, when twelve years of age, decided to become a master surgeon because he was profoundly attracted by the usefulness and helpfulness of the art. Alfred Velpeau, when a mere child, determined on seeking a surgical career. The elder Gross, when only six years old, aspired to be a surgeon and could never tell what gave him the desire. But such instances are very rare. Most men have become surgeons

3

because of a developed liking for it, because of some particular opportunity or of some chance which stirred the idea. Often a son will adopt the father's specialty, as did the younger Gross, the younger Pancoast, and the younger Kocher.

Some great surgeons did not lean to surgery at all. Sir William Fergusson began the study of law, but abandoned it. Robert Liston wished to be a sailor. Sir James Paget had an inclination toward botany. Syme was infatuated with chemistry. Simpson had, as a student, a horror of surgery. Sir Benjamin Brodie had no special liking for it. The great John Hunter was a mischievous lad and a ne'er-do-well and he was sent up to London to see if his brother William, the anatomist and obstetrician, could make something or anything out of him.

Most medical students are attracted to surgery. Its positive results please them. The bloody drama of the operation fascinates them, the dramatic force of some great operator stirs their admiration. They note decisive achievements and wonderful successes. They hear little of failures. They know nothing of the haunting anxieties, the keen disappointments, the baffling perplexities, the dread responsibilities, and the numerous self reproaches of one who spends his life as an operating surgeon. Yet few even of these admiring students become surgeons. Some suffer disenchantment during their student days. Many lack the necessary qualities. Many shrink from the responsibility. Some never get an opportunity. Many find an opening in general practice and seize it for a livelihood. The very best minds in a class seldom lean to surgery. This is a sad admission, but it is true. Men with deep, broad, philosophic minds usually tend to laboratory science and experimental medicine. That such minds are apt to be repelled by surgery is often the fault of a teacher. No mere knifesman can command their admiration and respect. If the teacher is what Bob Sawyer's landlady, Mrs. Raddle, held every surgeon to be, only "a cutter and carver" of "live people's bodies," he can never attract the best intellects of the class. No mere operator can do it, no factory of dramatic flourishes, no phrase maker, no exponent of surgery by epigram, or surgery by aphorism, no one ignorant of the other branches of medicine, of medical history, of surgical physiology, of experimental surgery, of bacteriology, of diagnosis, of prognosis, and of the natural history of disease. One of the highest problems of a teacher of surgery is how to save to the great practical branch of surgery intellects some of which might be of more use to humanity among the patients in a hospital than among the test-tubes in a laboratory.

Years ago I heard a medical student say that he was going into surgery because of the chance it gave to make great fees and get rich rapidly. I don't know what became of that youth. I have lost track of him. I never see his name to a surgical article in a medical journal. He may be so busy making great fees that he has no time to write, but I doubt it. I would venture a considerable wager that that mercenary gentleman has long since discovered his huge mistake.

The ideas held by the public regarding surgeons' fees are ludicrous exaggerations. The man who is going after surgical fees as a buccaneer goes after a laden galleon should fly the black flag of piracy in Wall Street. He doesn't belong in surgery and won't succeed there. A man who regards the dollar mark as the flowing curve of faultless beauty doesn't belong among us. A man who is ever looking into the beautiful eyes of his cash box will receive, if he is a surgeon, few dazzling glances in return. An able man who spends the same amount of preparation, thought, study, toil, anxiety, observation in any one of twenty other callings can obtain more than twenty times the reward he can get in surgery.

Here and there throughout the country there are to be found men who make huge incomes, but such men are rare. When we find one of them we may find a great surgical genius. We may find a man who combines business ability with surgical ability. We may find one of preeminent repute in a special line of work. We may find one who has organized his business as efficiently as a department store. We may find one who has the good fortune to command cases from over a vast area of country. We very seldom find a surgical Croesus.

I do not believe there is a surgeon in Philadelphia who makes more than $50,000 a year. I do not believe that more than two make nearly that much. Large fees are the exception. Small fees or no fees are the rule. The largest fee ever received by the elder Gross, the undisputed head of American surgery, was $2500. Every surgeon, even the most successful one, makes most of his income from small fees.

Year by year the incomes of most purely surgical specialists who practise in the large cities shrink. This is an inevitable outcome of the establishment of hospitals in all the smaller towns. A few years ago every one with a surgical trouble went to a large city for advice and, if operation was needed, for operation. Now comparatively few go. They stay at home, and are operated on in the neighborhood hospital. Year by year fewer and fewer surgical patients come from a distance to this city. This is the reason why there are so few pure surgical specialists. There is not enough work to go around. I am not arguing now for or against the hospitals in the small towns. The question as to how they are fulfilling their function is not, on the present occasion, up for dispute. I am simply stating the fact that because of them surgery in a city will seldom make a man rich.

A man does not have much time to make money in surgery and he is seldom a good enough business man to do nearly as well as he could. He spends years of breaking work and cruel anxiety to fit himself to be a surgeon. He is usually in the forties before he obtains a remunerative practice. Few are prosperous at twenty-five, as were Liston, Syme, and the first McClellan, or at thirty-two, as was Fergusson. Paget was in practice ten years before he obtained a fee for a private operation. Agnew was in the fifties before he had attained reasonable prosperity.

A surgeon can continue to operate only so long as his hand is steady and his eye keen. Hand and eye are apt to fail in the sixties. As a rule, at the best, a surgeon has only twenty-five years in which to make and lay by enough to provide for his old age and for the decent support of his family after his death. At any time during those twenty-five years a man's usefulness may be de-

stroyed by inoculation with a disease or by a crippling injury of
the hand. Thirty years ago one of the most promising men in
Philadelphia was inoculated with syphilis while doing an operation. He became a shattered wreck, went totally blind, and died
in a few years. Shortly afterward a noted hospital surgeon became inoculated with the same disease, and at once and permanently gave up practice for fear that he might inoculate his
patients.

The period for remunerative work in operative surgery is
probably shorter and more beset with perils than in any other
profession. The soldier and sailor must stop at sixty-two years,
but the government supports them for the balance of their lives.
The civil engineer, the mechanical engineer, the electrical engineer,
the chemist, can keep on indefinitely. The medical man can
continue as a consultant as long as he can get about, and we have
it on the authority of Oliver Wendell Holmes that many people
"like their doctors mouldy like their cheese." When the clergyman grows more and more prosy, doctrinal, and orthodox, he
takes a colleague and proses on. When a lawyer is about fit
to be put on the shelf, he is put on the bench instead. But when
the operating surgeon begins to fail, he has to stop. A man who
is something more than a mere operator can perhaps continue as
a pure consultant, but the pure operator is done and is done
forever.

It is evident that during his period of activity and opportunity
a surgeon must charge fair fees to those who can afford to pay
them. A failure to do so will mean an old age of privation and a
family left in want. The time during which a surgeon can charge
large fees is brief. Very few people are able to pay large fees.
Very few of those who are able to do so are willing. The surprise
of a professional philanthropist when asked to make a personal
contribution, the obstinacy of a government mule confronting
a stream which must be forded, the indignation of a reformer
when forced to be specific and to keep his promises, the wrath
of a politician on discovering an impending split in the party,
the horror of a superstitious colored man upon seeing a ghost

in a graveyard, when all combined do not quite serve to represent the state of mind of the average millionaire when presented with a fair bill for having had his life saved by surgery, I think that a consideration of these facts should convince any impartial mind that surgery is a poor field from which to glean a harvest of wealth.

A surgeon's life is a very hard one. It is a life of endless strain. During most of the hours of every day his faculties are keyed up tense almost to the breaking point, and physical tire goes hand in hand with mental exhaustion. He must carry and carry naturally the heaviest responsibilities. No matter how tired he is, his faculties must be alert, his judgment clear, his will inflexible, his knowledge accurate and instantaneously accessible for transmission into action. He must be calm, no matter what the clamor, the peril, the perplexity. Of course he will worry about his patients. Every conscientious man must do so. A man who doesn't worry at all doesn't care a whole lot. I should not want a man who did not care a whole lot operating on me or mine. Perhaps worry is a device of nature to make us try to do our very best. If we knew we should not worry, we might be tempted at times to be careless. If a surgeon analyzes his worry he can get a line on what sort of man he is himself. If he worries only because he fears he may be sued, may lose a bill, or may hurt his reputation, then with him the voice of conscience is the fear of getting caught. If he worries because of the poor patient and the credit of surgery, then he is a really conscientious man. He must expect much harsh and unjust criticism, and when he is the victim of it all he can do is follow Joseph Pancoast's advice and make his shoulders broad enough to bear the burden. A surgeon must learn thorough self surrender and all his life must wear the iron yoke of duty.

Yes! the life of a surgeon is toilsome, responsible, and anxious. It is a life of stress and strain. It is small wonder that surgeons as a class are not long lived. Pneumonia, angina pectoris, Bright's disease, vascular disease are the commonest agents of dissolution. The life is full of tragedy. Sometimes it seems as though a malign destiny were intervening in our affairs. This so impressed Velpeau that he came to believe in the rule of three. It so influenced Pirogoff that he wrote an essay on *Luck in Surgery*.

The days of waiting for practice are very hard and very dangerous. Those days may make a man or mar him. The same wind which blows out the penny dip urges the flames of the forest fire. Those days go far in determining what sort of a man he is and is to be. During them he should study ceaselessly, learn to work, to observe, to think, and to teach himself. He should ponder deeply and often on the responsibilities and the duties of his calling. Thus he should become a real man, an individual, a man with genuine ideas, definite beliefs, established principles, and high ideals. Thus he should avoid being a mere mimic and echo.

There is grave danger in those waiting hours, those dark hours of poverty and nonrecognition. A sensitive soul will shrink, falter, and probably fail. Brooding discontent is apt to dominate and it is a deadly peril. Jealousy may spring up, envy may attain rank luxuriance, bitterness may grow, selfishness, avarice, disloyalty, mental dishonesty may be planted. Low ideals are ever knocking for admission. From them come admiration for despicable things, desires for unworthy objects, and improper professional conduct.

Gradually, as a man becomes a surgeon, he tends toward one of the two fundamental groups into which all surgeons are divisible. The mental tendencies of an individual determine to which group their possessor or victim belongs. Each type has its strengths and its weaknesses. Each may be potent for good or active for evil. The ideal surgeon has not as yet been born. He would possess the strengths of both types and the weaknesses of neither. He would have wisdom as well as knowledge—tact as well as skill—confident hope as well as cautious doubt. His hand, like that of Joseph Pancoast, would be as light as floating perfume—his eye as quick as a flashing sunbeam—his heart as broad as humanity —his soul as sweet as the waters of Lebanon.

One fundamental class is the conservative, the other is the radical. The conservative is often a most valuable factor in surgery. He is a brake on the wheel and often stops the dashing automobile of progress when on a joy ride from upsetting in the ditch of folly. He smothers the torch of the fantastic, snatches the mask from pretense, and punctures the hot air balloon of egotism. He studies the past and reveres it, likes to penetrate its cities and its silences, to repeople its mouldering ruins, and to worship at its shattered shrines, and, in the words of Macaulay, looks back upon some Golden Age that has had no existence outside of his own mind. He attaches an exaggerated importance to books, and minimizes the value of new methods of communicating ideas. He has a great respect for authorities, and would rather "sin with Pope than shine with Pye." He is prone to write ponderous treatises, each of which has a name so complicated that it sounds like a sobriety test. He is apt to regard present-day claims through the dim sublimation of the foggy and remote. He regards each so-called "new" thing as a wrong basely done to the established order and agrees with Solomon that there is no new thing. He is very doubtful of the possibility of reforming anything or anybody. He follows custom even when it is unreasonable or actually absurd. His headlight, like the light of the glow worm, is on the wrong end. He progresses, but in a circle, like the hands of a clock. He is not the active minded man behind the gun, but the slow and often dull man behind the times. His ideas are from a reservoir and not from a spring. Such conservatism may be temperamental opposition to change, may be a mask for incapacity, or an excuse for laziness. He may block or drag back the auto of progress even when it is moving surely, in the right direction and on the right road. He is apt to be a pessimist—seeing the thorns and not the roses—seeing the hole in the doughnut, but not the doughnut.

The best and most useful conservative is one who has had the radicalism of youth and inexperience corrected by age and experience. He is cautious of accepting new things, but can be brought to believe them. He leans to traditional notions, but may be divorced from them after showing him the conduct of the correspondent Error. He will make no successes which will shake the world, but he will make few irremediable blunders. In trying conscientiously to reach decisions, he will often be plunged neck deep in a barrel of quandary. He will be a careful and successful but not a brilliant or notably rapid operator. He will probably be respected, learned, and prosperous.

A conservative man, when he looks through the spectacles of conservatism, will see common things with the greatest clearness and will come to know them with absolute certainty, but he will be unable to recognize the Good Fairy coming in the loathsome disguise of a Discovery.

Our most splendid triumphs, our worst mistakes, and our saddest failures come from the radical mind. It is a spring and not a reservoir. It is voice and not an echo. In the radical group are the original thinkers, the investigators, the discoverers, the combative spirits who "fight like raging devils for conciliation and hate each other for the love of God." The real radical believes a new statement because it is new, and doubts an old view because it is old. He glazes the way for lesser minds, but is always in danger of being lost in the jungle. His feet may be in the muck heap, but his head is among the stars of space. He is a dreamer of dreams. If he were to lose a leg, he would congratulate himself that he now had but one foot to keep warm. He habitually ignores the reasonably probable and revels in the doubtfully possible. His ideals are broad, expansive, on a great scale. He is ever seeking to make converts. He has an utter contempt for authority. He jumps to conclusions and may make the champion long distance leap from the frying pan into the fire. He has fierce controversies, devises operations, founds hypotheses, launches theories, discovers diseases, and dazzles all who know him by brilliant flights and amazing activities. As an operator he is brilliant, relying upon skill more than judgment, taking desperate chances, and skimming almost gaily within a hair's breadth of the deadliest catastrophes. He needs to have ever on duty by his side a peculiarly attentive guardian angel. He is never moderate, in fact, he scorns moderation. He is invariably convinced that he is always right. He will not brook contradiction and regards his opponents as instigated by the worst possible motives. His knife may cut for good or ill. He obtains wonderful successes and makes dreadful mistakes. He is often a copious and hasty writer, rather prone to recording things as certain long before they are proved. He loudly claims credit he thinks his due. He rides the Rosinante of a hobby as though it were a splendid charger. He often fails to reach his goal and, like a squirrel in a cage, rises only to fall.

The best type of the radical makes the real progress of humanity. Such a great man is a most attractive personality. He may die poor through adhering to some ideal. He may happen to become the fashion and get rich.

Unscrupulous and shallow impostors, who are good actors, are apt to pretend to be the best type of radical. Such a man never had a burning faith, never saw a vision, never had a dream which could not be turned into cash. He does not know a penny dip from a constellation of profundity, or a note on the golden trump of fame from a shriek on the penny whistle of notoriety. He tries to attract by cleverness and dexterity in order that he may become conspicuous and rich. He sends forth articles as bread upon the sea of medical journalism in hope that they will return to him as buttered toast. He flies toward notoriety as a bee to a buckwheat patch or a politician to a "divvy." He knows it all and consequently knows a lot of things which are not true. He appropriates the ideas of other persons and calmly puts them forth as his own, being as much at home in the stolen mansion as a hermit crab is in an appropriated cockle shell. He was born a lucifer match, but thinks he is an electric light. He can put a slender idea into more words than Newton used in his *Principia*, and even if he doesn't stretch the truth, he is likely seriously to twist it. His great hope is cash. If he attended a drowned man he would first of all go through the victim's pockets. He has the income of a taxicab driver or an evangelist. Next to cash (in the words of Doctor Holmes), his hope is to have an instrument, a method, or a disease named after him, in order that it may be fastened to him, and that the combination may go scuttling through the journals and books like a dog with a tin can tied to his tail.

Whether a surgeon is rich or poor, noted or obscure, conservative or radical, he has his trials and his triumphs. Many of his trials I have already alluded to. A man has few things harder to bear, until he has become well accustomed to it, than to be conscious of ability, integrity, and worth, and see the ignorant pretender, the fakir, the solemn ass, or the charlatan preferred in his stead. He may find comfort in the well-known story of John Abernethy (which I paraphrase). Abernethy, accosting a rich and famous quack, said: "Sir, you are no surgeon. You swindle the public. You deceive your patients. You are totally ignorant and utterly unscrupulous, and yet, you live in a palace, ride in a chariot, and actually smell of wealth. I, John Abernethy, surgeon of London, an operator, a student, an author, I, who strive to be an honest and conscientious man, must live in a humble abode, must walk my rounds, and only by the hardest work do I make a bare living. Why are these things?" The quack said: "Mr. Abernethy, yonder is London Bridge, how many people think you, cross it in a day?" and the surgeon answered, "I do not know, perhaps a hundred thousand." The quack responded, "And how many of them are fools? You, Mr. Abernethy, attend the wise men; I attend the fools."

One of the bitterest of bitter things is to find a truth and see our contemporaries neglect or repudiate it. This has often happened. In 1827 Mélier, a young intern in a Paris hospital, expressed the belief that inflammation in the right iliac fossa depended on disease of the appendix. He reported cases of undoubted appendicitis verified by autopsy. He described gangrene, perforation, concretions, and peritonitis. He sought to make it possible to diagnosticate inflammation of the appendix, and believed that if the diagnosis could be made, operation was demanded. The great Dupuytren arose and destroyed the young surgeon. For over half a century the profession followed Dupuytren, who was wrong, and rejected Mélier, who was right, and scores of thousands died when they might have been saved. Think of the feelings of the man who had the truth. What became of him I do not know. He was no more heard of in surgery. He probably went into obscurity, the victim of a broken heart.

The death of a patient after an operation is always hard to bear. It is particularly hard to bear if unexpected. Did any one of you ever have a patient die from an anesthetic? I did. It was horrible. Such an event will shake the strongest man. Sometimes a patient appeals to us so much that his death comes as a personal grief to the surgeon. A child often makes such an appeal to us.

I remember the venerable elder Gross. He operated for stone in the bladder upon a beautiful golden-haired boy. The next day he was walking along the hall of the hospital with bowed head and stern, set face. Someone went up to him and said, "Professor Gross, how is that pretty child you operated on yesterday?" Doctor Gross answered, almost fiercely, "that child is dying and I wish to God I'd never been a surgeon."

When death comes in spite of our best efforts, we are often dreadfully blamed and most unjustly criticized. A patient was shot in the abdomen. The bullet lacerated the spleen. I removed the spleen, but did not find the bullet. The patient died. A coroner's physician made such strictures upon my conduct in not finding the bullet that I had the narrowest escape from a law suit, yet I was absolutely right and the coroner's physician was an ignorant fool. It is very hard to bear. One cannot answer back. Yet even dignified reserve is often regarded as acknowledgment of our alleged mistakes. I have been criticized in some cases for which I deserved credit, but, conversely, I have also been praised when I did not deserve it, so perhaps it is as broad as it is long. Few things make me more unhappy than ingratitude—ingratitude of patients I have really served, ingratitude of assistants I have really helped. I have had my share from both sources. I do not wonder that poor, old, stricken Lear called ingratitude a "marble-hearted fiend," or that Milton spoke of it as "base" and "besotted."

But there are splendid compensations in surgery. Think of the mightly helpfulness of it—of how many it saves otherwise hopelessly lost—of how many it frees from loathsome disease, from racking torture, from cruel deformity. Think of its certainty, its quickness, its decisiveness, of the numerous sciences and infinite details all marshalled to aid us, and all put at our disposal.

It is a triumph to complete successfully a difficult and dangerous operation and know that we have done the best by the patient. It is a triumph to meet and master obstacles. It is a triumph and a splendid one to save a life by surgery. A man who has long practised surgery and practised it well has a right to feel that he has not lived in vain, but has done good to his fellowmen.

It is a proud moment when a surgeon faces some sudden peril or some unexpected difficulty and finds a way out of it that he knows will be of service to others—when he improves an operation—when he adds to the knowledge of diagnosis or treatment—when he contributes points to technic which make operating safer.

Years ago, when I first became Professor Keen's assistant (and never again shall I have so proud a title), I was immensely impressed with the usefulness of surgery. An old sea captain was suffering the agonies of hell from tic douloureux. Peripheral operations had been done in vain. As I gave him the ether he begged me over and over again, if Doctor Keen did not succeed in doing what he hoped, to kill him with ether. He said, "if you let me wake up to this awful pain I will first curse you and then kill myself." Doctor Keen removed the Gasserian ganglion and the man got well and lived for years tranquil, happy, and very grateful.

I once saw an important surgical principle evolved at the operation table. Doctor Keen was operating for chronic empyema. In those days we did not go farther than the removal of considerable pieces from several ribs. We found the lung shrunken up, and the parietal pleura nearly an inch thick. Doctor Keen said, "removal of pieces of rib won't cure this man. We must let his chest wall fall in. It can't fall in unless we practise extensive rib resection and remove that thickened pleura." He removed the ribs from the second to the ninth inclusive, removing them from their angles to their cartilages, removed the thickened parietal pleura, and let the soft parts drop in against the lung. The patient recovered, married his nurse, who gave birth to a child which was named after Doctor Keen. That operation was what we now call Schede's operation. Just as Doctor Keen was about to publish it, he saw in a journal the paper of Schede, of Hamburg, who first published his results about six months after Keen's operation. Keen had never heard of Schede's work and evolved the exact principle that Schede had done.

There is a keen delight, a luxury of feeling, a sense of triumph, on finding we have succeeded in an operation. I once saw in the Louvre a small picture which impressed me mightily. It represented King Charles X of France and Dupuytren in the hospital. The surgeon had just removed the bandage from a patient on whom he had operated for cataract. The patient's hands were raised up as in gratitude to God, as she cried out, "I see."

I have witnessed that very thing in the ophthalmological clinic. Whenever I see it, I feel a curious gripping at the throat and quiver of the heart. It has an unequalled dramatic intensity. Could anything be finer than to restore sight? I always envy the ophthalmologist that well-earned triumph and take off my hat to him in admiration.

Think of the triumph of Marion Sims when, for the first time in surgical history, a vesicovaginal fistula was cured—of Carrel when he succeeded in grafting viscera and anastomosing arteries—of Cushing when he saved a newborn victim of cerebral hemorrhage—of McDowell when he did ovariotomy—of Broca when he located the lesion of motor aphasia—of Walter Brashear when he successfully amputated at the hip joint—of Crile when he proved the value of, and showed the method of, transfusion—of Murphy when he succeeded in curing ankylosis—of Bigelow when he devised litholopaxy—of Kocher when he perfected the operation for goiter—of Matas when he performed endo-aneurysmorrhaphy—of Hunter when he tied the femoral artery for popliteal aneurysm instead of amputating through the thigh—of Jacobson when he restored trephining to its proper place in the treatment of trau-

matisms of the head—of Crawford, Long, and Morton when they
first used ether—of Simpson when he first used chloroform—of
Halsted when he had completed the methods of his operation for
malignant disease of the mammary gland—of Sir William Macewen
when he removed the first brain tumor ever operated upon. The
list of such triumphs might be indefinitely added to. The history
of surgery is strewn with them.

It is given to few to be Columbuses of great continents of
surgery—given to but few to discover such a principle as antisepsis as did Lord Lister—but all of us have at times our small
triumphs, all of us are workers in the cause and all of us add something to knowledge.

During my nearly thirty years of membership in the medical
profession many truths have crystallized in my mind, some as
apothegms, some as aphorisms, some as epigrams. I will cite a
few of them.

1. A trial at law, often a severe trial to the surgeon, is the
lawyer. Plato said he had seen in the courts "men keen and
shrewd, and skilled in the use of words, with dwarfed and
grovelling souls, deprived of mental enlargement, uprightness,
and independence."

Milton spoke of "men allured to the *trade* of law, who ground
their purposes, not on the prudent and heavenly contemplation of
justice and equity, but on the promising and pleasing thoughts of
litigious terms, fat contentions, and flowing fees."

I fancy you need no mental effort to catch my drift.

Lawyers sue us on the slightest provocation—put us under
subpoena even when we know nothing of the case on trial—cross
examine us with scorn and with a morbid interest in authorities
and in our private affairs, and combat us when we try to collect
a proper fee from a reluctant millionaire.

It is only just to say that lawyers collect accounts for us,
defend us when we are in trouble, and give us good advice if they
first receive retaining fees. Now and then a judge moderates the
extravagances of a bitter cross examination, but as a rule he pays
no attention to it and sits in dignified isolation from all mundane

cares, duties, and responsibilities. Every now and then I see a judge on the bench who reminds me of a fly in amber. I know he is there, but I can't imagine how he got there.

2. The lawyer's denunciations of medical experts are often just. They do disagree—in fact, sometimes they disagree like the supreme court. Many a one answers to Mark Twain's description of Fenimore Cooper "and deals freely in important omissions." Some present the naked truth, but many prefer to go no further than the truth décolleté. Every now and then an expert witness is found to possess one of those well-trained memories which is able to remember everything advantageous and nothing harmful to that side of the case. Some medical experts cheerfully swear to things they would not bet on.

3. It is the solemn and imperative duty of a surgeon to give to able and worthy young men a chance to become surgeons. He should train them—weed out the unfit—stimulate and encourage the fit—stand by them till they can go it alone. Next to a good name there is no heritage I would so much like to leave as a group of fine young surgeons to whom I had had the good fortune to open the doors of opportunity. Think of the benefit to humanity of such a heritage. Think of those men remembering the man who helped them with enduring affection. Could anything be finer? I venture to say that Professor Halsted is as proud of nothing in his distinguished career as of that splendid group of brilliant men he trained and started on the road to eminence.

A surgeon who deliberately fails to train young men is guilty of a crime against humanity. A hospital management which makes a surgeon fail in this duty is criminal.

4. In some hospitals there is a certain evil tendency. Now it slumbers—now it turns uneasily in sleep dreaming of power— now it wakes to harmful deeds. Now it fastens upon an institution as the Old Man of the Sea fastened upon the neck of Sinbad the Sailor. That evil tendency may be called "the system." All of you who have read of the murder of Rosenthal the gambler know what the system was in the New York police force. The system in a hospital is the same sort of thing to a less degree.

It means that certain medical men improperly and unjustly acquire supreme power and use that power for selfish interests and not for the public welfare. In an institution in which the system is in full sway, some of the staff get more than they deserve and most less than they need. Those who speak the truth are regarded with fear and aversion. Abuses accumulate. Ignorant neglect is tolerated in some, the best effort is censured in others. There is an outward appearance of the highest efficiency, when in reality the institution is a whited sepulchre. No man is appointed to the staff purely for fitness, but personal reasons sway the result. On one side we see the suffering poor, on the other the foul and loathsome rule of the system. Everything is passed to the man higher up. If I had my way, I'd strike that thrice accursed system dead.

5. I have noticed a tendency on the part of an occasional elderly and distinguished man to think that the rules of medical ethics were meant for young fellows just starting out, but not for him.

6. Sometimes a man tells the truth out of pure meanness.

7. A man who has a theory which he tries to fit to facts, is like a drunkard who tries his key haphazard in door after door, hoping to find one it fits.

8. The way of the medical transgressor who violates the obligations due his fellow practitioners is sometimes as hard as the way of the thoroughly decent and honorable man usually is. The good man knows that man wants but little here below, and that's what he usually gets.

9. Many a man who is brooding over alleged mighty discoveries reminds me of a hen sitting on billiard balls.

10. One of the never mentioned causes of all the proclamations about higher medical education is the secret conviction that there are too many doctors and too little money in circulation.

11. A fashionable surgeon, like a pelican, can be recognized by the size of his bill.

12. When a man finds his "idea" doesn't appeal to the tired and indifferent world, he is apt to speak to posterity. I heard a

4

man do this once and before he finished he almost had his audience there.

13. Diagnosis by intuition is a rapid method of reaching a wrong conclusion.

14. Some people get credit for using a big word instead of a shorter one, yet every now and then a synonym is used because we forget how to spell the word we want to use.

15. Now and then a very learned article or lecture, like the talk of the man mentioned in Wolfville, increases the sum total of human ignorance.

16. The Master of Trinity is correct; "none of us is infallible, not even the youngest of us."

17. Many young men, laboriously climbing the ladder of Fame, get knocked off by older men engaged in coming down. Sometimes a man who thinks he is on a treadmill is really on the ladder of Fame and *vice versa*.

18. Some who approach the summit don't stay there long. They can't stand the altitude.

19. A patient who says he must borrow the money to pay you, *will* borrow the money, but *won't* pay you. He will rob Peter to pay Paul and will cheat Paul.

20. It is not enough for a surgeon to have "go"; he must also have "stay."

21. Each one of us, however old, is still an undergraduate in the school of experience. When a man thinks he has graduated he becomes a public menace.

22. A surgeon is often and easily misunderstood. People always draw the worst possible inferences. What would certainly be said of a scientist who, in a moment of abstraction, tried to blow the froth off of a charlotte russe?

23. It is said that the good die young. I am not sure of this, but I am quite sure that only the young die good. If the good do not die young, they will grow up to be as lonely as a moralist on the police force.

24. Sometimes cowardice, sometimes laziness, sometimes selfishness saves a man from being called irritable, combative, and

cantankerous. What a man doesn't do is not always a sign of what he is and isn't. We must know why he doesn't do it in order to reach a conclusion.

25. A man who pays his surgeon many gleaming compliments, seldom pays him anything else.

26. The world is very small if we would avoid an enemy— huge if we would find a friend.

27. The public has an idea that a consultation is a meeting of accomplices.

28. A surgeon is worried about the past, anxious about the future, or up to his neck in present trouble. Often he suffers from the three inflictions at once and then feels as if he had taken a boil, rheumatism, and religion at the same time.

29. We waste much time blushing for the evil things done by our friends. In fact, the wisdom of some surgeons consists in knowing with certainty what other surgeons should or should not have done.

30. Appearances are deceptive. I knew a man who acquired a reputation for dignity because he had muscular rheumatism in the neck and back.

31. Sometimes when a doctor gets too lazy to work, he becomes a politician.

32. One man and one only should be in charge of a case. Other physicians may be assistants or consultants. Two men in charge is a surgical duet and like a musical duet is an arrangement by which each one may lay the blame on the other.

33. It won't help a young man much to be 100 years ahead of his time if he is a month behind in his rent.

34. It has been said that ignorance is bliss. If that be so the antivivisectionists must dwell in a veritable paradise.

35. Tact is a valuable attribute in gaining practice. It consists in telling a squint-eyed man that he has a fine, firm chin.

36. Patients can't understand surgical technicalities, but they want to be told them. When patients insist on learning in detail the reason why, one often feels like answering them as the negro preacher answered a number of neophytes awaiting baptism:

"Now, my breddern, you all want to know what's de reason dat immursion is de only mode of baptism. Well now, my breddern, bless de Lord, taint none o' yoah damned business."

37. The longer a person practises surgery, the more shy he becomes of venturing predictions and the more he respects Lowell's advice—"don't prophesy unless you know." Great ingenuity is often employed in avoiding the explicit. A patient approached a dear old chief of mine and insisted on specific statements as to the future of his sick son. The grizzled old professor said: "If your son gets well he will get about again. If he does not, he will not. If the balance of events shall remain equal, then he will remain in a state of status quo." I take it there has been no opinion equal to this since the immortal opinion of Jack Bunsby of the Cautious Clara. Strange to say, the man was entirely satisfied. He had seen the professor and had obtained his information from the highest source.

38. There is a splendid chance to do good in surgery, especially if you don't care who gets the credit.

39. It may rain upon the just as well as upon the unjust, but when it does the unjust usually have the umbrellas of the just.

40. To write an article of any sort is, to some extent, to reveal ourselves. Hence, even a medical article is, in a sense, something of an autobiography.

41. When I read some statistics I wish it was the law that statistics could be written only in the shade of the Peepul tree. You know it is the tradition in India that in the shade of that tree only truth can be told. To tell a lie kills the liar.

42. There are fashions in surgery just as there are in morals, millinery, religion, and war boats. They are just as transitory and often just as bizarre.

43. To tell a surgeon he reminds you of another surgeon is apt to offend two people. No genuinely able man ever consciously imitated anybody. Every real man is an individual and has his own personality.

44. There are two ways to injure the repute of surgery. One way is to slander it. Another and worse way is to exploit it purely for profit.

45. What we call experience is often a dreadful list of ghastly mistakes.

46. A genius for personal detraction is not a desirable attribute in a surgical brother.

47. Many patients are as oblivious to all sense of gratitude as a stone stag to a vote of condolence.

48. As one mounts in years he is apt to specialize less and less upon the purely ideal.

49. Some men don't try to leave footprints on the sands of time nearly as hard as they try to cover up their tracks and to avoid leaving finger prints in the central station.

50. The first patient I ever had stole my only umbrella. In those days patients regarded the "9 to 1" on my sign as a notice of the odds against them.

51. The spirit of the times is a cruel tyrant. One may fail to conform to it because of ignorance or laziness. Only the brave, honest, unselfish man dares knowingly to defy it.

52. In surgical operations some people do not know enough to be afraid. The position is like that of the little girl who went up in the flying machine and was not afraid.

53. The less a man knows about the cause of the disease and the exact condition of affairs, the more apt he is to tell the family all about it. Once the mother of a patient of Sir William Gull's said, "you do not tell me anything definite, are there any doctors who will?" and Sir William Gull answered, "yes, there are lots of them who are ignorant enough to tell you all about it."

54. Many times, when operating, the highest wisdom is to stop. The same rule ought to apply to a surgeon's address and I shall therefore proceed to amputate my remarks.

We are all brothers, marching shoulder to shoulder in the army of healing. We have the same banner, the same bugle calls, the same hopes and aspirations. We follow, as the pillar of smoke by day and the pillar of fire by night, two objects—the mitigation of human suffering and the prolongation of human life.

A like spirit is in all true surgeons. It was with Paré when he invented the ligature. It was with Larrey when he civilized warfare. It was in the lion heart of Abernethy. It filled the lordly soul of Hunter. It guided the scalpel of Agnew. It illumined the splendid intellect of Gross. The spirit which instigates, dominates, inspires, ay, and sanctifies—the magnificent science of modern surgery.

In the preceding remarks I have spoken much of the weakness and frailty of the strength and virtue of men. I have scoffed and gibed. I have praised and blamed. Yet what am I that I should judge?

> "In men whom men condemn as ill,
> I find so much of goodness still,
> In men whom men pronounce divine,
> I find so much of sin and blot,
> I do not dare to draw a line
> Between the two, where God has not."

ADDRESS ON THE OCCASION OF THE GRADUATION EXERCISES AT THE NAVAL MEDICAL SCHOOL IN WASHINGTON ON MARCH 30, 1907*

I ESTEEM it a great privilege to address this class. You are graduates in medicine, and something more; you are specialists in a branch of work that absolutely requires special knowledge; you are members of a corps that can never be diluted and defiled by the introduction of numbers of the unfit and ignorant; you are members of the great medical profession; and you patriotically serve your country as officers in her navy.

Medical men are, and ought to be, patriotic. Five physicians signed the Declaration of Independence, viz., Lyman Hall, of Georgia; Oliver Wolcott, of Connecticut; Joshua Bartlett and Matthew Thornton, of New Hampshire, and Benjamin Rush, of Pennsylvania. The first sacrificial blood of the revolution flowed from the veins of Dr. Joseph Warren, on the slope of Bunker Hill; and numbers of our profession have sunk to final rest on all the battlefields of the republic. It seems to me a glorious thing to serve in the navy of the United States. The navy commands the admiration, the affection, the gratitude of the people. Its record is lustrous with achievement, and the traditions of the service speak in a thousand voices to the noblest instincts of the human mind.

I once had the aspiration, the hope, the dream to be a naval surgeon. Fate willed otherwise; but ever since there has been an unsatisfied something in my nature, which makes me dream of

> "Sailor songs to sailor tunes,
>   Storm and adventure, heat and cold,
>   Schooners and islands and maroons,
>   And buccaneers and buried gold."

* Reprinted from the Army and Navy Register, April 20, 1907.

It is pleasant, in this sordid age, to see a group of professional gentlemen seeking to serve their country, entering an honorable career, a career which insures a competence, but never wealth; and, putting aside the chance for riches, to which the hearts of most men turn.

I speak of this sordid age. The real character of the age is a matter for grave dispute. Most cover it with praise; call it the glorious age, the age of education, of philanthropy, of progress. But there are discordant voices. Some call it the hypocritical age. The great Carlyle refers to "the mean, barren, baleful nineteenth century." Hear Elizabeth Barrett Browning:

"We burst in acclamations of self-praising, self-admiring;
　At every mile run faster (oh, the glorious, glorious age!);
Not asking if we work our souls as worthily as our iron,
　Or if angels will reward us at the goal of pilgrimage.

"What means this ceaseless entrance into Nature's vast resources;
　But the child's most gradual efforts to walk upright without bane,
As we lead out from our clouds of steam majestical black horses,
　　we greater than those first men who led white ones by the mane?

"If we trod the depths of ocean, if we struck the stars in rising,
　If we wrapped the globe intensely in one hot electric breath,
'Twere but power within our tether, no new spirit-power comprising;
　And in life we were not greater men, nor bolder men in death."

Often in the world's history the essential hopes and fears, the genuine joys and griefs, the real aspirations and characteristics of an age have been embodied not in the volumes of the historian, not in the essays of the philosopher, not in the tomes of the chronicler, not in the tables of the statistician, but in the song of a master poet; but no Homer or Dante, no Shakespeare or Milton has sung the real song of the present age; and no one will sing it, unless Kipling's old Fleet Engineer obtains his wish, and God sends "a man like Robbie Burns to sing the song of steam." The real song of our time does not ring in martial ardor, as the broadsword strikes upon the shield; it does not flow in liquid numbers from the lute of Arcadian simplicity; it does not burst in intoxicating harmony from the harp of lascivious passion; but it emanates from the sounding loom and the rattling spindle, the roaring blast and the churning propeller, the clanging anvil and the screaming shell; and the whistle of the locomotive is the proclamation of our civilization.

The last one hundred years constituted a century of science, of invention, of mechanical advance, of enormous increase in wealth-producing power. Tens of thousands of marvelous inventions have economized time, abridged distance, increased production, facilitated exchange, stilled pain, and subdivided labor. The railroad, the telegraph, the telephone, the phonograph, the ocean cable, the electric light, photography, the cylinder printing press, the breech-loading repeating rifle, the steamboat, the battleship, wireless telegraphy, the submarine boat, the x-ray, the board of brokers, lucifer matches, illuminating gas, petroleum, the gigantic trust, the laws of the correlation of forces and the conservation of energy, the doctrine of evolution, the science of embryology, physiology and her daughter pathology, bacteriology, scientific chemistry—which can conjure flame from the wave and water from the flame—geology—which shows the footprints of the Creator—spectrum analysis, hypodermatic medication, antiseptic surgery, the divine gift of anesthesia—these are a few of the great achievements of this wonderful age. We see, resulting from the foregoing discoveries and inventions, modifications, changes, or complete alterations in business methods, financial ideas, political beliefs, scientific tendencies, religious tenets, moral views, modes of thought, tastes, habits, customs, and amusements. Some of these inventions—for instance, the one that enables us to take the imprisoned sun's heat and force it to draw our chariots, and the one that permits us to harness the lightning and make it illuminate our streets—have destroyed ancient callings and given rise to new vocations.

It might be thought that all this material progress is absolutely synonymous with genuine mental and moral advance, and the conclusion that we must all be gentler, happier, and more humane than our forefathers be drawn; but, unfortunately, this is not the

case. The present age has some startling faults, and many
tendencies portentous of evil and pregnant with disaster. We
have more homes than had our ancestors, but also more prisons;
more libraries, but also more almshouses; more philanthropists,
but more lawyers; more school children, but more tramps; and
when we estimate the losses and the gains, the sorrows and the
pleasures, the griefs and the joys of one hundred silent years we
are inclined to cry with the poet:

> "Are God and Nature then at strife,
> That Nature lends such evil dreams?
> So careful of the type she seems,
> So careless of the single life!"

One hundred years ago Baron Boyer, the celebrated French
surgeon, wrote a treatise that was supposed to embody, and did
embody, all that was known of surgery at that time; and in that
treatise he makes the statement that any notable progress in the
art and science of medicine is impossible. This prediction justifies
Lowell's assertion that one should not prophesy unless one knows.

What has been added to medicine in the hundred years that
have elapsed since Boyer's prediction was written? The achromatic microscope; auscultation; hypodermatic medication; modern
chemistry; the erection of physiology into a separate science by
the genius of Magendie and of Müller; the foundation of histology
by Bichat; the ophthalmoscope; the laryngoscope; the endoscope;
the cystoscope; the x-rays; radium; electric illumination as a diagnostic aid or an operative adjunct; the therapeutical use of electricity; the clinical thermometer; the stethoscope; physiologic
therapeutics in place of the old-fashioned bald empiricism; the discoveries by Pasteur, which make him the Columbus of the great
continent of bacteriology, and the wonderful application of these
principles by Lord Lister, who promulgated the system of surgical
cleanliness that we now know as aseptic surgery; the discovery of
the anesthetic uses of ether by Jackson and Morton, and of chloroform by Sir James Y. Simpson; local anesthetics; antitoxins and
opsonins; the study of the blood and of the urine; cerebral localiza-

tion; the sciences of ophthalmology, neurology, laryngology, and dermatology; the infectiousness of puerperal fever; scores of diseases; the abandonment of copious blood-letting and violet purgation; the humane and proper treatment of the insane; numbers of new drugs; elegant pharmaceutical preparations; the injection of saline fluid into the veins; the subcutaneous tissues, or the rectum; the remarkable products of coal tar; the cold bath treatment of fevers; the surgery of the brain, chest, and abdomen; intubation; Bigelow's operation for the crushing of vesical stone; the catgut ligature; the hemostatic forceps; and scientific and humane military and naval surgery.

When Boyer wrote his treatise the grim specter of sepsis was ever present where there were wounded men or men that had been subjected to surgical operations; and the world was to wait until 1869 for the publication of Lister's article on *The Prevention of Sepsis in Compound Fractures*. In Boyer's day almost every wound suppurated; erysipelas, tetanus, hospital gangrene, and pyemia were very common; the mortality of compound fractures 70 to 80 per cent; cancer was practically never cured; the Esmarch apparatus and the hemostatic forceps were not employed; and it was not unusual for patients to die of pain or to bleed to death during operation. In fact, the surgeon's operating room was a dripping shambles, echoing with the shrieks of the dying.

And then we would note that the nurse of the earlier days was usually ignorant, often dirty, and frequently drunk; while the trained nurse of the present day is the right hand of the surgeon. The surgery of Boyer's day consisted chiefly in extirpating tumors, closing wounds, amputating limbs, removing dead bone and bullets, correcting deformities, cutting for stone, trephining the skull, and performing tracheotomy. Much of the horror of surgery has passed away. An anesthetic is administered, and the patient passes through the dreadful drama of the operation without knowledge and without pain. The surgeon, it has been said, is clothed in purity, as the lady in Comus was arrayed in chastity; and he unhesitatingly opens the abdomen or the skull and operates upon any organ that may demand it. Sepsis has been practically banished, erysipelas is very rare, and hospital gangrene is never even heard of. The mortality in compound fractures is extremely small; an amputation stump heals in a week; the patient suffers very little pain after the operation; and a pauper in the almshouse is now better cared for and more comfortable during and after a surgical operation than was a king one hundred years ago.

It has been said that the chief glory of the age is its scientific spirit. That is its chief glory, but it was the work of a very few. The cultivation of pure science is not nearly so popular as practical and applied science, and chemical technology claims far more devotees than does entomology or the higher mathematics. The chief characteristic of the age is mechanical invention, made not for glory, not for pure science, but for solid cash. Many of the brightest minds of the race are now not devoting themselves to writing literature, to painting pictures, to chiseling statues, or to composing operas; they are founding companies, projecting schemes, devising machines, promoting plans, building railroads, and setting up jobs. Some of these men are doing many acts that in a former age would have been regarded as disgraceful in the extreme, but are now often looked upon as evidences of creditable shrewdness or of praiseworthy finesse. The man that looks upon the dollar-mark as the flowing curve of beauty, and whose modes of thought are as purely mechanical as are his machines, has a narrow mind and a contracted view. He may be an honest man in many things, a kindly man, a good husband, an indulgent parent, a faithful officer; but you can no more get the highest out of him than you can extract a beefsteak from a nightmare. The highest is not in him, and it will not come out. On a final analysis, he really loves but money; and this, after all, is only what Judas sold his Master for.

In this age men tend to become machines, whether they wish it or not—machines whose valves are smoothed with hearts' blood. A great peril of the present day springs from this tendency, and that peril is the decay of individualism. By the term "individualism" I do not mean crankiness or fanaticism, but I mean the possession of self-reliance, and of the power and the courage to think and speak for one's self. Individualism requires tremendous energy; no lazy man can possess it. It is much easier to accept blindly other persons' thoughts, use other persons' words, and follow other persons' teachings than it is to seek the truth; it is easier to embrace a theory than to hunt a fact. Most men do not really think at all; they only think they think, and their ideas are as barnacles clinging to a vessel's keel. Such persons love proverbs, dogmas, and formulas; they bow abjectly to catchy phrases; and they accept such phrases, instead of thoughts, opinions, reasons, and facts. It is easier to use such phrases than it is to think, and the world is ruled by the formulas of shallow men.

The medical profession often suffers from this tendency. It listens to what old Dryden called "the mutterings of robustious nonsense"; and these mutterings creep into authoritative teaching. It is a peculiar spectacle to watch a man echoing out this intellectual garbage; thus exhibiting, according to Hanfield Jones, the imitative faculty, which is an evidence of his simian ancestry. The person that delivers such a formula is always cocksure, positive, and peremptory. Everyone that differs with him is in error, is a fool, or is one of the wicked. As one of the unregenerate, that do not bow in reverence before formulas, I would quote Mercier, who says: "To be treated as a rogue, an assassin, an imposter does not mean anything; it merely signifies a difference of opinion."

We should be particularly careful, in these modern days, in accepting surgery by dogma or surgery by aphorism. Such phrases are easily learned. They are remembered more readily than is a logically reasoned exposition; but, in picking them up, you clutch for a star and often gather up a jellyfish, you reach for a comet and fall into a hole, and "you often mistake"—as Victor Hugo has said—"for the constellations of profundity the stars that ducks' feet make in the soft mud of the pond." These hard formulas in medical science often lead to the most disastrous results; in fact, hard formulas from selfish principles in any field lead to wrongs innumerable.

A notable characteristic of this age is the persistent attempt of so many to do something new and something big, instead of trying to do something great or pure or noble or useful. Those who would constantly do something new are like Cleopatra, and would rule the world by change; they would give implicit faith to every new theory from the laboratory, and to every new suggestion from a scientific dream-book. As the result of the love for large things we have great hotels, enormous ships, gigantic bridges, tremendous schemes, large fortunes, big scoundrels, and monumental fools. We often seem to mistake size for quality and extent for virtue; but long ago Sir Joshua Reynolds said: "The man who paints with a big brush is not of necessity a great painter." The foundation of this love of bigness is ostentation, egotism, and empty vanity; and it is linked with hurry, incompleteness, superficiality and weakness, and, in consequence, with hypocrisy, deception, fraud, and adulteration. Big things are sometimes attempted in science in order to deceive and impress the ignorant and appeal to the galleries. I am sorry to say that all medical teaching is not absolutely free from the loathsome leprosy of sordid thought. At the present day, in medical education, the world is trying to put a quart of material into a pint pot; and the consequence is that most of it turns to froth and runs over. We are pretending to do what cannot be done—that is, to make men specialists in every branch—but we are forced to do this by the exigencies of the times, and it is to be hoped that we are only in a transitional stage and have not reached a final conclusion.

All of us, in all countries, give a great deal of attention to laboratory methods of supposed precision, and very little to absolute bedside acquaintance with disease; and yet the great physician of a thousand years ago was one that possessed, in a high degree, the power of observation and good common sense, the capacity to analyze, the learning to compare. The great physician of today must have identical qualities. The great physician of a thousand years from now will be the same sort of man. I take off my hat in respect and admiration to the

microscopist. His labors have been fruitful of invaluable information, and have opened up a new world—that of the infinitely
little; and the first few words of truth have, as yet, but scarce
been lisped by the baby lips of science. But the microscope is
not infallible; it is not a supreme court; it is not to abolish clinical
study. It is to be an aid, an assistant, an adjunct, a collaborator,
if you will; but not, as we are rapidly making it, a tyrant and
a despot. We have come to lean upon it as a staff; we accept its
formulas as so many revealed truths. We thus shift the responsibility and avoid thinking, to the great detriment of practical bedside diagnosis. We are trying to drive the microscopist into doing
our work—that is, into making the diagnosis for us. We must
know disease, not merely specimens in a bottle; symptoms, not
merely charts; signs, not merely pictures; and, as has been said,
we must always remember that it is not only disease with which
we are dealing but also diseased individuals. In fact, men should
be trained to observe, to think, and to practice; not merely to
answer questions. As the great Trousseau said: "In my younger
days we tried to fit men for life; now, we merely try to fit them
for examinations."

The tendency to petrifaction into formula, to reliance upon
others, to abandonment of individual thought and personal aspiration puts aside some of the strength of life and lays a sadden-
ing hand upon humanity. It destroys the true appreciation of
beauty; it impairs moral excellence; it leads to adulteration of
science and adulteration of character; it puts the ideal out of
man's nature—and I would not put aside the ideal. Every real
advance since man came upon the earth was first a dream in the
mind of a single individual. The greatest men of all time—the
leaders, the conquerors, the explorers, the navigators, the scientists, the authors, the poets, the novelists, the inventors—have
been dreamers at heart. They have conjured up the pathway in
their visions. The real progress of humanity has come from the
enthusiast, and he is the dreamer of dreams. This spirit instigated those who traversed the sullen ocean, tracked the dusky
canon, bled the veins of the mountains, plowed the polar sea,

penetrated the trackless forest, and crossed the arid desert. It inspired the man that first struck fire from flint-stone, gave the car its wheel, invented the alphabet, devised the calculus, introduced vaccination. It inspired the noblest productions of human genius; the eloquence of Demosthenes, the patriotism of Washington, the comprehension of Gladstone, the masterly genius of Napoleon, the humanity of Lincoln, the majesty of Homer, the persistence of Columbus, the wisdom of Franklin, the learning of Bacon, the incomparable superiority of Shakespeare, and the splendid force of the President of the United States. It carved the Venus of Milo and painted the Sistine Madonna. It wrote the aphorisms, described the circulation, invented the ligature, discovered anesthesia, and laid a healing hand upon the wounds of mankind by means of antiseptic surgery.

A notable characteristic of the present day is the great number of persons that devote themselves entirely to attending to other persons' business. Such persons have a positive genius for criticism. They see the defect, and never the beauty; they observe the ill, and never the good; they discover flaws in the diamond, and call attention to spots on the sun. It is a sad fact that bowlegs excite more comment than pure conduct, and a red nose than a blameless life. The species contains many varieties. There are long-haired men and short-haired women; anti-vaccinationists, who, like Mr. Bettridge in the Moonstone, are "constitutionally superior to reason, and thank God for it"; anti-vivisectionists, who are self-constituted oracles of the Creator; ultra-temperance advocates, who would forbid the use of alcohol in the treatment of disease—persons who forget that drunkenness cannot be stopped unless the cause is removed, for no law can be passed that will prevent thirst. There are the diet cranks, who prove by statistics that everything is harmful. It has been pointed out that bread, rice, and potatoes cause diabetes; that beef is responsible for tapeworm, and pork for trichinosis; that strawberries produce nettle rash; that cucumbers and watermelons induce colic; that grapesr dates, figs, raspberries, and soft-shelled crabs are responsible fo, appendicitis; that the use of pie and cheese is followed by dyspepsia; of ice cream, by tyrotoxicon poisoning; of pickles, by copper poisoning; of canned goods, by lead and ptomaine poisoning; of lettuce, by poisoning with opiates; of milk, by tuberculosis; of beer, by Bright's disease; of alcoholic liquors, by liver diseases, and of water, by lead poisoning and typhoid fever. In fact, things have come to such a pass that a human being, to be safe and virtuous, will be obliged to live in what has been called a pious vacuum.

To go on with the classification, we have the professional Irishman, fierce, uncontrolled and defiant, a collector of dimes and dollars, an individual that sails for a divvy as a hungry dog loose in a meat shop does for a joint. There is the professional patriot, who justifies Doctor Johnson's definition of patriotism as "the last refuge of a scoundrel"; there is the professional philanthropist, who puts forth, from time to time, what Carlyle loves to refer to as the "bray of Exeter Hall." Prominent in this procession of pernicious cranks we see the Pharisee, the religious hypocrite, the scandalmonger, and the assassin of character. In medicine at one end of the scale are the systematized delusions of medical systems; at the other, the criminal obsessions and slobbering imbecility of Christian Science, beliefs that show we are as credulous as our ancestors. The whole combination is a witches' sabbath of paretic hopes. When we contemplate this heterogeneous collection and listen to the various opinions that are shrieked forth, we realize that Lord Houghton spoke the truth when he said that everything really pleasant in life is unwholesome, expensive or wicked.

The Christian Scientist is a production so remarkable that he is entitled to rather special consideration. I once had a personal experience with one. Some years ago, in association with a colleague, I had a quiz-room in the same building with a Christian Scientist. One night he remained in his office until the building was locked up. Finding himself unable to get out, he called to a policeman to go around to my house for the key. I accompanied the police officer, and viewed the Christian Scientist through the bars. I told him that, in my opinion, he had a great opportunity

5

to demonstrate his theory and make a convert; that, according to his point of view, if a sick man were to make up his mind that he did not have a disease, why, he did not have it; and that, therefore, all that was necessary for the prisoner to do was to make up his mind that he was not there, and he was not. I also said that if he remained there, after making up his mind, he did so either because he wanted to stay there or because he was a scoundrel; and that in either case I felt that it would be improper for me to liberate him. My well-meant advice was received with fierce denunciation, and I left him in the care of the policeman, who subsequently brought the prisoner down on a ladder.

Sometimes a Christian Scientist is wise in his own generation; he has what might be called clinical judgment. For instance, a patient of a former distinguished professor of therapeutics in Jefferson College went to one of these individuals. The Christian Scientist asked what brought her there, and the patient said that Doctor Bartholow had told her that she was suffering from organic disease of the heart. Then the Christian Scientist, after profound cogitation, refused to undertake the case, justifying his conduct by the statement that it was his experience that the Lord very rarely interfered in the progress of organic heart disease. We can, therefore, draw the inference that the difference between a scoundrel and a Christian Scientist is certainly no greater than that between an alias and an incognito.

An interesting phenomenon that has become very noticeable in our age is the "new woman." She is an individual who repudiates anatomy, scorns physiologic necessities, derides history, and purposes forthwith to eject man from his calling and to rule the world. She is the modern representative of an antediluvian reptile known as the pterodactyl, which was part fish and part bird. It was a poor sort of fish, and had wings with which it could not fly. The new woman seems to be part man and part woman, possessed of the weaknesses of both and the strength of neither. Man's life has been defined as a duel with his enemies; the life of the new woman is a duel with her friends. Russell tells us that. The late Lord Coleridge was an advocate of woman's rights, and he maintained that there is no real difference between the masculine and the feminine intellect. He asserted that some of the best qualities of judicial genius, *i. e.*, quickness of apprehension, delicacy, and sensibility, are essential feminine characteristics. Sergeant Dowse made an interesting comment upon Lord Coleridge's assertion. It was as follows: "The argument of the honorable and learned member, compendiously stated, amounts to this: because some judges are old women, therefore all old women are fit to be judges." The new woman is not a pleasing production. Can we imagine a man dying for the defense of a restaurant or for the salvation of a person in steel spectacles and bloomers?

But enough of these glances through the long annals of human folly; enough of these sketches of mental aberration. You follow the most useful of callings, the most interesting of occupations, always full of new and striking problems; one of the best of callings, because its only aim is to benefit man. Medicine is the most ancient of professions; it is older than Christianity and more ancient than the civil law. As Sir Thomas Watson said, it has its own system of rewards and punishments, its own dignities, and its own glories. It is a profession that has a mighty broadening influence upon the human mind, and is characterized by the most splendid charity. It is an acquiescence in the best tendencies and a protest against the worst tendencies of the age. It constructs no trust; it founds no monopoly; it excludes no qualified competitor; it retains for its own profit no valuable discovery; and it has no real standing room for the crank, the scoundrel, or the advertiser. Its best work is not done in the bright light that beats upon a throne; not in the arena of politics, stimulated by the cheers of thousands; not in the cloister, sustained by the hope of eternal joy; but in the wind-swept country and the back alley of the reeking town, in the sick-bay of the warship, on the desolate field of battle, with naught but pestilence and misery and death and God to see. It furnishes a curiously checkered life—a life in which storm clouds alternate with sunbeams, but one in which even the darkened pathway is spanned by the rainbow. It stands closer than any other calling to the secret of eternity, and watches Death, ever busy with her shuttle, as she weaves her somber thread into all the warp and woof of the affairs of men. It seeks to mitigate human suffering and to prolong human life. These have ever been its watchwords, are still, and always will be; its pillar of smoke by day and its pillar of fire by night. One should enter it with properly exalted ideas; with a belief in its greatness, its dignity, its stability, its real importance, its essential strength. You should resolve at the very start to learn to observe, to think, to compare, to analyze, to study, to avoid formulas, to cast out sordid thought, to repudiate shallowness, advertising, and vain pretensions; to be originals, and not simulacra; to be honest, gallant, patriotic gentlemen, worthy to be priests of Aesculapius, and to be officers of the Navy of the United States.

DICKENS'S DOCTORS*

CHARLES DICKENS was incomparably the master. His most notable strength was in the marvellous exactitude of his powers of observation. He saw a hundred things where ordinary mortals would see but one. Pathos was his forte; humor, an integral part of his nature. The writings of no other man impress us so much with the close and vital relationship between humor and pathos. He was fond of oddity and revelled in the whimsical. He loved bravery, honesty, simplicity and generosity, and always gave them praise. He detested falsehood, pomposity, meanness, presumption, and pretence, and abhorred all quacks and impostors with the hearty hatred of a vigorous, truthful, and clear-headed man. He never hesitated to attack wrong with splendid power, even though it sat upon a throne, and even though that throne were twined with the ivy of precedent and green with the moss of tradition. He was always examining, exposing, analyzing, dissecting, and cauterizing; and no one who merited it was too high or too powerful to escape exposure or castigation.

Dickens has given us numerous pictures of lawyers, and he seems to have known the legal profession thoroughly, from its highest, the Lord Chancellor and Mr. Tulkinghorn, to its lowest, Dodson, Fogg, Brass, and Pell. We remember Uriah Heep, Spenlow, Jorkins, Stryver, and Vholes. We are obliged to acknowledge, too, that the majority of his pictures are the reverse of complimentary, although he names some decent ones, among whom are Jaggers, Lightwood, Perker, Wrayburn, Wickfield, Traddles, Sergeant Buzfuz, and Sergeant Snubbin.

For honest, virtuous clergymen he had nothing but regard; but he often paid his compliments to ranting and hypocritical preachers. He drew as types—which, we regret to say, are not

* A paper read before the Philobiblon Club, Philadelphia, May 28, 1903.
Copyright, 1905, by The Philobiblon Club.

uncommon in this country—Mr. Chadband, Melchisedech Howler, and Mr. Stiggins. Among the good ones we recall Septimus Crisparkle and Frank Milvey.

It has occurred to me that it would not be uninteresting to learn his views about doctors, and discover what types of medical men he has drawn in his stories. In that early contribution known as the *Report of the Mudfog Association* we have set before us some physicians whose words and whose views are depicted in a spirit of the broadest caricature. The Mudfog Association was a meeting of scientists, assembled to discuss notable advancements and achievements, and the book is really a species of parody upon the proceedings of the British Association for the Advancement of Science, which had then been but recently organized. For instance, at this meeting Doctor Kutankumagen, a distinguished practitioner from Moscow, reports a case of extraordinary interest. He had taken a perfectly well man and subjected him for a definite period to the recognized treatment of blood-letting and purgation; and he reports to the society the interesting fact that, by persistence in these beneficial measures, he has succeeded in making his patient now able to walk about with the slight assistance of a crutch and a boy. He now eats little, drinks little, sleeps little, and never laughs.

Before this same association Mr. Knight Bell reports the very remarkable case of an individual who had swallowed a door-key. When the postmortem examination was made, an unscrupulous student took a cast of the mold in the stomach wall made by the retention of the key; he then had a door-key made from this cast, and by means of it succeeded in entering a house and committing a most extraordinary robbery.

Another gentleman reports to this association a peculiar case of monomania; and still another presents some interesting experiments upon a dog by means of prussic acid. The dog objects, and the experimenter laments "that the interests of science should " be sacrificed to the prejudices of a brute creature." There is no character of a physician drawn in the article. With broad humor Dickens satirizes some of the profound convictions of the

time—for instance, blood-letting and purgation. The papers
show Dickens's abhorrence of the practice of vivisection, and his
appreciation of the owllike solemnity with which our learned
bodies sometimes debate perfectly obvious propositions. He
likewise laughs at homoeopathy, by presenting Professor Muff
who sobers up on one-twenty-fifth of a teaspoonful of soda water,
and who advocates a diet for paupers of one-twentieth part of a
grain of bread and cheese. The Mudfog papers are rarely bound
up in Dickens's works today. They are well worth reading.
They will be found in the "Gadshill Edition." They were originally published in "Bentley's Miscellany" for 1837–38.

In *The Uncommercial Traveller* we find an article known as
The Great Tasmania's Cargo. The cargo consisted of men starved
to the last extremity because of the ignorance, the red-tape, and
the incapacity of the officials in charge of the transports. In
this article Dickens pays a tribute to the intelligence of the medical officers of Liverpool, who had the courage to denounce the
official, Pangloss.

In *The Uncommercial Traveller*, in the chapter headed *A Small
Star in the East*, Dickens showed that he had an appreciation of
the good that the profession does; and we may read with pleasure
his praise of the children's doctor, who realized to him the memory
of the children's doctor that he had seen years before on the
Paris stage.

Again, we find the picture of a doctor in another chapter
entitled *Some Recollections of Mortality*. This doctor testifies at a
coroner's inquest. The author describes him as follows: "He
" was a timid, muddle-headed doctor, and got confused and con-
" tradictory, and wouldn't say this, and couldn't answer for that."
I fancy few of us have attended trials in courts of justice and
listened to medical men testifying without seeing a medical witness that answers pretty accurately to this description.

In the above story Dickens pays a fine tribute to a surgeon,
Mr. Wakley, the coroner. He was patient and humane; and the
author says that he felt grateful to him then, and does now to
his memory.

Many of us remember when the Uncommercial Traveller returned to Dullborough Town, in which community he had passed his childhood days, although he had not visited it since reaching manhood. Dullborough is meant as the type of an ordinary country town, and Dickens says: "Most of us come from "Dullborough who come from a country town." The Traveller saw nobody he knew but a green-grocer until he "was suddenly "brought up by the sight of a man who got out of a little phaeton "at the doctor's door, and went into the doctor's house." He at once recognized the man as his boyhood's playfellow, Joe Specks, the individual who had once studied Roderick Random with him. The Uncommercial Traveller passed into a room which was half surgery and half study, and found it "bestrewn with testimonials "to Joe. Portrait of Mr. Specks, bust of Mr. Specks, silver cup "from grateful patient to Mr. Specks, presentation sermon from "local clergyman, dedication poem from local poet, dinner-card "from local nobleman, tract on balance of power from local "refugee." Mr. Specks entered, but did not recognize his visitor. The Traveller smiled and said he was not a patient, but Mr. Specks "seemed rather at a loss to perceive any reason for smiling "in connection with that fact." The Traveller is finally recognized, is introduced to the doctor's wife, dines with the family, takes part in a conversation about things in general, and leaves. Nor could he "discover one single flaw in the good doctor" . . . "except that he had forgotten his Roderick Random." The Uncommercial Traveller went to the railway station to catch his train. Specks had intended to go with him, but was called away inopportunely. There is nothing characteristic in the above except the appreciation of the local status of the country doctor, the rarity with which he sees any one but patients, the fact that he educates his son highly as a barrister-at-law, the dulling of the imaginative faculties of boyhood by the exigencies of life, and his liability to be called out at any and all times.

In *Bleak House* we find several members of the medical profession; for instance, Harold Skimpole, the child who had no knowledge of money, "had been educated for the medical pro-

" fession, and had once lived, in his professional capacity, in the
" household of a German prince." But as he was "a mere child
" in point of weights and measures, and had never known any-
" thing about them (except that they disgusted him), he had never
" been able to prescribe with the requisite accuracy of detail."
When he was summoned "to bleed the prince, or physic any of
" his people, he was generally found lying on his back, in bed,
" reading the newspapers, or making fancy sketches in pencil,
" and couldn't come." Skimpole's two chief characteristics, as
set forth by himself, were that he had no idea of money and no
idea of time. A man can practice medicine with benefit to the
community, although he may have no idea of money; but it is
needless to say that he cannot do so with benefit to himself.
A man who has no idea of time is usually foreordained to failure
in the medical profession. The elder Gross, one of the world's
greatest surgeons, insisted on a punctilious observance of all
appointments, was forgiving to many things, but not to avoidable
lateness, and was accustomed to quote on such occasions, "punc-
" tuality is the politeness of kings."

It will be remembered by the readers of *Bleak House* that a
poor and miserable law-writer, who called himself Nemo, lodged
in the Rag and Bottle Warehouse of Mr. Krook. This strange
lodger died, and Miss Flite, the unfortunate chancery suitor, ran
out for a doctor, and returned "accompanied by a testy medical
" man, brought from his dinner—with a broad, snuffy upper lip,
" and a broad Scotch tongue." The medical gentleman examined
the deceased, and said, "He's just as dead as Phairy!" Mr.
Tulkinghorn, the eminent legal gentleman, asked how long the
man had been dead, and the testy practitioner said, "It's probable
" he wull have been dead aboot three hours." This view is
assented to by a dark young man who has just come in. "Air
" you in the maydickle prayfession yourself, sir?" inquired the
physician. The dark young man says that he is. "Then I'll
" just tak' my depairture," replied the other, "for I'm nae gude
" here!" The young surgeon examines the deceased, and recalls
that he is a man who has often bought opium from him. This

young surgeon is Allan Woodcourt; and in this character Dickens would have been able, had he had the wish, to show some of the relations which exist between the good physician and poor patients. The author pays a tribute to this physician as a man whom the poor loved; he endeavors to show him as charitable, kindly, brave, and indefatigable. Woodcourt knows how to talk to the poor, being neither familiar nor condescending; yet it rather grates upon us to reflect that he sells opium to habitués. This man becomes a ship's surgeon, behaves with great courage in a wreck, returns to England, takes up practice, and finally marries Esther Summerson; but, as a matter of fact, he is throughout but a lay figure used to develop and bring out the plot.

Richard Carstone, one of the unfortunate wards in chancery, makes an attempt to study medicine, but gives it up because it requires too much effort; and in this connection the advice given him by Mr. Jarndyce would be eminently wise if given today to any medical student—advice which emphasizes the absolute necessity of being in earnest. Carstone undertakes the study under Mr. Bayham Badger, a surgeon of some note in Chelsea, who was connected with a large public hospital; but Mr. Bayham Badger shows us nothing of the characteristics of the medical practitioner. We learn that he was an honest man, because he advised Richard to give up the study of medicine, in which pursuit he was sure to fail. Mr. Badger thus lost a paying pupil. Mr. Badger is chiefly noted in the book as the third husband of Mrs. Bayham Badger; and he is extremely proud of the fact that his predecessors have been such eminent men as Captain Swosser, of the Royal Navy, and Professor Dingo, who had had a European reputation.

Old Krook, the keeper of a rag-and-bottle shop, died of spontaneous combustion. He was sodden with alcohol, and burnt up, so that nothing remained but a cinder like a charred log of wood. Dickens evidently believed in the possibility of such an occurrence, and cites cases reported by Le Cat and others. In 1692 the subject of spontaneous combustion of the human body began to excite interest. An alleged case was reported in 1725, but the victim, the wife of the Sieur Millet of Rheims, was found only one foot and a half from the kitchen fire. (Tidy's *Legal Medicine*.) Tidy analyzes all of the alleged cases, and reaches the following conclusions:

I. There is no authentic case of genuine spontaneous combustion on record, although there are many authentic cases in which the clothing has been set on fire, and the body has been thus ignited. In some cases the body has been more completely burned than the clothing.

II. It is probable that the body of a habitual drunkard, especially if he is fat, is more inflammable than the body of an ordinary person; hence a spark or the upsetting of a candle might ignite such a body and it might be destroyed by burning.

The Mystery of Edwin Drood and *Great Expectations* contain no medical references. We may say the same of *American Notes;* though we find in this book a noble tribute to Doctor Howe, who trained Laura Bridgman, and also a strong commendation of the Medical Superintendent of the Massachusetts State Hospital for the Insane.

The Old Curiosity Shop has a touch or two regarding matters medical. When Little Nell, ill and exhausted, arrived at the inn, the landlady gave her a drink of hot brandy and water, put her feet in a hot mustard foot-bath, tucked her up warmly in bed, and sent for the doctor. The doctor quickly arrived, and is described as a "red-nosed gentleman with a great bunch of seals " dangling below a waistcoat of ribbed black satin." He entered majestically, seated himself solemnly by the bed, drew out his watch, and felt the girl's pulse. Then he looked at her tongue, then he felt her pulse again, and while he did so he eyed the half-emptied wine-glass as if in profound abstraction. "I should " give her—" he said, "a teaspoonful, every now and then, of hot " brandy and water." The delighted landlady stated, "Why, " that's exactly what we've done, sir!" The doctor had observed the foot-bath on the stairs as he came up, and his next order was to "put her feet in hot water, and wrap them up in flannel." He further directed them to "give her something light for supper— " the wing of a roasted fowl." The landlady, affected with great personal gratification, announces that the chicken is cooking at the kitchen fire that instant; and the author goes on to tell us that the doctor might have smelt it if he had tried, and that perhaps he did. The doctor then arose, and with great gravity ordered for the patient a glass of hot mulled port wine. The landlady suggested toast with it. "Ay," said the doctor, in the tone of a man who makes a "dignified concession." "And a toast—of " bread. But be very particular to make it of bread, if you " please, ma'am." The author describes the doctor as departing " slowly and portentously"; and the entire household was "in " admiration of that wisdom which tallied so closely with their " own."

There can be no doubt that the general public are particularly anxious to appear possessed of medical knowledge. They have an indescribable fondness for prescribing drugs and methods of treatment, and they simply delight in bestowing aphorisms and threatening admonitions. Just as certainly, there is no doubt that when one of these public prescribers happens to be right, he is complacently satisfied, and is inclined to regard the physician that agrees with him as a very knowing fellow; but that any educated medical man should grovel to this sentiment is unbelievable, even to obtain the regard of his patients and to have it said of him, as was said of a Dickens doctor, that "he was a very shrewd " doctor indeed, and knew perfectly what people's constitutions " were." In fact, many physicians grow restless, irritable, or actually ferocious at domestic suggestions and household medication, and thus awaken the enduring hatred of each old woman, who has had many children and is awful in her learning; and of each maiden aunt, who, it is needless to say, has not had any children, but who is simply terrifying in her profundity.

Little Dorrit contains a most atrocious medical blackguard. It will be remembered that Mrs. Dorrit, the wife of that celebrated person who became the Father of the Marshalsea, was about to be confined. Doctor Haggage was a prisoner in the Marshalsea. When Mrs. Dorrit's confinement was beginning, the doctor and a companion were seated in a wretched, ill-smelling little room, engaged in playing at all-fours, smoking pipes, and drinking brandy. "The doctor's friend was in the positive degree of hoarse-" ness, puffiness, red-facedness, all-fours, tobacco, dirt, and " brandy; the doctor, in the comparative—hoarser, puffier, more " red-faced, more all-fourey, tobaccoer, dirtier, and brandier. " The doctor was amazingly shabby, in a torn and darned rough-" weather sea-jacket, out at elbows and eminently short of buttons " (he had been, in his time, the experienced surgeon carried by a " passenger ship), the dirtiest white trousers conceivable by mortal " man, carpet-slippers, and no visible linen." The turnkey summoned this pleasing scientist to attend Mrs. Dorrit. He jumped up instantly, characterizing himself as just the boy for a child-bed, and prepared himself for his arduous duties as follows: "With " that, the doctor took a comb from the chimney-piece and stuck " his hair upright—which appeared to be his way of washing him-" self—produced a professional chest or case, of most abject " appearance, from the cupboard where his cup and saucer and " coals were, settled his chin in the frowsy wrapper round his " neck; and became a ghastly medical scarecrow."

The whole of the ensuing scene is very interesting. The progress of the doctor on his way to the patient's room; the excitement of the women; the retirement of the men, because they felt at a disadvantage; the heat of the weather, and the sufferings of the poor patient, whom Mrs. Bangham was fanning with a cabbage leaf. Mrs. Bangham bestows incoherent comfort upon the sufferer, and comments upon the flies as follows: "What between " the buryin' ground, the grocer's, the waggon-stabless, and the " paunch trade, the Marshalsea flies gets very large. P'raps " they're sent as a consolation, if we only know'd it." Doctor Haggage assumes charge with the greatest cheerfulness, and says, " We are as right as we can be, Mrs. Bangham, and we shall " come out of this like a house a-fire." The author tells us that the most notable feature of the doctor's treatment was his evident determination to keep Mrs. Bangham up to the mark. He orders her to go outside and bring in some brandy, so as to prevent her giving in. Mrs. Bangham declines to bring in any liquor on her

own account, but the doctor grows peremptory and says, "I am
" in professional attendance on this lady, and don't choose to
" allow any discussion on your part. Go outside and fetch a little
" brandy, as I foresee that you'll break down." Mrs. Bangham
bows to this superior authority, and tells the doctor that he is
looking poorly himself, and "If you was to put your own lips to
" it, I think you wouldn't be the worse." The brandy was
obtained. The doctor gave himself a dose and administered one
to the nurse, and repeated this treatment every hour, being very
determined with Mrs. Bangham.

     After some time a little girl was born. The doctor announced
the birth, and at once sent Mrs. Bangham for more brandy, on
the ground that without this potent reviver that good woman
would inevitably have hysterics. The poor debtor paid the doctor;
and the doctor, "who was an old jail-bird, and was more sodden
" than usual, and had the additional and unusual stimulus of
money in his pocket," bestowed a piece of philosophy upon his
client—a germ like those which dropped from the lips of Micawber,
sayings which were probably resurrected from Dickens's early
recollections of boyish visits to his own father when that gentleman was a prisoner in a debtor's jail. The poor debtor thanks the
doctor, and says, "—though I little thought once, that——"
The doctor interrupted him, and continued, "That a child would
" be born to you in a place like this? Bah, bah, sir! What does
" it signify? A little more elbow-room is all we want here. We
" are quiet here; we don't get badgered here; there's no knocker
" here, sir, to be hammered at by creditors and bring a man's
" heart into his mouth. Nobody comes here to ask if a man's at
" home, and to say he'll stand on the door mat till he is. Nobody
" writes threatening letters about money to this place. It's
" freedom, sir, it's freedom! I have had today's practice at home
" and abroad, on a march, and aboard ship, and I'll tell you this:
" I don't know that I have ever pursued it under such quiet cir-
" cumstances, as here this day. Elsewhere, people are restless,
" worried, hurried about, anxious respecting one thing, anxious
" respecting another. Nothing of the kind here, sir. We have

" done all that—we know the worst of it; we have got to the bot-
" tom, we can't fall, and what have we found? Peace. That's
" the word for it. Peace." With these comforting reflections, the
doctor returned to his friend, his cards, his tobacco, and his brandy.

A very different medical man in *Little Dorrit* is the fashionable
physician that attended Mr. Merdle, the great financier. He is
an educated, cultivated gentleman. He is described as a famous
physician, who knew everybody, and whom everybody knew.
He first appears after a dinner given by Mr. Merdle in his Harley
Street house. A crowd of dignitaries are gathered in the drawing-
room. The physician touches Mr. Merdle on the arm and asks
him whether he is feeling any better. Mr. Merdle answers that
he is no better. The physician says he must come to see him the
next day. A lawyer and a bishop overhear a part of the dialogue,
and each suggests to the physician a diagnosis and a plan of treatment; but the physician knows better, and speaks as follows:
" Yes, yes, you are both right; but I may as well tell you that I
" can find nothing the matter with Mr. Merdle. He has the
" constitution of a rhinoceros, the digestion of an ostrich, and the
" concentration of an oyster. As to nerves, Mr. Merdle is of a
" cool temperament, and not a sensitive man: is about as invul-
" nerable, I should say, as Achilles. How such a man should sup-
" pose himself unwell without reason you may think strange.
" But I have found nothing the matter with him. He may have
" some deep-seated, recondite complaint. I can't say. I only
" say, that at present I have not found it out."

It will be observed from the foregoing how little Dickens
appreciated the imperative rule of professional secrecy. We cannot conceive a physician discussing, as an ordinary topic of conversation, the disease of one of his patients. It is quite needless
to say that no reputable man would even think of doing anything
of the sort.

This same fashionable physician, at one of Mr. Merdle's
dinners, was asked by the bishop how to lessen that common disorder of young curates, relaxation of the throat. He answered
that the best way to avoid it "was to know how to read before

" you made a profession of reading"—good, sound advice to those that contemplate a clerical career. Preachers as a class are notoriously the worst readers in the world.

When speaking of this fashionable physician, Dickens makes several statements which are eternally true. For instance, he describes a dinner-party at the physician's house at which a number of prominent people were present. "Few ways of life " were hidden from Physician, and he was oftener in its darkest " places than even Bishop. There were brilliant ladies about " London who perfectly doted on him . . . as the most charm-" ing creature and the most delightful person, who would have " been shocked to find themselves so close to him if they could " have known on what sights those thoughtful eyes of his had " rested within an hour or two, and near to whose beds, and under " what roofs, his composed figure had stood. But Physician was " a composed man, who performed neither on his own trumpet nor " on the trumpets of other people. Many wonderful things did " he see and hear, and much irreconcilable moral contradiction " did he pass his life among; yet his equality of compassion was " no more disturbed than the Divine Master's of all healing was. " He went, like the rain, among the just and unjust, doing all the " good he could, and neither proclaiming it in the synagogues " nor at the corners of streets. As no man of large experience " of humanity, however quietly carried it may be, can fail to be " invested with an interest peculiar to the possession of such " knowledge, Physician was an attractive man. Even the daintier " gentlemen and ladies who had no idea of his secret, and who " would have been startled out of more wits than they had, by " the monstrous impropriety of his proposing to them, 'Come and " ' see what I see!' confessed his attraction. Where he was, " something real was. And half a grain of reality, like the small-" est portion of some other scarce natural productions, will " flavour an enormous quantity of diluent. It came to pass, " therefore, that Physician's little dinners always presented people " in their least conventional lights. The guests said to themselves, " whether they were conscious of it or no, 'Here is a man who

" ' really has an acquaintance with us as we are, who is admitted
" ' to some of us every day with our wigs and paint off, who hears
" ' the wanderings of our minds, and sees the undisguised ex-
" ' pression of our faces, when both are past our control; we may
" ' as well make an approach to reality with him, for the man
" ' has got the better of us and is too strong for us.' Therefore,
" Physician's guests came out so surprisingly at his round table
" that they were almost natural."

Dickens goes on to say that "Bar's knowledge of that agglom-,
" eration of Jurymen which is called humanity was as sharp as a
" razor; yet that a razor is not a generally convenient instrument.
" Physician's plain bright scalpel, though far less keen, was
" adaptable to far wider purposes. Bar knew all about the
" gullibility and knavery of people; but Physician could have
" given him a better insight into their tendernesses and affections,
" in one week of his rounds, than Westminster Hall and all the
" circuits put together, in threescore years and ten. Bar always
" had a suspicion of this, and perhaps was glad to encourage it
" (for, if the world were really a great Law Court, one would
" think that the last day of Term could not too soon arrive); and
" so he liked and respected Physician quite as much as any other
" kind of man did."

It is this physician who, while reading late at night, is sent for
to go to a near-by bath-house; and in this establishment he finds
the body of the eminent Mr. Merdle, the cause of death being
suicide by cutting the throat.

It might be assumed that the story of *Doctor Marigold* in
Christmas Stories deals with a medical man, but it does not.
Doctor Marigold was a Cheap Jack, who was born on the highway, and who was called Doctor Marigold out of gratitude to the
physician that had officiated at his birth, "a very kind gentle-
" man," who accepted "no fee but a tea-tray."

Martin Chuzzlewit, which in many respects is one of Dickens's
greatest works, contains the inimitable nurses, Sairey Gamp and
Betsy Prig. Mrs. Prig was a hospital nurse that came from St.
Bartholomew's. She had a voice like a man and a pronounced

6

beard, and was very skeptical as to the existence of Mrs. Harris.
Mrs. Gamp's nose "was somewhat red and swollen, and it was
" difficult to enjoy her society without becoming conscious of a
" smell of spirits." She lodged in Kingsgate Street, High Holborn, "at a bird-fancier's, next door but one to the celebrated
" mutton-pie shop, and directly opposite to the original cat's-
" meat warehouse." Were we dealing with nurses in this article,
we should present these two distinguished persons at length, and
gather some amusement concerning what the immortal Sairey
calls "this Piljian's Projiss of a mortal wale." No story that has
ever been written portrays so clearly the nurse of forty years ago.
She was a hideous affront to intelligence and an insult to humanity,
often dirty, generally unscrupulous, usually drunk, and always
ignorant. The modern trained nurse is the antithesis of the old-
time hireling. Well educated, clean, intelligent, refined, conscientious, she is truly the right hand of the physician.

At the funeral of old Mr. Chuzzlewit, Mr. Mould, the undertaker, with a tact that was habitual, pretended not to know the
family physician, and fitted black kid gloves on the hands of
that medical gentleman as if he had never seen him before. The
doctor was just as particular; and though he and Mr. Mould were
near neighbors and very often "worked together," regarded that
urbane funeral director with a look "as distant and unconscious as
" if he had heard and read of undertakers, and had passed their
" shops, but had never before been brought into communication
" with one." The doctor, after much trouble, was arrayed in
gloves, cloak, and hat; took some cake and a glass of port; and
got into the carriage, while relating to Mr. Pecksniff an interesting
episode in practice. This story continued without intermission
during the progress to the cemetery. At the grave, Chuffey, the
poor old faithful servitor, broke down and kneeled in the dust;
and the doctor remonstrates because "it's a clayey soil," and
endeavors to comfort the sufferer by telling him that his conduct
is not only weak, but "bad, selfish, very wrong," because he is
not connected by ties of blood with the deceased. After the
funeral, Mrs. Gamp returned to her home at the bird-fancier's,

and "was knocked up again that very night for a birth of twins; " Mr. Mould dined gaily in the bosom of his family, and passed " the evening facetiously at his club." The doctor "got merry " with wine at a wedding-dinner, and forgot the middle of the " story, which had no end to it."

We meet this same physician again, as the story advances. His name is John Jobling, Esquire, M. R. C. S. He was the Medical Officer of the fraudulent insurance company. We see him at lunch with the Chairman of the Company. It was the doctor who had suggested the advisability of taking lunch. He tells the Chairman, "If you don't make a point of taking lunch, " you'll very soon come under my hands." He illustrates this axiom by a demonstration of Mr. Crimple's leg. He explains that in Mr. Crimple's leg there is a certain amount of animal oil; and that if Mr. Crimple neglects his meals, the oil will become exhausted and "Mr. Crimple's bones sink down into their sockets, " sir, and Mr. Crimple becomes a weazen, puny, stunted, miser- " able man!" Mr. Crimple becomes very indignant, resenting this personal application of scientific truths, and demands to know whether the same isn't true of other people's legs. Doctor Jobling was extremely fond of thus solemnly giving out medical informa- tion. For instance, after explaining that the medical profession is acquainted with many secrets of nature and that the general public knows practically nothing about this subject, he makes the following inquiry: "where do you suppose Mr. Crimple's stomach " is?" Mr. Crimple was somewhat agitated by this question, and put his hand below his waistcoat. The doctor showed that this was a common popular mistake. Mr. Crimple said that all he knew about it was that he felt it there when it was out of order. " 'You think you do,' replied the doctor, 'but science knows " ' better. There was a patient of mine once': touching one of " the many mourning rings upon his fingers, and slightly bowing " his head: 'a gentleman who did me the honour to make a very " ' handsome mention of men in his will—in testimony,' as he " was pleased to say, 'of the unremitting zeal, talent, and atten- " ' tion of my friend and medical attendant, John Jobling, Esquire,

" ' M. R. C. S.,'—who was so overcome by the idea of having
" all his life laboured under an erroneous view of the locality of
" this important organ, that when I assured him on my pro-
" fessional reputation, he was mistaken, he burst into tears, put
" out his hand, and said, 'Jobling, God bless you!' Immediately
" afterward he became speechless, and was ultimately buried at
" Brixton." During the lunch previously alluded to, "the Med-
" ical Officer grew more and more joyous and red-faced."

Jobling was a useful man to the Company. He had a large
practice among well-to-do tradesmen, and the fact that he was
Medical Officer brought considerable business to the concern. But
Jobling was entirely too knowing to connect himself with the
Company in any other capacity than that of a paid (and well-
paid) official. He evidently estimated its financial standing at its
real worth, and was extremely careful to explain to every one
abroad that he was merely the Medical Officer paid by the month;
that he never recommended any one; and that, as he had no head
for figures, he knew nothing whatever touching the responsibility
or capital of the Company. He would point out that the President
of the Company was a remarkably handsome man, and quite the
gentleman in every respect, who, he was informed, held property
in India. He would then say to the person with whom he was
conversing that if he should ever think of being insured, he would
pass him beyond doubt, because he could conscientiously report
him a healthy subject. During the lunch a commission was paid
to Jobling on four new policies. As he pockets the money, he
says that it is really like robbing the Company to take it, because
he does not recommend anybody there; but only tells them what
he knows.

It is within the memory of the present writer, sad to say, that
during the popularity of the "Get-Rich-Quick" concerns a few
years ago, the attempt was made by these organizations to gain
an appearance of respectability by having supposedly decent men
for medical officers. More than one man, previously respectable,
was seriously smirched by this connection. At this time, when
insurance companies, at least in this part of the country, are closely

watched and regulated, the existence of such a company as Dickens describes is practically impossible; and whereas Joblings may exist potentially, they do not have such a chance to be publicly recognized.

The physician who attended the stranger ill in the Bull Inn in Holborn, the stranger that was nursed by Mrs. Gamp and Mrs. Prig, is not even presented to us; for he simply drops in now and then and shakes his head, which "was all he could do, under the " circumstances, and he did it well." This physician orders that the patient shall be kept cool and quiet; that his draughts shall be given regularly, and that he shall be carefully looked to; to which directions Mrs. Gamp makes answer: "And as long as Mrs. Prig " and me waits upon him, sir, no fear of that."

Mr. Lewsome, the mysterious patient, had been educated as a surgeon, and for some years had been assistant to a general practitioner in the city. He was a gambler and a drunkard, was accustomed to carouse with Jonas Chuzzlewit, and had gone heavily into debt to that miserly scoundrel. Jonas used to talk about the desirability of having old Mr. Chuzzlewit die. One night he went to Lewsome and asked for two deadly drugs to poison cats. The drugs were furnished, with the proviso that Jonas forgive the debt. Thus Lewsome became the accomplice to an attempted murder.

There is nothing to show that Dr. Ginery Dunkle was a medical doctor. As far as the description carries us, he might have been a doctor of divinity, a horse doctor, or a corn doctor. He was a member of the committee that welcomed the Honourable Elijah Pogram. He was supposed to possess great poetical ability, and is described as a "shrill boy."

The only doctor in *Hard Times* is the nameless surgeon who cared for Stephen Blackpool when he was lifted, fearfully injured, from the pit. The only medical men in *Barnaby Rudge* are those that attended John Willet, reached the conclusion that he had a stroke of apoplexy and that he ought to die, and took it "very ill" that he did not.

In *Dombey and Son* we meet Mr. Pilkins, the family Surgeon that attended Mrs. Dombey in her confinement and was so

obsequious to the Court Physician. He had "regularly puffed the
" case for the last six weeks, among all his patients, friends, and
" acquaintances, as one to which he was in hourly expectation
" day and night of being summoned in conjunction with Dr.
" Parker Peps." Dr. Parker Peps was a distinguished practitioner
who fashion demanded must be called in to assist "at the increase
" of great families." He is observed walking "up and down the
" drawing-room with his hands behind him, to the unspeakable
" admiration of the family Surgeon." The following conversation
takes place:

    " 'Well, Sir,' said Dr. Parker Peps, in a round, deep, sonorous
" voice, muffled for the occasion, like the knocker; 'do you find
" ' that your dear lady is at all roused by your visit?'—'Stimu-
" ' lated as it were?' said the family practitioner faintly: bowing
" at the same time to the Doctor, as much as to say, 'Excuse my
" ' putting in a word, but this is a valuable connexion.' " As a
matter of fact, Mr. Dombey has not thought at all of the patient,
and has thought only of the recently born heir; and the question
as to Mrs. Dombey comes quite as a surprise. He requests Dr.
Parker Peps to walk upstairs again. " 'Good! We must not
" ' disguise from you, sir,' said Dr. Parker Peps, 'that there is
" ' want of power in Her Grace, the Duchess—I beg your pardon;
" ' I confound names; I should say, in your amiable lady. That
" ' there is a certain degree of languor, and a general absence of
" ' elasticity, which we would rather—not'—'See,' interposed the
" family practitioner with another inclination of the head. 'Quite
" ' so,' said Dr. Parker Peps, 'which we would rather not see.' "

    After pointing out some further particulars about the patient,
the distinguished physician says that the only hope of a rally is
that she will make a vigorous effort. " 'Mr. Pilkins here, who,
" ' from his position of medical adviser in this family—no one
" ' better qualified to fill the position, I am sure.' 'Oh!' murmured
" the family practitioner, 'praise from Sir Hubert Stanley!' 'You
" ' are good enough,' returned Dr. Parker Peps, 'to say so.' "

    The two medical gentlemen go into the sick room and stand
by Mrs. Dombey's bed and look upon her compassionately. In

the solemn stillness nothing was audible but "the loud ticking
" of Mr. Dombey's watch and Dr. Parker Peps's watch, which
" seemed in the silence to be running a race." Mrs. Chick, a
sister of Mr. Dombey, a domineering woman with the Dombey
instincts, insists that the invalid must exert herself; but the
sufferer does not even open her eyes until her little girl comes in,
when a slight trace of consciousness is evinced. The poor woman's
eyelids tremble, the faintest shadow of a smile appears on her
face, and immediately afterward she dies.

When Paul Dombey grew into childhood, his health became
feeble, and Mr. Pilkins ordered him sea air. He was therefore
taken to Brighton, where he resided at the house of Mrs. Pipchin,
whose husband had been ruined in the Peruvian mines. Later
Paul lived at the learned establishment of Doctor Blimber. At
one time Paul was taken sick while at Brighton, and was attended
by a "certain calm Apothecary," of whom we learn nothing
except that he was kind, thoughtful, and sensible.

When Paul, drooping and fading, was taken to his home from
Brighton, he grew gradually but certainly worse, and was attended
by "three grave doctors—they used to assemble downstairs and
" come up together—and the room was so quiet, and Paul was so
" observant of them (though he never asked of anybody what
" they said), that he even knew the difference in the sound of
" their watches. But his interest centred in Sir Parker Peps, who
" always took his seat on the side of the bed. For Paul had heard
" them say long ago that that gentleman had been with his
" mama when she clasped Florence in her arms, and died. And
" he could not forget it, now. He liked him for it. He was not
" afraid." But in spite of these medical luminaries, Paul Dombey
died.

In *Nicholas Nickleby* Sir Tumley Snuffim is a mere name. He
attended Mrs. Wititterly, who was an unprincipled, superficial,
stupid, socially ambitious, and hysterical female. Poor gentle
Kate Nickleby was Mrs. Wititterly's companion; and Sir Tumley
gave it as his opinion that Kate disagreed with Mrs. Wititterly's
constitution.

Mr. Lumbey, the family physician of the Kenwigs's, is more distinctly outlined than is Sir Tumley. He is met with in the Kenwigs's sitting room. He has just delivered Mrs. Kenwigs of a child, and he is resting from his labors with the new baby while he dandles the old baby on his knee. "He was a stout bluff-looking "gentleman, with no shirt-collar, to speak of, and a beard that "had been growing since yesterday morning; for Doctor Lumbey "was popular, and the neighbourhood was prolific; and there "had been no less than three other knockers muffled, one after "the other, within the last forty-eight hours." The doctor tells Mr. Kenwigs that the new baby is the finest boy he ever saw in all his life.

The condition of affairs in the house was such as is commonly encountered today in such circumstances. "All this time there "had been a great whisking in and out of the other room; the "door had been opened and shut very softly about twenty times "a minute (for it was necessary to keep Mrs. Kenwigs quiet); "and the baby had been exhibited to a score or two of deputa-"tions from a select body of female friends, who had assembled "in the passage, and about the street-door, to discuss the event "in all its bearings. Indeed, the excitement extended itself over "the whole street, and groups of ladies might be seen standing "at the doors (some in the interesting condition in which Mrs. "Kenwigs had last appeared in public), relating their experi-"ences of similar occurrences. Some few acquired great credit "from having prophesied, the day before yesterday, exactly when "it would come to pass; others, again, related how that they "guessed what it was directly they saw Mr. Kenwigs turn pale "and run up the street as hard as ever he could go. Some said "one thing, and some another; but all talked together, and all "agreed upon two points: firstly, that it was very meritorious and "highly praiseworthy in Mrs. Kenwigs to do as she had done; "and secondly, that there never was such a skilful and scientific "doctor as that Doctor Lumbey."

Doctor Lumbey reminds Mr. Kenwigs that the new arrival "makes six," and that he will have "a fine family in time." Mr.

Kenwigs thinks six is about enough. "'Nonsense! not half
"'enough,' said the doctor scoffingly. With this, the doctor
"laughed; but he didn't laugh half as much as a married friend
"of Mrs. Kenwigs's, who had just come in from the sick chamber
"to report progress, and take a small sip of brandy-and-water:
"and who seemed to consider it one of the best jokes ever launched
"upon society."

When Smike, after his second escape from the schoolmaster,
became ill, he was seen by a "physician of great repute," who gave
the following extremely noncommittal opinion. He said, "there
"was no cause for immediate alarm. There were no present symp-
"toms which could be deemed conclusive. The constitution had
"been greatly tried and injured in childhood, but still it *might*
"not be." This seems to rank, though unintentionally, in the
same class as the famous opinion of Captain Jack Bunsby.

In *A Tale of Two Cities* Doctor Manette is met with, a physician
of Beauvais, who practised his profession in Paris, under the old
régime. He became possessed of a terrible secret relating to a
great and aristocratic family—a brutal barbarity that he declined
to conceal. His bold and menacing attitude led to his seizure and
incarceration in the Bastille, in which he remained for years.
During this imprisonment he lost his mind. The story of his
release from the Bastille; of the slow reconstitution of his shattered reason; of his life in England, where he practised his profession; of the marriage of his daughter to the son of the aristocratic scoundrel that had caused his imprisonment; of his journey
to France and of his residence in Paris during the most bloody and
dreadful scenes of the French Revolution—though replete with
living interest, does not in any way deal with his life as a physician, except that during his Parisian residence he was attending
physician to several of the prisons; was treated with great regard
and affection as a former Bastille prisoner; and was respected,
admired and tenderly loved even by the drunken, brutal, bloody
mob of Revolutionary Paris.

In the earliest pages of *Oliver Twist* the birth of the hero is
carefully described. There was some difficulty in inducing

respiration; and the author says that if "Oliver had been sur-
" rounded by careful grandmothers, anxious aunts, experienced
" nurses, and doctors of profound wisdom, he would most in-
" evitably and indubitably have been killed in no time. There
" being nobody by, however, but a pauper old woman, who was
" rendered rather misty by an unwonted allowance of beer; and
" a parish surgeon who did such matters by contract; Oliver and
" Nature fought out the point between them. The result was,
" that, after a few struggles, Oliver breathed, sneezed, and pro-
" ceeded to advertise to the inmates of the work-house the fact
" of a new burden having been imposed upon the parish, by setting
" up as loud a cry as could reasonably have been expected from
" a male infant who had not been possessed of that very useful
" appendage, a voice, for a much longer space of time than three
" minutes and a quarter."

The mother raised herself with difficulty in the bed and
weakly asked to be permitted to see the child before she died.
"The surgeon had been sitting with his face turned toward the
" fire, giving the palms of his hands a warm and a rub alternately.
" As the young woman spoke, he rose, and advancing to the bed's
" head, said, with more kindness than might have been expected
" of him: 'Oh, you must not talk about dying yet.' " The surgeon picked up the baby and put it into the mother's arms. She
kissed it and fell back dead. The surgeon announced that it was
all over. Then, turning to the nurse: " 'You needn't mind sending
" 'up to me if the child cries, Nurse,' said the surgeon, putting on
" his gloves with great deliberation. 'It's very likely it *will* be
" 'troublesome. Give it a little gruel, if it is.' He put on his
" hat, and, pausing by the bed-side on his way to the door, added,
" 'She was a good-looking girl, too; where did she come from?' "
The old woman answered that the patient had been found lying
in the street the night before; had evidently walked a long distance, for her shoes were completely worn out; and had been admitted by the overseer's order. "The surgeon leaned over the
" body, and raised the left hand. 'The old story,' he said, shaking
" his head: 'no wedding-ring, I see. Ah! good-night.' "

When Oliver Twist was rescued from the peremptory magistrate, Mr. Fang, and was taken to the house of Mr. Brownlow, he became seriously ill; and as he improved, he became conscious of "a gentleman with a very large and loud-ticking gold watch in his "hand, who felt his pulse, and said he was a great deal better. "'You *are* a great deal better, are you not, my dear?' said the "gentleman. 'Yes, thank you, sir,' replied Oliver. 'Yes, I know "'you are,' said the gentleman: 'You're hungry, too, an't you?' "'No, sir,' answered Oliver. 'Hem!' said the gentleman, 'No, I "'know you're not. He is not hungry, Mrs. Bedwin,' said the "gentleman, looking very wise. The old lady made a respectful "inclination of the head, which seemed to say that she thought "the doctor was a very clever man. The doctor appeared much "of the same opinion himself. 'You feel sleepy, don't you, my "'dear?' said the doctor. 'No, sir,' replied Oliver. 'No,' said the "doctor, with a very shrewd and satisfied look. 'You're not "'sleepy. Nor thirsty. Are you?' 'Yes, sir, rather thirsty,' "answered Oliver. 'Just as I expected, Mrs. Bedwin,' said the "doctor. 'It's very natural that he should be thirsty. You may "'give him a little tea, ma'am, and some dry toast without any "'butter. Don't keep him too warm, ma'am; but be careful that "'you don't let him be too cold; will you have the goodness?' "The old lady dropped a curtsey. The doctor, after tasting the "cool stuff, and expressing a qualified approval of it, hurried "away; his boots creaking in a very important and wealthy man-"ner as he went downstairs."

Mr. Grimwig, the irascible and peremptory friend of Mr. Brownlow, entertained strong suspicions regarding a surgeon in the neighborhood. Finding a piece of orange-peel on the pavement, he came in in a state of great indignation, saying that orange-peel was always lying about in the street, and that he was sure that it had been deliberately placed there by the surgeon's boy. "A "young woman stumbled over a bit last night, and fell against my "garden-railings; directly she got up, I saw her look toward his "infernal red lamp with the pantomime-light. 'Don't go to him,' "I called out of the window, 'he's an assassin! A man-trap!'"

When Mrs. Corney, the matron of the workhouse, was taken to listen to the death-bed confidence of the old crone that had nursed Oliver's mother, she found the apprentice of the parish apothecary warming himself in front of the fire and cutting a toothpick from a quill. They passed the compliments of the evening together, complained about the quality of the coal, and growled about the management of the board. The apprentice tells Mrs. Corney that the old woman is dying from a complete break-up of the system. This budding physician stands in front of the fire for a little time, actively using his toothpick; but, finding the situation dull and uninteresting, he wished Mrs. Corney joy of her job and took himself off on tiptoe.

After Oliver Twist had been shot during the attempted burglary, he was placed in bed in the house of Mrs. Maylie. The morning following the tragedy, Mr. Losberne, a physician, came to attend Oliver. He was a stout, eccentric, jovial, and impetuous old bachelor, who was loved and highly respected by the whole community. He complimented Mr. Giles, the old butler, on his marksmanship; and then went upstairs to see the patient, talking all the time. He was absent for a long while, sending downstairs for his instrument-box, which was brought up from the gig. The bell was rung at frequent intervals; and the servants were constantly running up and down stairs, bringing things that he required. Finally he came downstairs with a mysterious look, closed the door carefully, and told Mrs. Maylie that the wounded marauder was not some large, hulking, black-browed villain; but was a poor, weak, miserable little boy.

The sympathy of the ladies was warmly excited for Oliver; but the matter was seriously complicated by the arrival of Blathers and Duff, the Bow Street runners, who had been sent for to investigate the crime, and who would be certain to take Oliver into custody. Mr. Losberne devised an ingenious plan to throw the officers off the scent and save Oliver from prosecution, maintaining that the lad had been accidentally wounded by a spring gun while trespassing upon someone's grounds; that he had come to the house to obtain assistance, and had been immediately taken hold of and accused by the butler, Mr. Giles. The detectives cross-examined Mr. Giles, who involved himself in such an extraordinary maze of contradiction that Blathers decided that he had been drinking, and Duff looked upon him as absolutely muddle-headed.

The only other medical appearance of Mr. Losberne is during the sickness of Rose Maylie. Although we see him frequently in the book, it is not in his medical capacity.

In *Our Mutual Friend* we do not find any physician; but we do find a business man closely connected with hospitals and the medical profession. This is Mr. Venus, of Clerkenwell, who was accustomed to float his "powerful mind" in oceans of tea in his little dark shop. Mr. Venus's occupation was to prepare anatomical specimens; and in the course of business he had become possessed of the amputated leg of Mr. Silas Wegg, the literary man of Mr. Boffin. Mr. Wegg, having got on in life, and having obtained the position of reader to Mr. Boffin, feels that it is not respectable that his leg should be lying around in a shop; and he visits Mr. Venus, to make an effort to buy it. On entering the shop, Mr. Wegg greets Mr. Venus; and the latter gradually remembers who Mr. Wegg is. Mr. Wegg introduces himself by name, and Mr. Venus responds that he remembers that it was a hospital amputation. Mr. Wegg then propounds the following inquiry: " 'Where am I?' " Mr. Venus makes answer: " 'You're
" ' somewhere in the back shop across the yard, sir; and speaking
" ' quite candidly, I wish I'd never bought you of the Hospital
" ' Porter.' 'Now, look here, what did you give for me?' 'Well,'
" replies Venus, blowing his tea: his head and face peering out of
" the darkness, over the smoke of it, as if he were modernizing
" the old original rise in his family: 'you were one of a warious
" ' lot, and I don't know.' Silas puts his point in the improved
" form of 'What will you take for me?' 'Well,' replies Venus,
" still blowing his tea, 'I'm not prepared, at a moment's notice, to
" ' tell you, Mr. Wegg.' 'Come! According to your own account,
" ' I'm not worth much,' Wegg reasons persuasively. 'Not for
" ' miscellaneous working in, I grant you, Mr. Wegg; but you
" ' might turn out valuable yet, as a—' here Mr. Venus takes a

" gulp of tea, so hot that it makes him choke, and sets his
" weak eyes watering: 'as a Monstrosity, if you'll excuse
" ' me.' "

In *Sketches by Boz* we find a few medical references. In the
Story of *The Four Sisters* the birth of Mrs. Robinson's child is
described. The fact was anticipated by noticing "that Mr.
" Dawson, the surgeon, &c., who displays a large lamp with a
" different colour in every pane of glass, at the corner of the row,
" began to be knocked up at night oftener than he used to be; and
" once we were very much alarmed by hearing a hackney-coach
" stop at Mrs. Robinson's door, at half-past two o'clock in the
" morning, out of which there emerged a fat old woman, in a cloak
" and nightcap, with a bundle in one hand, and a pair of pattens
" in the other, who looked as if she had been suddenly knocked
" up out of bed for some very special purpose. When we got up
" in the morning we saw that the knocker was tied up in an old
" white kid glove; and we, in our innocence (we were in a state
" of bachelorship then), wondered what on earth it all meant, until
" we heard the eldest Miss Willis, *in propriâ personâ*, say, with
" great dignity, in answer to the next inquiry, '*My* compliments,
" ' and Mrs. Robinson's doing as well as can be expected, and the
" ' little girl thrives wonderfully.' "

In one of the *Tales* included in the volume of *Sketches by Boz*,
we are introduced to Doctor Wosky, who appears in *The Boarding-
House.* He is described as "a little man with a red face—dressed
" of course in black, with a stiff white neckerchief." He was well
off. "He had a very good practice, and plenty of money, which
" he had amassed by invariably humouring the worst fancies of
" all the females of all the families he had ever been introduced
" to." For instance, to a selfish woman, fond of food, luxury,
and ease, he gives the following advice: " 'We must take stim-
" ' ulants,' said the cunning Wosky—'plenty of nourishment, and,
" ' above all, we must keep our nerves quiet; we positively must
" ' not give way to our sensibilities. We must take all we can get,'
" concluded the doctor, as he pocketed his fee, 'and we must keep
" ' quiet.' "

In this story of *The Boarding-House* we are also introduced to Mr. Septimus Hicks, a student of medicine; but his adventures are amatory, and not medical. He is described as a "tallish, " white-faced young man, with spectacles, and a black ribbon " round his neck, instead of a neckerchief." After Mr. Hicks married, his conduct was not absolutely above reproach. The author dismisses him as follows: "Mr. Septimus Hicks, having " walked the hospitals, took it into his head to walk off altogether."

The Black Veil, another of the *Tales* included in the volume of *Sketches by Boz*, is a peculiar story. On a cold, rainy evening a woman came to a physician's office and requested the doctor to call the next morning and see a person that would, she knew, be by that time beyond all human aid; although she would fain think otherwise. The physician was amazed at a request for him to see a man the next morning, when that man was probably dying at the moment the request was made. Thinking the woman insane, he humored her, and promised to go. The next morning he kept this promise. On reaching the house he found the man stone dead, the corpse having just been brought home after the execution. This story will not appear an absolute improbability to those Philadelphians who remember the elaborate preparations that were made before the hanging of Jerrold Eaton, and recall the prolonged attempt to bring him back to life, after the corpse, wrapped in hot blankets, had been driven madly from Moya-mensing Prison to a house on Tenth Street. In the old days, before the drop was used, the neck was not broken; and now and then a person could be resuscitated. A notable instance of this occurred in Scotland in the last century.

In *The Hospital Patient*, one of the *Characters* included in the *Sketches by Boz*, we are taken to a Police-office, where a man is being examined on the charge of having assaulted a woman with whom he lived. Testimony had been submitted to prove that he had attacked her most brutally. "A certificate was read from the " house-surgeon of a neighbouring hospital, describing the nature " of the injuries the woman had received, and intimating that her " recovery was extremely doubtful." The magistrates decided to visit the hospital and take the woman's deposition, and ordered that the man be taken there also. The man, in the custody of an officer, was waiting at the hospital when the magistrates arrived. "After a short interval, the magistrates and clerk were bowed in "by the house-surgeon and a couple of young men who smelt "very strong of tobacco-smoke—they were introduced as 'dressers' "—and after one magistrate had complained bitterly of the cold, "and the other of the absence of any news in the evening paper, "it was announced that the patient was prepared; and we were "conducted to the 'casualty ward' in which she was lying." The woman declined to charge the brute with having injured her. In fact, she declared that he had not and that he would not hurt her, and died with the vindication on her lips. We have seen more than one similar occurrence.

In *The Drunkard's Death*, another of the *Tales* included in the *Sketches by Boz*, the not uncommon feeling of the poor toward poor district doctors is shown by the father's attitude when he finds his daughter ill. He says: "You must get better somehow, "for we must have money. You must go to the parish doctor "and make him give you some medicine. They're paid for it, "damn 'em." That this feeling so often exists is due partly to the fact that a few—and, we believe, a very few—district doctors are harsh, unsympathetic, and dictatorial; but it depends chiefly upon the common human tendency to attach no value to what is given, to look upon a kindness extended as a right, and to regard the doctor that practises among them as extremely foolish and as a poor lot, anyway. In a Memoir of the late Dr. J. Mason Warren, of Boston, we find the following anecdote, which exhibits something of this tendency. For many years, out of pure kindness, Doctor Warren had attended a woman free of charge. He had given her any amount of his very valuable time, and had not sought a penny of remuneration nor expected it. All this was at a time when he was the most distinguished surgeon in Boston. He then lost sight of the patient for many months. One day he met her and asked what had become of her. The answer was that she had thought it better to consult a pay doctor.

In *David Copperfield* there is only one physician. During the trials and tribulations that attended the ushering of David into the world, Miss Betsey Trotwood, grim, rigid, and determined, sat before the parlor fire, stopping her ears with jewellers' cotton and waiting for a girl to be born. She had a presentiment that it must be a girl, and would not hear the faintest suspicion that it might be a boy. Mr. Chillip, the attending physician, having examined the patient, came downstairs and took a seat near Miss Trotwood to await developments. He is described as follows: "He was the meekest of his sex, the mildest of little men. He " sidled in and out of a room, to take up the less space. He " walked as softly as the Ghost in Hamlet, and more slowly. He " carried his head on one side, partly in modest depreciation of " himself, partly in modest propitiation of everybody else. It is " nothing to say that he hadn't a word to throw at a dog. He " couldn't have *thrown* a word at a mad dog. He might have " offered him one gently, or half a one, or a fragment of one; for " he spoke as slowly as he walked; but he wouldn't have been rude " to him, and he couldn't have been quick with him, for any " earthly consideration." Mr. Chillip looked mildly at Miss Trotwood, observed with surprise her occupation with the jewellers' cotton, and asked her whether it was "some local irritation." Miss Trotwood pulled the cotton out of one ear like a cork and said: "What!" This alarmed Mr. Chillip extremely, but he repeated his inquiry. Miss Trotwood said, "Nonsense!" and corked herself again. Mr. Chillip was then called upstairs, remained there for quite a little time, and then came down again. Miss Trotwood uncorked her ear and inquired, "Well?" Mr. Chillip feebly said: "We are—we are progressing slowly," whereat Miss Trotwood uttered the contemptuous remark "Ba-a-ah!" and corked herself as before. He was called upstairs again, was subjected to the same inquiry on returning, and made the same answer, at which Miss Trotwood snarled at him with such fierceness that he decided "to go and sit upon the stairs, in the dark " and a strong draught," in preference to remaining with her. Finally David was born, and Mr. Chillip came downstairs to tell

7

Miss Betsey. "The mild Mr. Chillip could not possibly bear
" malice at such a time, if at any time. He sidled into the parlour
" as soon as he was at liberty, and said to my aunt in his meekest
" manner: 'Well, ma'am, I am happy to congratulate you.'
" 'What upon?' said my aunt, sharply. Mr. Chillip was fluttered
" again by the extreme severity of my aunt's manner; so he made
" her a little bow, and gave her a little smile, to mollify her.
" 'Mercy on the man, what's he doing!' cried my aunt, impa-
" tiently. 'Can't he speak?' 'Be calm, my dear ma'am,' said Mr.
" Chillip, in his softest accents. ' There is no longer any occasion
" 'for uneasiness, ma'am. Be calm.' It has since been con-
" sidered almost a miracle that my aunt didn't shake him, and
" shake what he had to say out of him. She only shook her own
" head at him, but in a way that made him quail. 'Well, ma'am,'
" resumed Mr. Chillip, as soon as he had courage, 'I am happy to
" 'congratulate you. All is now over, ma'am, and well over.'
" During the five minutes or so that Mr. Chillip devoted to the
" delivery of this oration, my aunt eyed him narrowly. 'How is
" 'she?' said my aunt, folding her arms with her bonnet still
" tied on one of them. 'Well, ma'am, she will soon be quite
" 'comfortable, I hope,' returned Mr. Chillip. 'Quite as com-
" 'fortable as we can expect a young mother to be, under
" 'these melancholy domestic circumstances. There cannot be
" 'any objection to your seeing her presently, ma'am. It may do
" 'her good.' 'And *she*. How is *she?*' said my aunt, sharply.
" Mr. Chillip laid his head a little more on one side, and looked
" at my aunt like an amiable bird. 'The baby,' said my aunt.
" 'How is she?' 'Ma'am,' returned Mr. Chillip, 'I apprehended
" 'you had known. It's a boy.' My aunt said never a word, but
" took her bonnet by the strings, in the manner of a sling, aimed
" a blow at Mr. Chillip's head with it, put it on bent, walked out,
" and never came back."

In the *Posthumous Papers of the Pickwick Club* Doctor Slammer,
of the Ninety-seventh Regiment, and his friend, Doctor Payne, are
of interest only because of the ludicrous manner in which Doctor
Slammer and Mr. Winkle became involved; but the real Æscu-

lapian luminaries of this book are Bob Sawyer and Benjamin
Allen, who are first encountered at Mr. Wardle's country place.

On Christmas morning Sam Weller brings some warm water
into Mr. Pickwick's bed-chamber, and says to his master: "There's
" a couple o' Sawbones downstairs," explaining that by a Sawbones
he means a Surgeon, and that the specimens of the family then in
the house are not "reg'lar thorough-bred Sawbones," but "only in
" trainin'." Mr. Pickwick finally understands that two medical
students are among the guests. He pays a cordial tribute to medical students as a class, and says: "They are fine fellows; very fine
" fellows; with judgments matured by observation and reflection;
" tastes refined by reading and study." Sam says to Mr. Pickwick:
" They're a smokin' cigars by the kitchen fire." Mr. Pickwick
strongly approves of this conduct. " 'And one on 'em,' said Sam,
" not noticing his master's interruption, 'one on 'em's got his legs on
" ' the table, and is a drinkin' brandy neat, vile the tother one—
" ' him in the barnacles—has got a barrel o' oysters atween his
" ' knees, wich he's a openin' like steam, and as fast as he eats 'em,
" ' he takes a aim vith the shells at young dropsy, who's a sittin'
" ' down fast asleep, in the chimbley corner.' "

At breakfast Mr. Pickwick meets the students. "Mr. Benjamin
" Allen was a coarse, stout, thick-set young man, with black hair
" cut rather short, and a white face cut rather long. He was em-
" bellished with spectacles and wore a white neckerchief. Below
" his single-breasted black surtout, which was buttoned up to
" his chin, appeared the usual number of salt-and-pepper coloured
" legs, terminating in a pair of imperfectly polished boots. Al-
" though his coat was short in the sleeves, it disclosed no vestige
" of a linen wristband; and although there was quite enough of
" his face to admit of the encroachment of a shirt collar, it was
" not graced by the smallest approach to that appendage. He
" presented, altogether, rather a mildewy appearance, and emitted
" a fragrant odour of full-flavoured Cubas.

"Mr. Bob Sawyer, who was habited in a coarse blue coat,
" which, without being either a great-coat or a surtout, partook of
" the nature and qualities of both, had about him that sort of

" slovenly smartness, and swaggering gait, which is peculiar to
" young gentlemen who smoke in the streets by day, shout and
" scream in the same by night, call waiters by their Christian
" names, and do various other acts and deeds of an equally face-
" tious description. He wore a pair of plaid trousers, and a large
" rough double-breasted waistcoat; out of doors he carried a thick
" stick with a big top. He eschewed gloves, and looked, upon
" the whole, something like a dissipated Robinson Crusoe."

The foregoing uncomplimentary portraits certainly do not
represent the average student of today, and probably did not the
student of that day. Nevertheless, we admit that the average
medical student is unconventional and convivial and is somewhat given to nocturnal gaiety. The writer can admit this without being invidious, for he was a student himself.

At breakfast Ben and Bob agree that there is "Nothing like dis-
" secting to give one an appetite," and enter into an appropriate
breakfast argument about legs, arms, and brains. Ben asks Bob
whether he had "finished that leg yet?" Bob says he nearly has,
and that "it's a very muscular one for a child's." Mr. Allen
states that he has put his name down for an arm; that they are
"clubbing for a subject, and the list is nearly full"; but that, as,
so far, no one would promise to take a head, Bob had better do
so. Bob says he "can't afford expensive luxuries"; he wouldn't
mind a brain, but he couldn't stand a whole head.

At the termination of the meal Mr. Bob Sawyer, "enlivened
" with the brandy, and the breakfast, and the talking, gradually
" ripened into a state of extreme facetiousness, and related with
" much glee an agreeable anecdote, about the removal of a tumour
" on some gentleman's head, which he illustrated by means of
" an oyster-knife and a half-quarten loaf, to the great edification
" of the assembled company."

Bob Sawyer lived in Lant Street in the Borough, in the house
of Mrs. Raddle. He determined to give a bachelor's party, to
which Mr. Pickwick was invited. Just before the guests arrived
Mrs. Raddle came up, fierce and denunciatory, and demanded
her back rent. After a tremendous blow-up, she burst into an

hysterical fit of weeping, threw down all the umbrellas, and disappeared into the back parlour, closing the door after her with an awful crash.

At this party Jack Hopkins tells the credulous Mr. Pickwick of a wonderful case illustrating the surgical skill of Mr. Slasher, a good operator; and also gives the clinical history of a boy who had swallowed his sister's necklace of wooden beads. While in the hospital it was found necessary to "muffle him in a watchman's " coat"; because, as he walked about, the rattling of the beads in his stomach made "such a devil of a noise" that it was feared he would wake the patients.

A "prim personage in clean linen and cloth boots" commences a long story which he has been in the habit of telling with great applause for ten years, "but for the life of him he couldn't recollect " at that precise moment what the anecdote was."

A "scorbutic youth in a long stock" becomes involved in a row with Mr. Gunter. The warm water for the punch is intercepted by Mrs. Raddle; and finally the voice of Mrs. Raddle is heard screaming Mr. Sawyer's name, ordering the company out, and complaining about being swindled out of her rent. The guests rapidly depart, the prim man being particularly indignant because he was just beginning to have a dawning recollection of the story he had forgotten.

Mr. Ben Allen was much inebriated and "knocked double " knocks at the door of the Borough Market office, and took " short naps on the steps, alternately, until daybreak, under " the firm impression that he lived there, and had forgotten the " key."

After Bob had finished his medical studies, he practised in Bristol; and Ben spent much time there, "wavering between in- " toxication partial and intoxication complete." Bob adopted various expedients to obtain practice. The lamplighter was paid " eighteen pence a week to pull the night-bell for ten minutes every " time" he went his round. A boy of the establishment would rush into church just before the psalms with "horror and dismay " depicted on his countenance," and call Mr. Sawyer out. Every-

body would say, "What a business that young man has!" But
half the drawers in the shop did not open and the other half had
nothing in them. There was, in the words of Bob, "hardly any-
"thing real in the shop but the leeches, and *they* are second-hand."
The patients he did have never paid, under any circumstances.
He finally went away on a jaunt with Mr. Pickwick. Mr. Pickwick
remonstrates with Bob for leaving his patients without anybody
to attend them.

" 'Why not?' asked Bob, in reply. 'I shall save by it, you
" 'know. None of them ever pay. Besides,' said Bob, lowering
"his voice to a confidential whisper, 'they will be all the better
" 'for it; for, being nearly out of drugs, and not able to increase
" 'my account just now, I should have been obliged to give them
" 'calomel all round, and it would have been certain to have dis-
" 'agreed with some of them. So it's all for the best.' "

Bob wafers a notice on his office door. The notice reads:
"Sawyer, late Nockemorf. Enquire of Mrs. Cripps, over the way."
Mrs. Cripps was the mother of Bob's office-boy, and was directed
to say to anxious questioners that Mr. Sawyer was very sorry
but there was to be a "tremendous operation," and he had been
called to attend "a consultation of the very first surgeons in the
" country." Bob says: "It'll do me more good than otherwise, I
" expect. If it gets into one of the local papers, it will be the
" making of me."

Bob and Ben went through many interesting adventures together, and finally received surgical appointments from the East
India Company and passed over to Bengal. "They each had the
" yellow fever fourteen times, and then resolved to try a little
" abstinence; since which period they have been doing well."

Such are Dickens's Doctors—fools, drunkards, blackguards,
criminals, coarse, common, ignorant men, impostors, solemn
ignoramuses, clowns, and a few gentlemen. Truly, as a general
thing he has not been complimentary. Most of his pictures are
broad caricatures, in which a single failing is exaggerated into the
essential part of the man. There is some truth in his amusing

pictures of professional solemnity and owllike assumption of almost superhuman wisdom. Let us profit by the sketch.

But Dickens has not used to the best, except from a humorous point of view, the mighty life experiences of a busy doctor. He has not understood the weary years of toil, the perplexities, the period of hope deferred which maketh the heart sick, while waiting for recognition, the trials of a brave and worthy man who sees the shallow trickster preferred and successful, the physical tire, the mental exhaustion, the corroding anxiety that knows no end, the sights that stir pity and the words that awaken sympathy, the failure in spite of effort and the success snatched at last from the reluctant hands of fate, the vast power for good or evil, the heartbreak that ensues upon failure, and the disenchantment that too often follows success. It is all there, the tragedy, the comedy, the farce; and he just hints at it in his description of the fashionable physician in *Little Dorrit;* but he scarcely tapped this mine of precious wealth. What a pity that he never delineated such a lion-heart as Abernethy's, such a lordly soul as Hunter's, such a noble career as Paget's, or such a helpful life as Gross's. The world will always be the poorer because he did not.

BARON LARREY: A SKETCH *

AMONG the many remarkable men that stood with the greatest
captain of modern times in his Titanic combats was one whose
career attracts the particular interest of surgeons. He was a
military surgeon for over half a century, and he participated in
twenty-six campaigns, from Syria to Portugal, and from Moscow
to Madrid. He followed Napoleon with love that never failed,
with constancy that never faltered; and gave all his best skill to
friend and foe alike, as duty called. He was brave on the battlefield and in the plague-hospital, but he was braver in the Tuileries
and in the imperial tent; for he always dared to tell his master
the truth. That master loved and trusted him; ennobled him;
decorated him before the army; when at St. Helena, referred to
him in his will as "the most virtuous man I have ever known";
and bequeathed to him ten thousand francs as a souvenir of enduring affection.

It is needless to say that I refer to the greatest military surgeon that ever lived,† to Dominique Jean Larrey, Baron of the
Empire, Commander of the Legion of Honor, Inspector General
of the Medical Staff of the French Armies, Chief Surgeon of the

* Read at a meeting of the Johns Hopkins Historical Club, February 12, 1906
Reprinted from *The Johns Hopkins Hospital Bulletin*, vol. xvii, No. 184, July, 1906.
The chief sources of information for this article are the *Surgical Memoirs of Baron
Larrey*. (The first two volumes have been translated by Richard Willmott Hall;
the third volume, by John C. Mercer); Sloane's *Life of Napoleon*, Taine's *Ancient
Régime*, Levy's *Private Life of Napoleon*. The *Memoirs of Baron Marbot, The
Memoirs of Marshal MacDonald, The Hospitals and Surgeons of Paris*, by F. C.
Stewart, and *A Memoir of J. Mason Warren, M. D.*, edited by Howard Payson
Arnold. *The Life of Larrey*, by Paul Triaire, I was not familiar with when writing
this sketch and I did not see it until Dr. Harvey Cushing showed it to me in Baltimore. Had I been able to use this excellent and complete work errors would have
been corrected which doubtless exist in this article, and the subject would have
been treated more accurately.

† Mitchell Banks calls him so and I think justly. See "The Surgeon of Old in
War," *Medical News*, September 4, 1897.

Baron Larrey.

Grand Army, and First Surgeon of the Imperial Guard. He was born in 1766 in the romantic region of the High Pyrenees. His birthplace was the little village of Beaudeau, which is distant about a mile from Bigore, a well-known watering-place, celebrated since Roman days for the medicinal virtues of its mineral springs.

At the period of Larrey's birth centuries of misrule were about to culminate in a mighty catastrophe. All faith and loyalty had gone out of life; there were no real leaders; the nobles devoted their time to debauchery, intrigue, and the chase; love was dead, and gallantry reigned instead. The ambitions of the Bull's Eye were directed purely to getting influence, so that this influence might bring power and gold. Everything went by favor, and nothing by merit; and harlots wheedled from the king every appointment, from Archbishop to Gamekeeper. The nobles thronged Versailles, leaving their estates in utter neglect and ruin and permitting their peasants to starve and rot. The people, in the words of Macaulay, were beasts of burden and were soon to become beasts of prey. They were ignorant beyond conception, were brutal as pigs or oxen, and were regarded by the authorities as mere material for the tax-gatherers. Famine stalked through every district; and lust, anger, ferocity, and brutal hatred brooded in every workshop and hovel. The best that could happen to a son of the people was to become the steward of an estate and oppress his brothers; the best that could happen to a daughter of the people was to become the bed-room slave of a well-to-do captor. The people could truly say, as the Corn Law Rhymer was to say many years later:

> "Our sons are the serfs of the rich by day,
> And our daughters their slaves by night."

It was thirteen years before Larrey's birth that Lord Chester-field, traveling in France, wrote: "All the symptoms which I have ever met with in history previous to great changes and revolutions in government exist and daily increase in France"; but the rulers were blind and could not see. In 1766 the old Satyr, Louis XV, in spite of the dreadful poverty of the people, still kept four thousand horses in his stables, and still spent every year sixty-eight million francs for his household expenses, the equivalent of at least twice that sum today. Pompadour, who had cost him directly thirty-six million francs, and indirectly had cost him wars, famines, pestilences, and his immortal soul, had been dead but two years; and the beautiful and brazen DuBarry reigned in her stead. The easy view among the rich and powerful was that what had been would continue to be; but even Louis was a little wiser and said: "After me, the Deluge"—and after him the Deluge came. Charles Dickens said: "Rooted in the woods of France and Norway there were growing trees . . . already marked by the Woodman Fate . . . to make a movable framework with a rack and a knife in it terrible in history" (*A Tale of Two Cities*). The educated world had become skeptical, philosophical, utterly cynical, and prated and canted continually of philanthropy and the rights of man. A young fellow named Charles Henri Sansom was taking from his father the lessons that were to fit him to be the great M. de Paris, the public executioner of the time of the Terror. Voltaire was living at Ferney in Switzerland, was attacking with searing sarcasm and almost Satanic mockery the most cherished traditions of the court and of the church, and was placing in a pillory before all the world every hideous instance of public wrong and injustice. Diderot, with some great contemporaries—notable among whom were Grim, D'Holbach, and d'Alembert—was editing the Encyclopédie, and was helping to lay broad and deep the foundations of modern thought. Rousseau was in England, just preparing to return to France, where he was to hide in a garret, and in that garret brood out the dread retribution of the French Revolution. Marat, the future editor of *L'Ami du Peuple*, the future advocate of a sacrifice of 270,000 lives, the future victim of Charlotte Corday, was a poor, unknown doctor, and was leading a wandering existence. Robespierre, the future creator of the Terror, the sentimentalist who dearly loved dogs, the man who was to move the abolition of capital punishment, and was to resign a judgeship rather than impose a death sentence, the man who came to make

slaughter a creed and to kill friend and foe alike, was a school-
boy at Arras, living with his father, the advocate. Danton, the
lion-hearted Danton of later days, the one that was to defy the
threats of united Europe and was to "cast down as a gage of
battle the head of a king," was but seven years old and was
living at Arcis-sur-Aube. Napoleon Bonaparte, whose loving follower Larrey was destined to become, had not yet been born.
This illustrious man was born on August 15, 1769. It must have
been evident to all thoughtful minds in 1766 that the world was
on the threshold of great events, that the future was pregnant
with portentous happenings, and that Jean Jaques spoke the truth
when he said: "This is an age of revolutions."

Larrey, like most great men, was born poor. His parents
were too poverty stricken to pay for his education; and what
instruction he got was obtained gratuitously from the Abbé de
Grasset, a good and kindly churchman, who had originally become interested in the boy because he possessed a good voice
and sang in the choir. When Larrey was thirteen years of age
his father died; and the son went to Toulouse to live with his
uncle, Alexis Larrey, a successful surgeon of that city, and the
chief surgeon to a large hospital. The city of Toulouse had
recently rung in the ears of men; for it was there, in 1762, that
probably the most infamous verdict ever given by a judicial
tribunal had been rendered by the Parliament of Toulouse against
the Calas family. This verdict excited Voltaire to frantic rage,
and is dealt with in his book *Sur la Tolerance*.

While in Toulouse and under the guidance of his uncle, Larrey
finished his education in the College of Esquile, and then studied
medicine and surgery. He left Toulouse in 1787, when he was
twenty-one years of age, and went direct to Paris. This was
two years before the convocation of the States General. Soon
after reaching Paris he took a public examination and obtained
an appointment as auxiliary surgeon in the navy. He went to
the great naval station at Brest, underwent another examination,
was appointed chief surgeon of a war vessel, and was assigned to
the Vigilante.

As the boat was not to sail for some months, Larrey passed the time in lecturing to students on surgery and anatomy, an instance of that fiery activity that possessed him all his life. He was also interested in visiting the prison of the galley-slaves. Ten years later the notorious Vidocq, who afterward became chief of the French police, was a convict in this same dreadful Bagne of Brest, from which he made a remarkable escape. We learn of its terrors in his *Autobiography*, and the conditions were probably much the same at the time of Larrey's visit. In the Bagne Larrey saw a man seventy years of age, who was totally blind during the daytime, but could see at night. This condition of day-blindness had resulted from a confinement of over thirty years in a dark, underground cell. Larrey believed that the blindness was the result of the long exclusion of light, which, of course, is one of the known causes of this interesting condition. In a postmortem examination made upon a galley-slave at this time Larrey found transposition of the viscera.

The newly appointed naval surgeon sailed from Brest for Newfoundland in April, 1788, and was gone six months on his trip. He made many interesting observations, which are recorded in his *Memoirs*. For instance, he discusses seasickness, a condition from which he suffered himself, and which he justly calls "the most painful disease with which a mariner can be affected." He studied its development and theorized on its cause, and came to the conclusion that it results from oscillation of the brain, saying that when the brain is large and soft it is more liable to be affected. Hence, young persons, whose brains are voluminous, are most usually the subjects of seasickness; while persons of advanced ages, with firm brains, are less liable to the disease. He says graphically that the first effects are "sadness and panic, which seizes the individual. The face becomes pale, the eyes are suffused with tears, and the appetite for food is entirely removed. The patient is silenced; seeks solitude and repose; reels like one intoxicated; is affected with vertigo, tinnitus aurium, and unpleasant weight of the head. Nausea succeeds, and soon after vomiting, which becomes frequent and painful, and continues almost without intermission until the cause ceases." It, therefore, becomes evident to us not only that Larrey was seasick, but that he was most extremely seasick.

He also discusses frost-gangrene; the catching, cleaning and salting of codfish; and the tastes and habits of the Newfoundland caribou, which in some respects were extraordinary; as one of them broke into the fold, and as the result of this forcible entry a cow became pregnant. Larrey always wondered what the product of this ill-assorted love affair could have been.

He was very much interested in the change of plumage of the birds in Arctic climates, and noted that the blackbirds are red-brown in the summer and white in the winter. He also presents a dissertation on the habits of the Esquimaux. It had always been my impression that the Esquimaux, almost alone among races, use no intoxicants; but Larrey found the Newfoundland Esquimaux using a fermented liquor made of the buds of the fir tree. He speaks, likewise, of the insect pests in Newfoundland during the summer; says particularly that "a species of gnat called the mosquito is very troublesome, and produces by its sting local inflammation and fever, which are but ephermal. The effects of these stings were removed by washing with salt water and by rest and refreshment. By my advice our men protected their skins from them by anointing themselves with camphorated oil and by wearing a piece of gauze over the face." The phenomenon of phosphorescence also interested him greatly. This he believed to be the result of the presence of numerous animalcules "and putrid animal matter. The situation where these lights appear most brilliantly is consequently unwholesome if persons continue in it."

Larrey reached Brest on his return voyage in October, 1788; and early in the winter of 1789 he went to Paris. The winter of 1789 he justly calls "the memorable winter," and says that between the time of his return to Paris and of his departure for the campaign of the Rhine "many remarkable events transpired in this capital to which I was a witness"; but, unfortunately, he does not tell the events, but confines himself to speaking purely of surgical matters. He departed for the Army of the Rhine in April, 1792, just thirteen months before the beginning of the Terror, and the very month in which the guillotine was adopted as the official instrument of execution. Decapitation by an instrument had been suggested for France by Doctor Guillotin. The instrument had been invented by Louis and improved by Sanson, the executioner. A musician that boarded with Sanson suggested the obliquely set knife; and, irony of fate, Louis XVI suggested the neat little basket to catch the separated head.*

It was in the winter of 1789 that the people awoke to their wrongs and their power, and that the earthquake-tread of red Democracy began to echo through the land. Tumult and disorder became common in the capital. We read in history of the attack of the mob of the St. Antoine Quarter upon the paper warehouse of Réveillon, who was falsely charged with saying: "A workman can live well on fifteen sous a day." In this attack on the paper warehouse 500 were killed and very many were wounded; and Réveillon himself took refuge in the Bastille. Larrey saw many of those wounded in this affair. They were brought to the Hôtel Dieu in the service of the celebrated Desault.

Desault demonstrated these cases, and used them to emphasize his views upon the treatment of gunshot wounds. He strongly opposed the popular alcohol dressing, and used lead-water, as recommended by Paré. He opposed the attempt to alter the nature of the wound by excision and suture, except in wounds of the face and mouth, when he advocated it. He opposed immediate amputation, a view from which Larrey subsequently positively dissented.

Desault must have had many harrowing experiences during the Revolution. He was physician to several of the chief jails; he did not attend the Dauphin—Peleton having been the surgeon that had him in charge; but he saw most of the prisoners that went to execution from the Conciergerie. Desault must have freely moved among the prisoners, jailers, and revolutionists, just as did Doctor Manette in Dickens's *Tale of Two Cities;* and he seems

* *Memoirs* of the Sansons.   Also Lenôtre on *La Guillotine.*

to have been almost universally loved and respected. He was a
man of violent temper, as we learn from the following account of
him, given by Sir Astley Cooper (*A Book About Doctors*, by J.
Cordy Jeaffreson, Vol. I, p. 8):

It was in the winter of 1792 that Sir Astley Cooper was a
student under Desault and Chopart. A boy, sixteen years of
age, was brought to Desault's clinic. He was said to have paralysis of the right arm; but the surgeon suspected that he was
malingering. Desault spoke to the boy by name and calmly
said: "Take off your hat." The boy thoughtlessly took the supposedly paralyzed hand and removed the hat. "Hand me a
stick," called Desault; and then he attacked the boy before
everybody and soundly beat him. This remedy he called "club
cordial."

Once during the Revolution Desault was arrested, and was
confined in the Luxembourg Prison for three days. This was
in many respects the least terrible of all the Revolutionary jails.
It was considered the aristocratic prison. It was a palace that
had been made into a prison, and the first noble suspects in the
beginning of the Revolution were sent there. Later, however, the
ordinary, everyday citizen occasionally found his way there; and
finally, on a certain notable night, Danton, Camille Desmoulins,
and their friends were brought in, at the order of their one-time
friend, Robespierre. Desault was quickly liberated; returned to
his work as a teacher of surgery in the Hôtel Dieu, and was not
arrested again.

At the height of his fame 600 pupils attended his clinics.
The horrors of the Revolution depressed him greatly and embittered his final years. At his death he was attended by two
friends, both of them celebrated, and both remembered today:
Bichat, the founder of histology, and Corvisart, subsequently the
physician to Napoleon and a great authority on the heart. At
the present day we remember Desault particularly by his circular
amputation of three incisions, a cone being thus made, the apex
of which is the divided bone; by his long extension-splint for fracture of the thigh; by his bandage for fracture of the clavicle; and

by his operation for one form of salivary fistula. Chopart, Desault's hospital colleague, is still remembered in this age for his amputation through the middle tarsal joint, this articulation being yet called in anatomy the line of Chopart. The writings of neither of these men endure, but we may say with Longfellow:

"Happy those whose written pages
Perish with their lives,
If among the crumbling ages
Still their name survives."

Some writers have stated that none of the crowd was killed at the taking of the Bastille; but there must have been some of them injured, for Larrey says that he saw the wounded of the tumult of that day. The day that martial law was declared in the Champs de Mars, many wounded persons were brought into the Invalides; and our surgeon saw them being treated by Sabatier, whom we remember today as the surgeon that advocated suturing a divided intestine over a cylinder made of a playing-card smeared with turpentine. This method of Sabatier was a modification of the method of the Four Masters of the Thirteenth Century, who used the trachea of an animal; of the method of William of Salicet, who employed the dried and hardened bowel of an animal; and of the method of Watson, who used a cylinder of isinglass.

On May 13, 1789 Larrey seems to have seen a genuine case of anthrax. He tells us in his *Memoirs* that an ox having a carbuncle was purchased at a market by a butcher; and that the butcher killed the animal in haste, because he was afraid that the carbuncle would be fatal and that he would lose the sale of the meat. One of the boys that had killed the ox developed a black pustule of the face and stiffness of the left jaw. This tumor grew purple-red around its margins, and was black and depressed in the center; and the patient died within a few days, by which time the lesion had spread over half the face. Another boy in the family had the same fate, the tumor having arisen on the neck. The wife of the butcher also developed a similar condition; and when Larrey saw her, she seemed on the point of death. He ordered what he called "cordial antiseptic drinks," aromatic cataplasms, and mineral lemonade; and had vinegar evaporated in the chamber. He then held a consultation with M. Boyer, a celebrated surgeon of La Charité. Boyer is remembered as the author of a noted book which was supposed to embody all the surgical knowledge of his time, in which he makes the statement that any further progress in the art or science of medicine is impossible. The surgeons agreed that the pustules should be extirpated, and the raw surfaces cauterized. The patient so treated recovered.

During the winter that Larrey stayed in Paris he passed a competitive examination for the position of intern of the Hôtel Dieu; but the appointment was given to someone else having more influence. He also passed an examination for Second Surgeon of the Invalides, and this place was given him. A short time afterward war was declared; and Larrey was sent as a surgeon of the first class to the Army of the Rhine, then commanded by Marshal Luckner, but soon afterward put under the charge of Lieutenant-General Kellermann. Marshal Luckner, a fine old soldier, came to the guillotine during the Terror. Lieutenant-General Kellermann soon afterward won the great conflict of Valmy; and when Napoleon became Emperor, Kellermann was created a Marshal of France and Duke of Valmy. He was soon displaced from the command of the Army of the Rhine by General Biron, who was quickly succeeded by General Custine. The latter occupied Frankfort, and was then obliged to retire to the Rhine. In the fall of this year Dumouriez won the great battle of Jennappes, and thus secured possession of a large portion of the Austrian Netherlands.

It was in the Campaign of the Rhine that Larrey first became impressed with the "inconvenience to which we were subjected in moving the ambulances and military hospitals. The military regulations required that they should always be one league distant from the army. The wounded were left on the field until after the engagement, and were then collected at a convenient

8

spot, to which the ambulances repaired as speedily as possible; but the number of wagons interposed between them and the army, and many other difficulties, so retarded their progress that they never arrived in less than twenty-four or thirty-six hours; so that most of the wounded died for want of assistance." Larrey saw that it was absolutely necessary to construct vehicles that would readily convey the wounded actually during the battle. He was unable to perfect the plan at this period, but did so soon afterward; and the principle of actively treating men on the battlefield and quickly transferring them to a field-hospital seems to have originated in the mind of this distinguished surgeon.

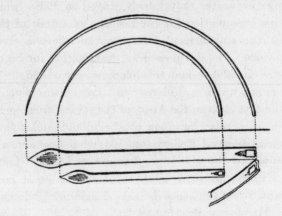

Larrey's needles (Larrey's *Memoirs*).

When he was at Mainz, or Mayence, a town in Hesse that the army occupied for some time, he attended the anatomical demonstrations of the celebrated Doctor Sömmering, whose method of numbering the cranial nerves is the one that we follow today; and he also repeated with Doctor Straak some of the very earliest experiments in galvanism. He was able to carry out on a recently amputated leg some experiments that had previously been made only upon animals. The contraction of the muscles that followed the galvanization of the popliteal nerve led Larrey to believe that galvanism might restore paralyzed limbs; but he says that the very slight benefit that had since been derived from galvanism and electricity in the cure of such conditions led him to give up this idea.

It was at this period of his career that he invented the needle that was long known by his name. These needles were made of fine and highly tempered steel and were of different sizes. The needle was curved into a semicircle, the extremities being parallel. The point was a small curve with sharp edges, and the edges terminated toward the body in obtuse angles. The edges were rounded and slightly thinner than the middle of the needle. There was a square, transverse opening through the eye, and a groove, so that a cord or ribbon could lie in it. The advantages that he claimed for these needles were the readiness with which they would pass through the skin and the fact that the ligature would lie free and keep its flattened form, thus supporting the wound edges.

Larrey was in several actions during this campaign, and became very seriously impressed with the difficulties of handling the wounded through the fact that at Limbourg the French were obliged to leave them on the field, and they fell into the hands of the enemy. He applied for permission to construct a flying ambulance. He at first thought of having the wounded carried on horses in panniers, but he soon gave this idea up; and he was led to devise a carriage that united "swiftness to solidity and ease." He began to use his ambulance in this campaign with great success.

He was in some very serious battles, in which he made some extremely interesting observations on gunshot wounds. His experience led him to advocate immediate amputation in certain grave injuries of the extremities—a view that he never abandoned. He became convinced that people were sometimes killed by what was known as "windage" of bullets; there being no external wound, but a postmortem examination showing grave internal injury. Surgeons then believed that such injuries were caused by the wind from a cannonball or a shell-fragment that had passed close to the body, but had not struck it. Larrey thought there must have been a blow by the projectile, in spite of the absence of

surface-contusions. Military surgeons have entirely abandoned
the idea that injury by the wind of a ball is possible, and attribute
the so-called "wind-contusion" to a projectile that has lightly
passed across the surface and in doing so has left no surface
bruise.

The health of the soldiers in this campaign was excellent,
although thousands of them were new recruits that had been
hurriedly gathered; but they received good food and had plenty
of exercise. It was in this campaign that Larrey first met General
de Beauharnais, a native of Martinique, of whom he became
extremely fond. The general addressed to the Convention a letter
highly commending the surgeon for his services and speaking in
flattering terms of the ambulances that he had recently invented.
This unfortunate gentleman likewise fell a victim to the guillotine,
and left a widow to become Empress of the French.

After the Army of the Rhine had lost several combats General
Pichegru took command. In a few days the army joined the
Army of the Moselle; and the chief command was given to that
brilliant young man, General Hoche. We remember Pichegru as
the able but unfortunate soldier who conquered Belgium and the
Netherlands; suppressed the Parisian insurrection in April, 1795;
became, later, involved in the conspiracy of Georges Cadoudal;
and, after being captured by the police of Fouché in 1804, committed suicide. Hoche was one of the most promising and brilliant soldiers of the Revolution. He suppressed the Vendean
revolt in 1795-96 when only twenty-nine years of age, and died
at Wetzler. Had he lived, he would unquestionably have been
one of the greatest of Napoleon's marshals.

During the campaign Larrey amputated a foot between the
tarsal and the metatarsal bones, doing what we now call the
amputation of Lisfranc. He also extirpated the head of the
humerus, saving the arm—an operation of which he afterward
became a warm advocate. When the troops went into canton-
ments an adynamic fever, which was probably typhoid, broke out.
Larrey was then sent for to go to Paris and complete the organization of an ambulance service, and to establish it in the different

armies of the Republic, as the value of these ambulances had been most conspicuously demonstrated in the campaign of the Rhine.

In 1794 Larrey was appointed Chief Surgeon to the army that was intended for Corsica, and was ordered to report at Toulon. This city had been captured from the English the previous year. At the siege a certain Napoleon Bonaparte had been a captain of artillery; and in the same company of which he had been captain Marmont and Suchet had been junior officers, and Junot had been a sergeant. In the army destined for Corsica Bonaparte was a general of brigade.

During the few days that Larrey remained in Paris he married a lady to whom he had long been engaged, a daughter of M. Leroux, who had been for a time Finance Minister under Louis XVI. On reaching Toulon Larrey met General Bonaparte for the first time. Bonaparte was then twenty-five years of age, and commanded the artillery. He was beginning to be known, and the command of Paris had been offered him by Robespierre; but he had had the good sense to decline to take Henriot's position. The uncertainty of official life, however, was well manifested; for about this time he was put in prison for thirteen days as a suspect, and not long afterward he lost his commission altogether.

The squadron was to repair to Nice and take on soldiers; and Larrey went there by land, traveling with the Inspector of Hospitals, M. Heurteloup, a man remembered by us as the inventor of the artificial leech and one of the devisors of lithotrity.

The presence of the English fleet prevented the French expedition from reaching Corsica, so Larrey spent some time with the Army of the Maritime Alps. At this time he formulated his views on the treatment of the apparently drowned, advocating a form of artificial respiration that consisted in blowing into the mouth of the person to distend his lungs, and pressing on his chest to empty them.

He then went to Spain as Chief Surgeon of the Army of the Pyrenees, and was present at the taking of Figuières and the sack of Roses. He speaks in his journal of individuals on whom he had amputated more than one extremity, and says that they had afterward become very fat; and, because their circle of nutrition was so much lessened in extent, their alvine evacuations became much more frequent.

At this time he became very much interested in the treatment of burns, and insisted that a person that has been burned requires a generous diet; although this view is entirely contrary to the opinion of Hippocrates, who restricted them to a low diet. This solemn quotation of Hippocrates suggests that the latter must still have been regarded as an authority. In fact, in the age of which we speak, surgery was in a chrysalis state and was barely emerging from its cocoon; and the first few hesitating words of truth had, as yet, but scarce been lisped by the baby lips of science. Another of Larrey's views regarding burns was that opium should not be given in their treatment.

He notes that the Spanish love of beauty and good taste appeared even in the preparation of their linen for dressings, which was like cambric; and of their lint, which was as fine as silk, and was tied up in small packages, tastefully arranged in different colors by the Queen of Spain and the ladies of the court.

In 1796 Larrey's health broke down, and he obtained permission to go to Paris. The city was at times somewhat turbulent, but there were no actual outbreaks; for young General Bonaparte had discouraged anarchy by filling several commodious graveyards with the bodies of enterprising revolutionists. Larrey soon went to Toulon, where he learned that the Corsican expedition had been postponed without date; so he stayed a while at Toulon, and began to teach military and naval surgeons, giving courses on anatomy and theoretical and clinical surgery. He pursued this custom wherever he went. We find that whenever the army remained for a few weeks or months in one place, this indefatigable man organized a school and caused all the surgeons of the army to attend it. In this school they would perform operations on the cadaver, study anatomy, and question one another about important topics of military surgery. It seems to have been an infinitely valuable method, and it probably affords one of the reasons why the French army surgeons of that day were the best in the world.

In May, 1797, Larrey set out as Chief Surgeon of the Army of Italy, which had been recently placed under the command of General Bonaparte. Since Napoleon and Larrey had met for the first time at Toulon, the former had gone through many trials, and had achieved some notable triumphs. He had lost his commission; had been harassed by poverty; had walked along the streets of Paris contemplating suicide; had thought of going to Turkey to fight under the Sultan; had, in a critical moment, when all others were afraid, accepted the command of the city from Barras; and had defeated the National Guard, which, at the behest of the Sections, had come 30,000 strong, to attack the Convention. As a reward for this achievement—in fact, probably as the price of it—the command of the Army of Italy had been given him; and he had married Josephine de Beauharnais, whom he had met at Madame Tallien's. At the age of twenty-eight years this remarkable man had won a coveted object of his ambition, the command of an active army about to enter a campaign.

While Larrey was proceeding to Italy he saw, among the Alps, the victims of goiter and the cretins. They interested him a great deal; and he believed that the drinking of snow-water was responsible for the conditions. The difference between travel then and now is well exemplified by the fact that the surgeon had to wait forty-eight days at the foot of Mt. Cenis, owing to the snowdrifts and the avalanches.

He visited most of the important towns of northern Italy, establishing schools of military surgery. He was particularly interested in Venice, a city then noted for its gaiety, its luxury, and its indolence. The contrast between the voluptuous, luxurious Venetians and the rough and hardy French soldiers is shown in the well-known pictures by Georges Clairin. The French are encamped in front of the Ducal Palace. Some soldiers and a woman are preparing dinner, and some men are resting on a great pile of straw. A grim, white-moustached, red-vested revolutionary soldier, with a gun in his hand, is looking with unspeakable disgust at the dandies of Venice, who, arrayed in laces and silks of many colors, are gazing at him with languid surprise and supercilious disgust.

Larrey tells us in his *Memoirs* that the Winged Lion, which he then saw in the Square of St. Mark, now adorns the Esplanade of the Invalides at Paris. It did adorn it for a while, but it went back home after the fall of Napoleon. Our traveler was very much struck with the Cathedral and the four gilded bronze Corinthian horses that surmount the front piece. These horses had been found, centuries before, on the Island of Chios; had been taken to Alexandria; removed to Rome by Augustus Caesar; taken to Constantinople by Constantine; and to Venice by the Doge Dandolo, who captured Constantinople in 1204. Larrey says that these horses have also been transported to Paris, and are now on the Triumphal Arch of the Tuileries. This arch is what we, at the present day, call the Arch of the Carrousel; and it has horses on it, but they are not the genuine horses from Venice. They were taken to Venice, as was the Winged Lion—a commentary, both these circumstances, on the mutability of human affairs.

The gondolas interested Larrey greatly, and he describes them in his journal. We cannot help thinking of Byron's description in a few words, when he says that a gondola is like "a coffin clapt in a canoe."

We gather from Larrey's account that the well-to-do inhabitants of Venice had a reasonably comfortable life. The custom of a fashionable Venetian was to rise from bed between two and three o'clock in the afternoon; to pass the remainder of the daylight in his apartment, clad only in a morning robe; to take a light meal, array himself in his finest, and walk to the Square of St. Mark or some adjacent island; to idle about for a time; to go to dinner, and then to the theatre, which did not begin until nine o'clock and did not let out until about one in the morning. After leaving the theatre he would pay any ceremonial calls he had to make, going from place to place in a gondola; keeping on making visits until five o'clock—or perhaps six—in the morning;

and then going home to bed. The law forced the workingmen
whose occupations produced noise to live in a remote section of
the town, so that the day-slumbers of illustrious personages might
not be disturbed.

While traveling to Trieste Larrey met Desaix, already a well-
known general, who was soon to go with Napoleon to Egypt and
to return with him, only to be killed at Marengo. The surgeon
became very fond of Desaix and regarded him as a most lovable
character. We remember Desaix at Marengo. Bonaparte said:
"The battle is lost." Desaix looked at his watch, found the hour

Ambulance (Larrey's *Memoirs*).

was four o'clock, and said: "Yes, this battle is lost; but there is
time to win another." The other battle was won. Desaix was
killed; and long years afterward Napoleon said that had Desaix
lived, he would have made him a king.

When at Pavia the surgeon called on Spalanzani and Scarpa.
The latter gave him a copy of his recent treatise on the nerves of
the heart. Scarpa's dissections of the nerves of the heart were
studied by Larrey with the utmost interest. He greatly preferred
them to the wax models of all the different portions of the human
system copied from those in Florence; because he loved reality
more than imitation, however accurate the latter might be.

Larrey was ordered to Toulon, with directions to prepare to assume the position of Surgeon in Chief to the expedition that was to go to Egypt and Syria under General Bonaparte. The Chief Surgeon wrote a letter to the medical schools of Montpelier and Toulouse, requesting them to send him at once a number of intelligent young surgeons whose health justified the belief that they could stand the fatigues of a most laborious campaign. This request met with an ample response, and Larrey appointed those that suited him. How differently it would have been done in this country! It would not have been possible for the Surgeon General of our army to write to any nonpolitical bodies to send him capable men; for these capable men could not have been appointed, unless they had had political endorsements; and most medical men with high political endorsements are not suitable men. In this country United States Senators, Congressmen, and other outcasts, would have sent peremptory orders to the War Department as to who was to be appointed; and most of them would have been appointed, irrespective of their fitness. I am not, of course, speaking of the regular army surgeons, who enter by examination, but of the volunteer surgeons, who go out in time of war.

This expedition had a Chief Physician, as well as a Chief Surgeon. The Chief Physician was Desgenettes, a most humane and able man. The expedition embarked on May 13, 1793; and its leader was filled with enthusiasm as to its destiny. The idea of conquering Egypt was not a new one to the French mind. Four centuries before Philip le Bel had thought of it. Sixty years before D'Argenson had suggested the cutting of the Suez Canal; and Choiseul had advocated the conquest of Egypt, because it was the highroad between the East and the West. This remarkable expedition carried the name of Bonaparte into the remotest parts of Asia, and led the Mamelukes and the Arabs to think that he was invincible and to call him El Kebir, the Exalted One; and through all these countries, his fame still lingers in stories and traditions.

Ever since, as a boy, he had read Plutarch and of the achievements of Alexander the Great, Napoleon had dreamed of and longed for the East. When in Paris without an occupation, his thoughts had turned to the East for a career. He went there as a poet goes to the source of his inspiration; and while there he acted a veritable epic. During all the rest of his life, and particularly near its close, when at St. Helena, he regretted that he had failed to found an Empire of the East.

In this Eastern Campaign we see some of the most impressive and some of the most dramatic events in the marvelous career of Napoleon. At Alexandria; near Cairo at the Pyramids, when he called upon forty centuries to look upon their deeds; at the bombardment of Jaffa; at the bloody, desperate, and unfortunate siege of Acre; at Mt. Tabor; and at Aboukir. Traveling the fiery deserts on a camel, sharing all the hardships of his soldiers, he was the great, forceful, inscrutable figure that ever since has entranced the imaginations of men.

He took with him on this expedition some of the best soldiers of France. He took Desaix, who afterward won the battle of Marengo and was killed there, and whom he said he would have made a king. He took Kleber, who was assassinated in the East. He took Berthier, who was so long his close companion; Menou, who turned Mohammedan; Davout, who afterward won Auerstadt and became one of the most celebrated marshals of France; Murat, the cavalry-leader who surprised the very Mamelukes by the splendor of his horsemanship, and who later became King of Naples; and his close friend, Lannes, who afterward became Marshal of France and Duke of Montebello, who lost his life at Essling, and of whom Napoleon said: "He was the most distinguished soldier in my army."

Three of the colonels in this expedition came later to great celebrity: Marmont, who became a marshal and a duke; Junot, who became one of the best known of the generals and a duke; and Bessières, who became Marshal, Duke of Istria, and Commander of the Imperial Guard, and who lost his life at Lützen. One hundred scientists skilled in various sciences, many of them students of the East, were taken along to study the country, the people, the inscriptions, etc. One find of the learned men of the

Army of Occupation (1799) was the Rosetta Stone, the key by which the hieroglyphics were deciphered by Young and Champollion.

The expedition visited Malta which was still ruled by that curious Order, the Knights of Malta, and had been so ruled since 1522. Napoleon broke up the Order and placed the Island under the flag of France; three months after he had left it was captured by Lord Nelson; and it has been an English possession ever since.

Larrey participated in all the dangers and troubles of this most harassing campaign. At Acre he was wounded; and Napoleon complimented him in public for his gallantry and usefulness. It was at this battle the great general saw that the surgeon was dismounted, gave him his own horse, and directed that the horses of the staff be placed at the disposal of the Surgeon-General to assist in removing the wounded soldiers. He had the satisfaction, he tells us, of bringing all the wounded off, and thus saving them from the Arabs. After the battle Bonaparte presented Larrey with a sword of honor; on account of his having operated, in the very midst of a conflict, upon one of the best generals, General Fougières. The operation was an amputation at the shoulder joint, and was done by the method that we still call Larrey's amputation. This sword was engraved, by the order of Napoleon after he became Emperor, with the words, "Aboukir and Larrey"; and Larrey wore it nearly all the rest of his active military life. When he was captured at Waterloo it was stolen from him by the Prussians.

On one occasion during this campaign the men were obliged to kill their horses to make soup of them. Larrey, in speaking of a later campaign, tells of flavoring soup with gunpowder, as a substitute for salt. He was constantly in the very midst of the plague, but he never took the disease. In the course of eight weeks, in one plague-hospital, every nurse that had, started in died of the disease; as well as three physicians, fourteen surgeons, and eleven apothecaries (see the *Memoirs*).

The journal of Larrey's campaign in Egypt and Syria is rich in striking incidents. He shows us how afraid the soldiers were

of being bitten by scorpions, and yet that the bites were not
dangerous; that severe homesickness compelled certain persons
to return to France; and that the Commander-in-Chief was kicked
by a horse, contusing his right leg severely, and threatening dangerous consequences. Larrey succeeded in curing this injury, in
spite of the marches and the great activity of the general, which
prevented him from giving the hurt member rest. Larrey also
tells us of a hernia that became strangulated and gangrenous, and
killed a man in the space of two hours. He speaks of the wounds
inflicted by the swords of the Mamelukes. One chief of brigade

Ambulance (Larrey's *Memoirs*).

had seven severe wounds; two on the shoulders, cutting through
the muscles and some of the bones, and one on the back, cutting
through the muscles and through the spinous processes of the
dorsal vertebrae. He also had a bullet in the chest, producing a
copious effusion of blood in the pleural sac, and followed by
empyema; but he recovered.

Larrey trephined a number of cases and warmly advocated
operation for meningeal hemorrhage, recording successful cases.
He describes cases in which leeches lodged in the nose and naso-
pharynx, and remained there for weeks before the condition was
understood, producing exhausting hemorrhage. He blames bad

water for liver abscess; and also for nervous putrid fever with bloody fluxes, which was probably typhoid. He points out that the inhabitants protected themselves from plague by inserting setons; that pannier-bearing camels were used to carry wounded men; and that maggots in wounds hastened the processes of nature and rapidly removed dead material. He tells us of the establishing of a school of practical surgery at Cairo; and discusses that dreadful disease, the Egyptian ophthalmia, which caused much blindness. We learn that many amputations were necessary, owing to the character of the missiles used by the enemy. He describes the bas-reliefs in the ruins of Luxor, representing surgical instruments similar to those used at the present time for amputating.

Tetanus seems to have been a veritable scourge among the French, killing many men; and it must have been a haunting nightmare to the surgeon. Larrey believed that when the body bent back into opisthotonos, the prognosis was much worse than when it bent forward into emprosthotonos. He insisted on the causative influence of a wound in this disease, and believed that cold and wet helped tetanus to develop. He advocates incision and cauterization in tetanus, if the wound is on the face or the body; and amputation, if it is on an extremity. He gives some notable examples of recovery from tetanus. One is the case of the celebrated General Lannes, who was wounded at Aboukir, and whom Larrey treated merely with internal remedies, emollient applications, and bleeding. General D'Estaing developed this disease after a wound through the right arm, and Larrey says that he cured him by amputation.

He tells us that at the Siege of Acre there were 2000 wounded; and that seventy amputations were performed, two of them being hip-joint amputations. One of these patients seemed on the high-road to recovery, when he took the plague and died of it. The other one died of shock. At the time it was considered useless to attempt hip-joint amputation. Larrey advocated it, in spite of Pott's view "that it is a bloody, dreadful, and unjustifiable procedure." Larrey was seven years ahead of Brashear of Kentucky in its advocacy. In his later campaigns he twice performed this

operation with success, although Brashear's success in 1806 ante-
dated Larrey's by several years. Larrey did six amputations at
the shoulder joint, and four of them were successful. He trephined
7 cases, and 5 were cured. General Caffarelli received a compound
gunshot fracture of the elbow joint. The arm was amputated;
but he developed "a nervous fever," and died of it. Undoubtedly,
however, this fever was pyemia; for the postmortem examination
disclosed an abscess of the liver and an abscess of the lung. General
Murat, afterward Marshal of France and King of Naples, received
a serious gunshot wound. A bullet entered the neck, below the
angle of the jaw, on the right side, and emerged on the left side,
passing in front of the jugulars, injuring the ninth pair of nerves,
and traversing the mouth. He was cured. M. Duroc, afterward
Grand Marshal of the Palace, received an enormous wound of
the right thigh by the bursting of a bomb. Eugene de Beauharnais,
Bonaparte's stepson, received a grave wound of the orbit. Both
these gentlemen recovered. General Lannes was wounded again,
by a bullet striking him in the face and passing behind the ear.
M. Arrighi, afterward Duke of Padua, received a wound that
divided the external carotid artery. One of the soldiers put his
finger into the wound to arrest the bleeding temporarily by
pressure; and Larrey was obliged to go to his assistance "in the
midst of a shower of bullets." He arrested the bleeding, strange
to say, by the use of a compress and a bandage.

He tells us that the wounds often became full of maggots, the
larvæ of the blue flies of Syria. He gives full accounts of the
plague, in all its horrors; speaks of the marvelous endurance and
great bravery of Bonaparte; tells the story of the sacking of
Jaffa, and of the martial deeds of Kleber; and mentions men
that swallowed leeches in their drinking-water, in spite of the
efforts to keep them from drinking from the pools. He speaks of
abscess of the liver, and says that there were many cures. His
rule was to open it when it had become glued to the surface. He
writes of atrophy of the testis; of leprosy; of elephantiasis; of the
death of Kleber, and of the military brilliancy of Desaix; of
scurvy, syphilis, Arabian horses, Syrian midwives, abortionists,

slaves, women, baths, seraglios, embalming, mummies, camels, sarcocele, wounds of the head, and incubators—truly a wide variety of subjects exhibiting enormous intellectual activity. He was very much interested in the bathing habits of the women, and engaged in the questionable proceeding of getting a female physician who was matron and proprietor of a bath at Cairo, to allow him to witness ladies bathing. He saw them through a small opening that commanded a complete view and also enabled him to hear. He describes the scene in an entertaining manner, and it evidently afforded him considerable personal satisfaction. He says that they "relate the adventures of the seraglio, dispute with each other of their charms and of the favors that they have received from the sultans."

Napoleon, it will be remembered, returned home on account of the critical state of public affairs and the peculiar conduct of Josephine. The army had been left under the command of Kleber. Kleber was assassinated by a fanatic, and Menou took command. The entire absence of reenforcements and supplies finally necessitated surrender. Alexandria was given up, and the army received all the honors of war. The officers and soldiers were returned to France in British vessels. In 1801 Larrey came back to Toulon. Thus ended the famous expedition to the East.

After his return, on December 24, 1801, the following letters were issued by the War Department: The first was one stating that the Commander-in-Chief had notified the Government of the devotion and success of Larrey and his colleagues in preserving the army. The next letter, dated January 8th, and signed by Berthier, tells Larrey that he has rendered most important service and has received the particular attention of the First Consul. The third is dated January 28th, and states that the Government has lost no chance to let the French Nation know of the services rendered by Larrey in Egypt, and tells him that his name will henceforth be regarded as that of a benefactor of his country. It also says that fifteen thousand francs had been sent to his wife, as a very small testimonial of gratitude; and that, to the personal knowledge of the writer, Larrey, with his brave associates, had attended the wounded under the fiercest fire, and even in the trenches.

The Revolution of the 18th Brumaire had cast the imbecile Directory out of power. The new Constitution, which was largely the work of the Abbé Sieyès, had established the Consular Government; and Napoleon had become First Consul. He was practically a king, without the title. He moved into the Tuileries in the beginning of the year 1800, and was soon afterward made First Consul for life.

It will be remembered that Larrey had remained in the East for a long time after Napoleon's return; and the Second Italian War, with its magnificent triumphs—the war in which the Battle of Marengo occurred—was fought before the surgeon returned. On his arrival he was received most affectionately by the First Consul; and was made the Chief Surgeon to the Consular Guards a few days before the signing of the Treaty of Amiens, which made peace between France and England. It was just about this time that the famous Concordat was drawn up, the agreement or understanding between France and the Papacy that has been under active discussion in the newspapers within recent months. Soon after Larrey arrived at Paris he commenced a course of lectures to a very large number of students; and it is extremely interesting to find that at that early day in surgery he was lecturing on Experimental Surgery, a branch that is still rarely taught and too seldom thought about.

In March, 1804, Napoleon became Emperor of the French. In the interval between his assumption of the office of First Consul and his becoming Emperor, his labors had been unceasing and marvelous. He had conquered Italy; had made peace with England; had adjusted matters with the Papacy; had built roads and canals, improved the drainage and the water supply of Paris, created numerous industries; had stimulated shipbuilding, science, and art; had become President of the Cisalpine Republic; had encouraged education—particularly the higher education—and had, with Cambacérès and others, drawn up the Code Napoleon, which is the basis of the criminal law of France today.

9

The peace with England was broken in 1803; and Napoleon gathered a large army in the neighborhood of Boulogne, with the intention of invading England. He had been beset by the Chouan Conspiracy, headed by Georges Cadoudal, General Pichegru, and probably Moreau. He had instigated—or, at least, accepted—the execution of the Duc d'Enghien. Soon after having been made Emperor, he also became King of Italy, and appointed his stepson, Eugene de Beauharnais, as Viceroy.

Larrey tells us in his *Memoirs* that the Emperor made mighty preparations for the invasion of England, and gathered vessels in

Pannier-bearing camel for the wounded (Larrey's *Memoirs*).

every harbor and soldiers at every port. Larrey, who was now Chief Surgeon of the Imperial Guard, went with his master to Boulogne. At this time, as never before, the Emperor felt the need of a great admiral. The Channel was practically open, and all he required was the escort; but the escort did not come. At the most there were probably but a few thousand regular troops in England; and could his army of veterans have crossed what Gladstone called the "silver streak" of the Channel, it seems as though London would have fallen. But the splendid activity of the English navy, in contrast to the supine imbecility of the French navy, together with the violent storms that beset the coast, hindered the passage. Just at this time, too, the European Coalition against the French power was formed, having been instigated by Austria.

Without a moment's hesitation Napoleon turned this gigantic army, marched it through France, crossed the Rhine, and was in Germany almost before the enemy knew that a single man had started. It was just then that Lord Nelson defeated the combined French and Spanish fleets in the memorable Battle of Trafalgar. Napoleon, as we have said, always wanted an admiral and never found one. It is an interesting speculation what might have happened had Paul Jones lived but a few years longer. It seems more than probable that he would have been the admiral that the Emperor was seeking. Had this daring sailor and most able seaman been in command of the French forces at Trafalgar, perhaps history might have had a different story to tell.

Larrey, as Chief Surgeon of the Imperial Guard, was under the direct orders of Marshal Bessières, the soldier in command of the Guard. The surgeon went to Strasburg and organized his ambulances, and the army marched rapidly toward the Danube. The Austrians were quickly cooped up in Ulm, where almost their whole army was lost. This was done by a masterly piece of strategy. They were unable to sustain a siege because there were no stores in the city. The remainder of the Austrians retreated toward Vienna, and the French followed them. While passing a few days in Munich, Larrey again visited Sömmering; and, although in the midst of the fierce excitement of war, he made a study of the anatomical museum. The Emperor soon established his headquarters at Schönbrunn, and the Marshal Prince Murat occupied Vienna.

This campaign throughout had been one of exposure, with almost constant snow or rain. The marches had been hard and harassing. The haste had been so great that there had been difficulty in transporting baggage, and even necessary articles had been left behind; yet there were very few sick. Larrey says, in his *Memoirs*, that as he watched the development of the army at this time, he was satisfied that the French soldiers were be-

coming more robust; and he insists that a soldier will stand almost
any fatigue, if he gets sufficient food. This view confirms the
axiom of Frederick the Great, that "an army, like a serpent,
travels on its belly."

The portion of the Austrian army that had escaped from
Vienna retired into Moravia, to effect a junction with the Russian
army; and the Emperor Napoleon set out to meet them. He found
them in a little town in Moravia, in the neighborhood of Brünn.
The name of the town will always be remembered. It is Austerlitz.

The Battle of Austerlitz was the greatest victory that Napoleon
ever won. It is often called the Battle of the Three Emperors;
the Emperors of Austria and Russia being on the one side, and
the Emperor of the French on the other. Napoleon had about
80,000 men; the allies, in the neighborhood of 100,000.

The direction of the Medical Corps of the army was in the
hands of Larrey, Baron Percy having remained in Vienna. The
night before the battle, the Emperor, without warning, rode along
the French line. Larrey tells us that the army "was electrified
by his presence. By a unanimous and spontaneous motion, the
whole army grasped wisps of straw and set them on fire; and in
a moment, you beheld a new kind of illumination, symmetrical
and brilliant, by more than 45,000 men."

The rain stopped during the night. Napoleon watched the
sun rise through the mists on the morning of the battle; and his
mystical nature was impressed with it as a favorable omen. He
always referred to it subsequently as the "sun of Austerlitz." At
seven o'clock in the morning the battle began; and the Russians
and Austrians were completely destroyed. A portion of the allied
army tried to escape by crossing a frozen lake; but the French
artillery fired at the ice with cannon and broke it up, and thousands drowned. Marshal Soult, the Duke of Dalmatia, was the
hero of the combat, and bore the brunt of it on the French side.

In this battle, Larrey tells us, the enemy lost forty stands of
colors, 500 pieces of cannon, twenty generals, 30,000 prisoners, and
12,000 killed; besides thousands of wounded, who were transported

to Brünn. Almost all the wounded of the French army were dressed on the field of battle. Inspector General Percy returned during the height of the engagement, and took charge of the General Medical Staff; and Larrey returned to his own position with the Imperial Guard. He had established a field hospital in a granary, and the French wounded were quickly removed there and satisfactorily cared for. He says that no battlefield ever presented such a fearful picture of destruction as did Austerlitz. The day afterward the French wounded were taken into Brunn, to quarters that had previously been prepared for their reception. Colonel Morland, of the Chasseurs, had been killed in the combat. The Emperor was very fond of him and desired Larrey to embalm the body, which he did most successfully by methods he had learned in Egypt. Soon after the battle, the Treaty of Presburg was signed, which forced Austria to give up Venice, the Austrian Tyrol, and Suabia.

Larrey describes the appearance of an epidemic disease in Brünn, among the French and the Russians. He speaks of it as a "malignant, nervous, and putrid hospital-fever (adynmico-ataxick)." It was characterized by severe headache, chills, and fever. The wounds that existed tended to become putrid and gangrenous. There was a quick and irregular pulse, turbid urine, and usually diarrhea. There were also tremor of the limbs, sub-sultus tendinum, delirium, pain in the belly, sweating, bleeding from the nose, and discharges from the bowel of black blood. The tongue was black in the center, and dry and red at the edges; and there were sordes on the gums and teeth. The patient was heavy and drowsy, and tended to become insensible. There was a most remarkable change in the features of the face; and when this facial condition, which was surely the Hippocratic face, was noticed early, it was always regarded as of fatal augury. The sick persons passed into very great debility, and often sank and died. Some patients died on the ninth, and some even on the seventh day of the disease. In this account, Larrey unquestionably describes typhoid fever, confusing it, perhaps, in some instances, with hospital-gangrene.

Soon after this period Larrey returned to Paris and again took up teaching. His *Memoirs* contain at this point an essay on aneurysm, in which he maintains that this condition arises only in a diseased artery, and that very frequently the artery has been diseased by syphilis. He also discusses the effect of rheumatism on the fibrous and osseous structures, and considers movable and preternatural cartilages of the joints. He tells us that the first instance of movable cartilage of the knee was reported by Ambroise Paré in 1558. That surgeon opened a suppurating knee joint, and a concretion about the size of an almond emerged. Larrey gives the other reported cases, and shows how many had been operated upon with success—particularly by his own masters, Sabatier and Desault. It is rather horrifying to us today to think of opening knee joints without asepsis, for the purpose of removing these movable bodies; and yet, Larrey seems to have operated with very great success. He also considers the subject of epilepsy, as met with among the soldiers; and says that in many instances mercurial treatment was curative; thus agreeing with our modern view that epilepsy that begins late in life— that is, after youth—if not alcoholic or due to organic brain disease, is usually syphilitic.

His memoir on amputations is a very important one, and somewhat lengthy. In it he strongly advocates immediate amputation for certain serious injuries. In amputating in continuity he employed the circular method, using several cuts. He did not sew up his flaps, but retained the edges together merely by applying a roller-bandage with a piece of lint over the wound. His operations were remarkably successful, probably because he had the freest kind of drainage and did not cover the wounds with foul and nasty greases, which would retain discharges. In confirmation of his views as to the value of early amputation, he quotes what he had heard of the experience of surgeons during the War of the American Revolution. He says that at this period the French surgeons would not amputate until late in the case, but that the American had the courage to amputate at once or within twenty-four hours. The mortality among the French was large, and among the Americans very small; yet the French hospitals were infinitely superior to the American. We thus see that even at this early day American surgeons had independent convictions and the courage to carry them out.

Not a great while after the battle of Austerlitz, Prussia, undeterred by the lesson just administered to Austria and Russia, made a league with Saxony and began war. The Emperor immediately took the field, and very soon the great Battle of Jena was won. There was some difficulty here about the ambulances. They were too far back of the line of battle, and there was considerable delay in dressing the gravely wounded. Larrey insists upon the necessity of placing the ambulances near the line of battle, and of establishing a headquarters to which the wounded requiring serious operations can be rapidly taken. He says that those dangerously wounded must be attended to first, entirely without regard to their rank or distinction; and that those less severely injured must wait until the gravely hurt have been operated upon and dressed. The slightly wounded can go to the hospital of the first or second line, especially officers; because officers have horses to transport them, and these merely trivial wounds do not immediately endanger life. The Emperor marched his army into Berlin, and the magistrates handed over to him the keys of the city. He also took back with him to Paris the sword of Frederick the Great. Prussia had to wait a great many years; but she frightfully punished her old conquerors in the fearful war of '70-'71; and now again France bends all her energies to keep up her army to the highest level, in the hope that she may take vengeance upon Germany and march her soldiers beneath the linden trees.

While in Berlin Larrey visited the distinguished physicians and scientists; and his relations with them seem to have been agreeable. He was particularly indebted to Humboldt, the great explorer; and to the elder and younger Walther, the eminent surgeons. A great many French soldiers, while in Berlin, became asphyxiated through having slept in rooms containing the stoves used by the inhabitants, after having closed the doors and windows of the rooms. It was in Berlin that the ravages of syphilis were particularly noticeable in the army.

The next campaign participated in by Larrey was that in Poland, where he saw for the first time that remarkable disease, plica polonica. He noted that it was most common among the Jews, and regarded it as a result of syphilis—especially of hereditary syphilis. He took part in the fearful battles of Eylau and Friedland. Eylau is in East Prussia, twenty-two miles from Königsberg; Friedland is in East Prussia, twenty-six miles from Königsberg. After the Battle of Eylau, both Larrey and Percy were made Commanders of the Legion of Honor. At this point in the *Memoirs* there is a treatise on dry gangrene produced by frost, which he calls "gangrene from congelation." In Poland he saw a number of cases of anthrax, which he thought came from eating the meat of animals that had the disease. In this campaign, for the second time, Larrey made a counter-opening in the cranium to reach a bullet. He introduced a gum-elastic catheter as a probe, and trephined over the point of it. He found a flattened bullet on the inside of the bone. The patient died five days afterward, of hospital-fever.

At Tilsit peace was made, the monarchs meeting on a pontoon anchored in the middle of the river. Königsberg interested Larrey greatly. Here he saw the point of a javelin that had been within the cranium of the Chevalier Erasmus for fourteen years without impairing his faculties. An abscess formed in the frontal region. It was opened, and this piece of javelin was removed. Larrey thinks that the javelin had probably been in the frontal sinus. He recalls that he himself, a little while after the Polish campaign, saw a French soldier who had had his head pierced with an iron ramrod from a gun accidentally discharged. He had no bad symptoms at all, although it seems that the ramrod must have penetrated the brain. In Königsberg the surgeon also saw a knife that a man had swallowed in 1613. Doctor Gruger, a Polish surgeon, had performed gastrotomy successfully; and the man had lived for ten years afterward. Larrey recalls that once, while he was a pupil, he had seen M. Frizac, Professor of Sur-

gery at Toulouse, make an incision into the abdomen parallel
with the linea alba, and discover the point of a knife sticking
through the wall of the stomach. He removed a fragment of knife-
blade, which was about 2 inches in length; sutured the stomach
with two sutures; and sewed up the integument. The man recovered. The sutures used were not inversion sutures, as the
Lembert suture was not introduced until the third decade of the
nineteenth century. Larrey then gives an account of a soldier
of the guard who was wounded in the left extremity of the stomach by the point of a saber, which penetrated the thorax between
the seventh and eighth ribs; injured the lung; split the diaphragm;
and entered the stomach. The man vomited blood, and fluids
that he had swallowed escaped from the wound. He was very
ill for several days. Cooling medicine and emollient enemata
were given, and venesection was performed. He was made to lie
continuously on the right side. The wound healed without
trouble. He got entirely well, and became one of the veterans
of the Old Guard. The only difficulty left as a legacy was a
hernia of the lung, which he kept in place by wearing a
bandage.

After this campaign Larrey again returned to Paris, where he
received from the Emperor the title of Knight of the Iron Crown
and was decorated with the insignia of that order. His *Memoirs*
set forth next the stories of the campaigns in Spain. On his way
to Spain he visited Toulouse and demonstrated to the students of
the College the views of Doctor Gall, which have been perverted
of recent years, and have been utilized by the quack and the
imposter; yet Gall seems to have been the first man that ever
really suggested the localization of cerebral functions. Larrey
also visited his own birthplace, and became much interested in
studying goiter in the Pyrenees. He disliked the bullfights of
Spain very much, and thought that they should be disapproved
by all that love tranquillity and humanity.

In Spain, as elsewhere, Larrey founded his military schools
and lectured on clinical surgery. He was in many fierce battles,
and had numerous striking experiences. At one time a hospital

was attacked by Spaniards; and he and the surgeons and the convalescents were obliged to take up guns and defend it.

He reports interesting cases of wounds of the brain; of penetrating wounds of the thorax; and of abdominal wounds with protrusion of the intestines, followed by recovery. He considers traumatic gangrene and the Madrid colic, which he thinks was due to some deleterious properties in the wine sold by the people, but which some of the French surgeons thought was due to the wine having been actually poisoned. In order to reach a conclusion as to the action of poisons and the way to treat cases of poisoning, he says that experiments should be made on living animals, in order to find remedies to counteract the poisonous effects. He was much impressed with the virtue of calisaya bark in treating intermittents.

He gives the following interesting case. The injury happened to Marshal Lannes, Duke of Montebello: The Marshal's horse fell down on a mountain covered with frozen snow; and, as a consequence, Lannes was severely bruised about the thorax and abdomen, and seemed to be gravely injured. He was completely covered with bruises. His abdomen was distended and very tender. He had violent pain and dyspnea, and could not voluntarily move. His pulse was small and tense. His face was deadly pale. His voice was weak, and his extremities were cold. The very slightest touch on the abdomen produced agonizing pain.

Larrey recalled a wonderful cure that he had seen made by the Esquimaux on some sailors of the Vigilante, whose boat had been cast against the rocks. These sailors had been dreadfully bruised. Larrey tried the Esquimaux treatment, and afterward used it on others besides the Marshal with success. He got a large sheep and had it stunned by a sudden blow on the neck, and two excellent butchers quickly flayed it. While this was being done the Duke was greased all over with camphorated oil of camomile. His body was then completely wrapped in the skin of the sheep, which had been taken warm from its back. This reeking skin was still covered with serous fluid, and it was fastened together at the edges so as completely to surround the injured man's body. His extremities were wrapped in warm flannel, and the Marshal was allowed to take internally a light tea with lemon juice and sugar.

His pain was very quickly relieved, although the sheepskin pricked and irritated the skin of his body for a little while. Ten minutes after its application he went to sleep and slept for two hours. When he awoke the sheepskin was taken off; and it was found that he had been sweating tremendously. The sweat was wiped off, and an embrocation of warm, camphorated brandy was applied to the injured regions. Camphorated enemata and mucilaginous drinks, with milk of sweet almonds, were given him. The next morning the swelling of the abdomen had abated, and the Marshal felt very much more comfortable. It was found that his urine contained quantities of blood. He was then put into a warm bath. The aromatic embrocations were continued, and he went on duty on the fifth day, being able to ride a horse.

In the wounds inflicted in the Battle of Benevento, Larrey did not think it proper to remove the dressings that had been applied until the third day; because they had been put in place by skilful surgeons, and he was evidently opposed to the meddling interference that is so often productive of harm. One of the Mamelukes, Ibrahim, received a pistol-shot wound of the knee joint that fractured the patella. Larrey removed the separated bone fragments, and this man recovered completely.

Larrey lays down the rule that in any severe wound of a hinge joint the surgeon should always take amputation into consideration; and before the days of antiseptic surgery, this must unquestionably have been sound practice.

We learn from the *Memoirs* that a Dragoon of the Guard received a saber cut in the right inguinal region. The abdomen was opened, and the epigastric artery was found cut. A large mass of the great omentum stuck out of the wound. The plug of omentum stopped the hemorrhage from the divided epigastric artery. The protruded part became cold, without tenderness, and of livid hue. Larrey cut away the part that exhibited these phenomena. He then tied the bleeding arteries, and restored the healthy portion of omentum to the abdominal cavity. The man was entirely well in six weeks.

We find the record of another remarkable case: The patient was a Chasseur of very vigorous constitution, and of a strongly amorous nature. A saber cut received in the Battle of Benevento chopped off a large piece of the occipital bone with a portion of the dura mater, and exposed the right cerebellar lobe. Pressure upon this lobe did not cause any pain, but produced immediate vertigo, convulsions, and then syncope. Larrey removed the loose portion of the occipital bone, which was stuck to the flap, and placed the skin flap directly in contact with the cerebellum, having retained an opening at the lower end for drainage. Quantities of fluid, which must have been cerebrospinal fluid, were discharged at each dressing. The day after the injury the man lost the sight of his right eye and the hearing of his right ear, and developed severe pains in the dorsal region and severe prickling, like the stinging of ants, in the testicles. These organs atrophied and, in the space of fifteen days, reached the size of Windsor beans. The man was taken from Benevento to Valladolid, and stood the journey very well; but inflammation appeared, and the pains in the head and back became agonizing. He had convulsions; and, on attempts at swallowing, had attacks of syncope. Tetanus developed; and the patient died of it, thirty-nine days after the injury. Postmortem examination showed that there was no suppuration in the wound. There was a great contraction of the right lobe of the cerebellum. The medulla oblongata and the spinal cord were dull white, indurated, and greatly shrunken; and the nerves that emerged from them were obviously atrophied. The cranium of this remarkable case was placed in Larrey's anatomical collection. The surgeon regarded this case as confirmatory of Gall's view that the cerebellum is the seat of the sexual instinct, a view long since abandoned. Larrey was aware that cortical injuries impair the intellect, and states that basal and ventricular injuries produce paralysis; and that in severe injury of one hemisphere, the limbs of the opposite side are paralyzed. He also knew that even when such conditions of the limbs are old, relief may follow the performing of an operation to relieve brain pressure on the side of the head opposite to the paralysis. He reports a case that Mumford* regards as undoubtedly a fracture of the base, in which there was coma and bleeding from the ears and mouth. A day after the injury, there was ecchymosis behind each mastoid, which we now call Battle's sign.

The health of the surgeon broke down in this campaign, and he consequently handed over his duties to M. Percy and returned to France. He was so ill that he was in great danger of dying. While he was still far from well, the Austrian campaign opened; and without waiting to recover his strength completely, he set out to join the army in Bavaria. On reaching Strasburg he found that the French had beaten the Austrians at Ratisbon.

Baron Marbot, in his *Memoirs*, gives a most interesting account of the fight at Ratisbon. It was in this engagement that the greatest difficulty arose in surmounting the walls in making an assault. Each party that went to take the scaling ladders was destroyed by the well-directed fire of the Austrians. Fifty volunteers were called for twice to place ladders, and twice every volunteer was killed or wounded. Marbot says that every man in the army would have gone, if ordered to do so; but when volunteers were called for a third time, no one responded. Marshal Lannes, who was in command, became extremely angry. He said that he had been a grenadier before he was a marshal, and would show them that he was a grenadier yet; and he grasped a ladder and alone started forward with it. The officers were ashamed to think of his making the movement personally, so they struggled with him for the possession of the ladder. When the soldiers saw a marshal of France and his staff fighting desperately to have the honor of an enterprise, hundreds jumped forward to participate. Among those that did so were Marbot and Labédoyère, who were the first two men up the ladders. They ascended side by side and hand in hand, steadying each other as they mounted. They got over; a swarm of grenadiers

* "Teachings of the Old Surgeons," by J. G. Mumford, *Boston Med. and Surg. Jour.*, October 3 and 10, 1895.

followed; and the city was taken. A fine aquarelle of these two men mounting the ladders may be seen in Sloane's *Life of Napoleon*.

It was in the fight at Ratisbon that Napoleon was wounded for the second and last time in his life. Some rifleman from the Tyrol succeeded in just grazing him with a shot. The Emperor and Marshal Lannes were talking together when the Emperor was struck. The injury was of the right ankle. Marbot makes a mistake in one point: he says that the pain was so sharp that the Emperor leaned upon the Marshal, and that Doctor Larrey quickly arrived and said that the wound was a trifle; but Larrey did not arrive, as we learn from his *Memoirs*. He was then at Strasburg. It was a young surgeon that took charge of the case. He felt extremely the responsibility of his position. This was obvious to the Emperor, who counseled him to proceed just as though he were dealing with the most unimportant man in the army—which was unquestionably the best of good advice.

The army marched forward and occupied the Island of Lobau, and soon afterward fought the desperate Battle of Aspern, from the field of which the French had to fall back, and in which Marshal Lannes was killed. There is a graphic account of this in Marbot's *Memoirs*.

Marbot tells us that the Marshal, tired out with his exertions, had dismounted from his horse and was walking about with Major General Pouset. At this moment the General was struck in the head and instantly killed. Lannes was warmly attached to the General; had, all through his life, advanced the latter's interests; and was grief-stricken at his death. The Marshal was almost overcome with grief. He walked about one hundred paces away, sat down on the side of a ditch, and seemed buried in deep thought. About fifteen minutes later some soldiers were carrying the dead body of an officer covered with a cloak, and they stopped to rest directly in front of the Marshal. The cloak fell aside, and Lannes recognized Pouset. He cried out: "Is this terrible sight going to follow me everywhere?" He then got up; walked a little distance away; and sat down again on the edge of a ditch, with his legs crossed and his hands held over his eyes. In a moment, a 3-pound shot ricochetted and struck him just where his legs were crossed. He was dreadfully injured, and Marbot rushed toward him. The Marshal said: "I am wounded, but it is nothing. Give me your hand and help me up." He tried to rise, but could not. He was suffering fearfully, and the soldiers started to carry him away. As they began to lift him, it was observed that he was not wrapped up. Someone ran and took the cloak from General Pouset's dead body, and laid it upon Lannes; but the Marshal recognized the cloak and said: "This was my poor friend's. It is covered with his blood. I will not use it. Drag me along, rather, as you can." So the grenadiers made a stretcher out of some boughs from an adjacent clump of trees, and carried the Marshal to the dressing-station, where Larrey took charge of him.

Larrey, in his *Memoirs*, says that a bullet of large size had struck the left knee, passed through the joint, grazed the right thigh, and lacerated the integument, and a part of the vastus internus muscle, just above the left knee joint; and that the Marshal also suffered from concussion of the brain and general prostration—by which, of course, Larrey means shock. He says that the face was livid, the lips pale, the eyes dull and watery, the voice extremely weak, the pulse almost absent, and the intellect deranged; and that the sufferer did not at all realize his danger. The surgeon was almost overcome at the sight of this devoted old-time friend, whom he had attended in Syria, Egypt, and Spain, and whose life he had saved on several previous occasions.

Larrey at once called some of his colleagues into consultation. The wound of the right knee was of the gravest description, there being a comminuted fracture of the bones, laceration of the ligaments and tendons, and destruction of the popliteal vessels. Marbot says that Larrey was in favor of amputating the right leg; another surgeon wanted to cut off both legs; but Doctor Yvan believed the Marshal's firm character would give him a chance of cure without any amputation at all, and that the operation performed in the hot weather would kill him. Larrey says that all of them were in favor of immediate amputation, but that each of the other surgeons hesitated to perform it because he was so sure that the result in any case would be fatal. Larrey hesitated to do it because his duty to the army called him elsewhere. Finally Larrey himself performed it, the operation requiring less than two minutes, and apparently causing but little pain.

The Marshal was then taken to the Island of Lobau, where the Emperor saw him, and where Larrey left him in the care of M. Paulet. He says that he left the Duke with great regret, and continues: "But I was the only inspector on the field of battle; and a great number of wounded on the island, whither they had been transported, still required our assistance. We never rested from our labor until all the wounded had been operated on and dressed."

The interview between Marshal Lannes and Napoleon has been told in many histories and memoirs, and a celebrated picture of it has been painted by Boutigny. It shows the Marshal, after his leg has been amputated and dressed, lying down, with the Emperor on his knees beside him, grasping the Marshal's hands. Larrey, with his apron still in place, stands back of them, looking upon the scene. Marbot tells us in his *Memoirs* that the interview between the Emperor and the Marshal was extremely touching; that Napoleon shed tears as he embraced the Marshal; and that the latter's blood stained the Emperor's white waistcoat. Marbot should have known; for he was at that minute supporting the Marshal's head and shoulders; although he is not put in the painting. Lannes was very much touched by the Emperor's grief. When Napoleon was obliged to leave, in order to provide for the safety of the army, he said: "You will live, my friend, you will live." The Marshal pressed the Emperor's hand and replied: "I trust I may, if I can still be of use to France and to Your Majesty."[*]

Marbot goes on to tell us that every moment Lannes asked the position of the troops, and exhibited pleasure when he learned

[*] Marbot's *Memoirs*.

that the enemy had not ventured to pursue. He asked how his wounded aides-de-camp were doing, and requested Doctor Larrey to examine Marbot's wound. Marbot says that they had to keep the Marshal all night on the island, lying on a bed of cavalry cloaks; and that there was not even good water to give him to quench his thirst. The water of the Danube was filled with mud, and Lannes would not drink it; so Marbot devised a filter, which he made of one of the Marshal's fine shirts. This water was eagerly taken. The next day the Emperor sent a boat to bring the Marshal to the right bank; and he was taken to a house in Ebersdorf, Marbot remaining with him.

We now return to Larrey's account in his *Memoirs*. On reaching Ebersdorf he found the Marshal extremely weak, pale, and incoherent. He was very restless, suffered with dyspnea, and sighed frequently. The next day the wounds were found to be purulent; but the stump looked well; and Larrey had some hopes of recovery. On the evening of the sixth day after the injury, a dangerous fever arose. Two hours after the first attack of fever, there was another attack; and in the course of the day, another, with delirium and gangrene. The Marshal died in the ninth day after the accident—in all probability of pyemia. Larrey had the unpleasant task of embalming the body of his old friend, so that it might be sent back to France.

After this battle there was dreadful mortality in the army from lockjaw and hospital fever. The next great battle participated in by the surgeon was the tremendous conflict of Wagram, upon which the fate of the Empire was staked. It was this fight that made Larrey a Baron of the Empire; and Macdonald, a Marshal of France. The latter had been regarded as one of the ablest soldiers of the Republic; but he was a personal friend of Moreau, and, although he had not joined in the conspiracy with Pichegru, the Emperor was suspicious of him. Furthermore, he was a man blunt of speech, truthful to a fault, and as courageous in counsel as on the battlefield. He had come from a family noted for courage; for his father, Macdonald of Glencoe, had agreed to go with Prince Charles Edward Stuart when all the other Scottish

10

chiefs had held back, and after the Battle of Culloden had gone to France and remained there.

The original list of Marshals was as follows: Augereau, Bernadotte, Berthier, Bessières, Brune, Davout, Jourdan, Kellermann, Lannes, Lefebvre, Masséna, Moncey, Mortier, Murat, Ney, Perignon, Sérurier, and Soult. It had caused surprised comment that Macdonald had been left out of this illustrious list. The Marshals afterward appointed by Napoleon were Grouchy, Marmont, Oudinot, Poniatowski, St. Cyr, Suchet, Victor, and Macdonald. The latter said himself that, in the long run, it was worth being left out; because his achievement at Wagram caused him to have the baton of a Marshal given him on the battlefield, and to have the distinction of being made a duke there—honors that had never come to anyone else on the field of battle.

Macdonald made at Wagram the charge upon which the whole battle hinged. It was his duty to break the center of the Austrian army. He had but 15,000 men with which to do it, and 100 cannon were playing upon them in a semicircle. He accomplished the task; but when it was done only 1500 men were left around him. The Emperor rode up to him and said: "No more trouble between us, Macdonald. You have been reserved for a higher honor than your brothers-in-arms. I make you a Marshal here, on the field of your glory."

In contemplating the names of the illustrious soldiers that were selected as Marshals of France, one is struck by the curious fact that all but three of them seem to have begun life in humble circumstances, with very few advantages. Of these three Poniatowski, the Polish Prince, was not made a Marshal until October, 1813; and he was drowned in the Elster six days later. He was a gallant soldier and an aide to Napoleon. The stories of the other two of better origin were different. One was Marmont, and the other Grouchy; and these two men ruined the man that had made them. Marmont surrendered Paris when the Emperor had almost reached there. If it had been held but a few days longer, far different terms could have been made. Grouchy, by indecision that is simply incredible, lost the Battle of Waterloo, which should have been won.

After Wagram a great many amputations had to be done on account of the severity of the gunshot wounds. In two of the Guard amputation at the hip joint was performed. In telling the story of one of these cases Larrey says that he ligated the femoral artery; and then amputated at the hip joint in fifteen seconds, without any loss of blood. One of these two patients died of shock within three hours; the other died at six o'clock the next morning.

One remarkable case was that of an artilleryman struck by a ball that had rebounded before hitting him. It buried itself behind the bone and lodged near the groin. The patient said that the ball had glanced from him and killed another artillerist. Larrey says: "On seizing the limb to amputate it, I found it unusually heavy; and I decided that there was a ball in it, as I had often seen while making incisions and during operations. Under this impression, and supposing that the thigh was injured high up, I wished to amputate with the flaps. I then made an incision parallel with the skin of the thigh, and discovered a 5-pound ball, which was extracted." The surgeon then completed the amputation.

With this campaign the second volume of the *Memoirs* of the surgeon is terminated. The third volume shows us that Larrey continued with Napoleon until the last. He went through all the horrors of the Russian campaign—the cold; the exposure; and the dreadful conflict at the Borodino, in which 30,000 Frenchmen lost their lives. He was at the desolation of Moscow, and at the passage of the Beresina, where he got safely over; but, finding that important hospital supplies had been left behind, he took his life in his hands and went back for them. The men cried: "Let us save the man that saved us." The frantic mob gave way, and the soldiers brought him in their arms safe to the army again. He was in the hideous tramp in midwinter, from Moscow back to France; and in all the actions of the winter of 1813–14, in which Napoleon fought united Europe and contested, step by step, the road to Paris.

The genius of the great captain never shone more brightly than in this period; for he won battle after battle against vastly superior numbers; but, as he had no reenforcements and few supplies, he was compelled, slowly and gradually, but surely, to fall back. On one occasion during this campaign he captured a whole German army corps; but the faces of the French had to turn to Paris, no matter what the result of the battles might be. We all remember that picture by Meissonier in which the Emperor and his staff, gloomy and depressed, but resolute, are going on their way back to the capital, through the desolate country, over a road cut to pieces by wagons and artillery.

When the order to send the Emperor to Elba was given, Larrey begged to be taken along; but Napoleon would not let him go, telling him that the army needed his services, and that it was his duty to stay with it. Bonaparte returned from Elba in 1815, and the old surgeon was one of the first to welcome his Emperor. The latter, after speaking of the joy that it gave him to be thus received, expressed regret that he had left Larrey so long without a fortune, and said that he hoped soon to be able to recompense him for his services. Soon after coming back from Elba, when the colors were being distributed to the different departments, the Emperor handed the flag of the High Pyrenees to Larrey and asked him to give it to the President of that Department; saying, as he did so, that he was glad that this color should be presented by their countryman, Larrey, a man that was an honor to humanity on account of his courage and his disinterested conduct—a man that had saved great numbers from death in the deserts of the East, had given water reserved for himself to suffering soldiers in Egypt and Syria, and had always loyally and faithfully served his Emperor.

On the eve of the Battle of Waterloo the surgeon was long with Napoleon in confidential conversation, seeking to rouse the Emperor from his depression; for this great man seemed to have dipped into the future, and to have had a glimpse of what was coming.

At Waterloo, when the news of the defeat arrived, Larrey, who was involved in the rout, endeavored to reach the French frontier. He had to fight his way with sword and pistol through a party endeavoring to take him. He succeeded in getting through this party, but his horse was shot under him; and before he could get up, he was struck on the head and the left shoulder with sabers. He was left for dead where he fell; but he regained consciousness, got on a horse, and proceeded on his road. He was, however, captured afterward. Nearly all his clothing was taken away, and the sword given him by the Emperor was also stolen. He was a short man, somewhat stout, and wore a gray great-coat. He thus somewhat resembled the Emperor in appearance, and was at first taken for him. Larrey's hands were tied together, and he was brought before a Prussian officer, who saw that he was not Napoleon and ordered that he be shot. Just as the soldiers were about to fire at him, the Prussian regimental surgeon recognized Larrey and succeeded in stopping the contemplated execution. He then took the French surgeon before General Bulow, who also recognized him. The general was grieved to see this distinguished man without shoes to his feet, almost without clothing to his back, wounded, hungry, and suffering. His hands were untied, and he was taken before Marshal Blucher, who knew of him; because in the Austrian campaign Blucher's own son had been wounded and taken prisoner, and Larrey had cared for him and saved his life. The Marshal at once liberated Larrey, gave him clothing and money, and had him sent forward into France; and he soon afterward reached Paris.

When the Bourbons mounted the throne Larrey lost his position and fell into a state of absolute poverty. His mother and one of his brothers died, and he almost made up his mind to go to the United States to practice surgery. The Emperor of Russia endeavored to secure his services in a high position with the Russian army, and Dom Pedro of Brazil made every effort to have him come to that country; but he refused both these offers.

Napoleon died in 1821 and Larrey was plunged into grief at the death of his old chief. He was greatly touched to learn that the Emperor had spoken of him in his will; had referred to him as "the most virtuous man that I have ever known"; and had left him some money, as an evidence of his continued affection.

Soon afterward Larrey was restored to the army. In 1826 he took a trip to England, and was received with the greatest distinction by the English surgeons. He then returned to Paris, and continued to practice and teach his profession; and he was again made Surgeon-in-Chief of the army, and Chief Surgeon of the Invalides. In the Revolution of July, 1830, which overthrew Charles X, he directed personally the care of the wounded. A year later, at the invitation of the King of Belgium, he visited all the army hospitals of that country and suggested regulations and improvements.

In 1834 he made a tour through southern France, visiting his birth-place. He was received with the greatest honor by all the citizens, and members of the Imperial Guard flocked from long distances to see him. At his birth-place he found the Abbé de Grasset, his old instructor, still living.

In 1842 he was sent to visit the army in Algeria. He inspected it carefully, and then turned toward home; but when at Lyons he was taken ill; and he died there on July 25, 1842.

We find an interesting picture of Larrey in his old age at Paris in *A Memoir of J. Mason Warren*, the father of the present distinguished Professor of Surgery in Harvard College. This interesting volume is edited by Howard Payson Arnold. Doctor Warren was a student in Paris during the reign of Louis Philippe, that greatest day of French medicine and surgery, which I have discussed in another paper*; the day of Dupuytren, Lisfranc, Roux, Marjolin, Civiale, Velpeau, Ricord, Falret, Trelat, Calmeil, Fauville, Dubois, Baudelocque, Guerin, Vidal-de-Cassis, Cazenave, Jobert, Lugol, Rostand, the younger Larrey, Boyer, Maisonneuve, Richerand, Blandin, Chassaignac, Hugier, Sanson, Denonvilliers, Cloquet, Amussat, Nélaton, Cullerier, Breschet, Sappey, Magendie, Andral, Gay-Lussac, Broussais, Malgaigne, and others. On November 5, 1832, Doctor Warren wrote as follows:

"*My dear Father:* I made a very pleasant and instructive visit, a few days since, to the Hôtel des Invalides, where I attended Larrey in his wards. He is a

* "Medical Paris During the Reign of Louis Philippe," by J. Chalmers DaCosta M. D., *University of Penna. Med. Bul.*, March, 1904.

short, corpulent man, with a very agreeable face. His hair, which is gray, falls in curls over the straight, ornamented collar of the military coat that he wears during his visits. He was very polite to Doctor Pierson, who was introduced to him by an Italian gentleman, and took great pains to show us all the remarkable cases, many of which he referred to as being described in his books. He also showed a case of amputating instruments that he had had with him in Egypt. He spoke much of his inventions of different kinds, particularly of an amputating knife with a curved blade, which, he said, cuts off the leg more expeditiously from its embracing a greater surface. I think I have heard you state in your lectures that, no matter how much a blade was curved, nothing was added to the celerity of the operation; as it cuts only on one point at the same time. Larrey, however, if he has anything he thinks his own, will not give it up for anybody. The most remarkable cases were:

"1. Lower jaw shot off, the tongue hanging down upon the front of the neck. To remedy this a curved plate was tied to the head, having a silver lip. When this was on, the man was able to articulate distinctly. He had been nourished with broth for ten or fifteen years.

"2. Three cases of disarticulation at the shoulder joint, with a beautiful union. One of the cases had been operated on two days previously, and was doing well.

"3. Baron Larrey showed us a case of neuralgia of the arm from amputation having been performed too low down. The flap is not sufficient, and the cicatrix presses on the bone. He says he has seen a number of cases like this, and the best remedy is to amputate again.

"He is very fond of the hot iron.* He says he applies it to large ulcers of the leg, forming an eschar over the whole. He stated that he had wrought some wonderful cures in erysipelas of the face by passing an iron over the whole surface. The patients were cured in twenty-four hours but he did not say how their faces looked after the operation.

"4. He showed us a case of cataract in which the man had been totally blind, but had been restored to sight by applying moxas to the back of the neck. From this he infers that cataract always depends on inflammation of the capsule. I did not see him operate, but intend to go there again for the purpose."

We have said more than once in these pages that Larrey was noted for his truthful and decisive character, and never hesitated to tell the Emperor what he thought, even though it irritated his master. As an illustration of this we may mention the disagreement between the Emperor and Larrey after the Battle of Bautzen. This is related in the sketch of Larrey in F. C. Stewart's book on the *Hospitals and Surgeons of Paris*, and is briefly referred to in Larrey's own *Memoirs*.

* Larrey, in his *Memoirs*, says he used the hot iron around an area of erysipelas to prevent its spread.

There were very large numbers of wounded in the Battle of Bautzen, which misfortune Larrey attributed to the very large percentage of recent recruits present; the fierce nature of the combat, and the positions occupied by the armies. Some of the officers, who wished the war to end and wanted to get home, said that the army could not be depended on; that the troops were dissatisfied; and that the soldiers, in order to make the army go home, had in many instances wounded each other, or had pretended to have injuries that they had not sustained. The Emperor ordered Larrey and some other surgeons to examine all the wounded, so that he might signally punish anyone guilty of such a lack of patriotism.

Larrey went to the Emperor for the purpose of insisting that these statements were untrue. Napoleon was extremely angry, and told the surgeon that any observation he might make must be official, and not personal; and that he should at once go on with the duty he had been ordered to perform.

Larrey, with quiet dignity, went about this duty; and he refused to be hastened, although the Emperor was in a passion of impatience. The surgeon obtained, with the utmost care, every particular about each wounded man. He was told by his companions in arms that he had better not be so careful, and should hurry for his own good, or the Emperor would punish him; but he took the time that he knew was necessary to do this duty thoroughly and well.

When he had finished the Emperor asked him whether he still retained his former opinion. Larrey said: "More than that, Your Majesty. I come to prove to you that our brave soldiers have been subjected to calumny. I have not discovered a single one that is guilty. There is not a wounded man that has not been examined. I have here a wagonload of manuscripts; and I shall be pleased, if Your Majesty has them all read." Napoleon snatched the report out of Larrey's hands, and said sternly: "I will have it attended to." He then paced uneasily up and down the room; but after a few moments his frown broke away. He stopped before Larrey; shook him warmly by the hand; and, with every evidence of affection, said: "Good-bye, M. Larrey. A monarch is extremely lucky who is served by such men as you; and my further orders shall be conveyed to you." That same evening the Emperor sent Larrey his portrait set with diamonds, six thousand francs in money, and a pension of three thousand francs a year. This story is creditable to both these distinguished men.

The surgeon's decision of character and willingness to assume responsibility are shown by the following anecdote: After a battle many officers complained that their horses had been shot by Larrey's order. The Emperor sent for him and said: "Why have you dared to have these horses shot? Was it to feed the wounded?" Larrey answered simply: "Yes, Your Majesty"; and Napoleon thanked him for it.

In summing up the achievements of Baron Larrey we should mention the following:*

1. The avoidance of meddlesome surgery, leaving a simple healing wound practically to take care of itself.

2. The use of warm salt solution to wash out wounds; and the use of Labarraque's solution, a powerful antiseptic, to wash putrid and sloughing wounds.

3. The demonstration that the union of two granulating surfaces may take place, if one surface is laid against the other and the wound is cleansed frequently with an antiseptic. We call this today union by third intention.

4. The belief in the necessity of supporting treatment after severe injuries, stimulants, and nourishing food being given the patient, instead of fierce purgatives and copious bleedings. In certain cases Larrey fed persons by the stomach tube; in others, by means of a catheter passed through the nostril, as is often done in lunatic asylums today.†

5. The demonstration of the very great value of heat in suppurating areas. We now know why heat is of such value; as it

* In this connection see the admirable article on "Teachings of the Old Surgeons," by J. G. Mumford, in the *Boston Med. and Surg. Jour.*, October 3 and 10, 1895.

† J. G. Mumford.

relieves circulatory stasis, and brings millions of leukocytes to encompass the area of infection. Napoleon's great surgeon knew clinically its usefulness.

6. The view that granulating wounds require no special dressing, some ordinary nonirritating ointment being sufficient; Larrey's rule was to abandon poultices as soon as the pain abated, the inflammation disappeared, and the temperature became normal.

7. The employment of rest in the treatment of wounds. Larrey believed rest to be imperatively necessary, in order to permit nature to do her work; and he would allow a first dressing, if properly put on, to remain undisturbed for several or many days. He associated rest with judicious compression, made by bandages—particularly flannel bandages.

8. The belief in the imperative necessity of drainage for large wounds, for certain injuries of the skull, and for some injuries involving the pleural cavity.

9. The use of the conservative operation of the resection of joints. The view regarding the usefulness of this had been put forth, but three or four years before, by Mr. Park, of Liverpool; and had been originally suggested by Bilgner, the Surgeon General of Frederick the Great.* Larrey showed that resections save a large number of amputations.

10. The insistence upon the necessity of enlarging, by incision and drainage, all punctured wounds—a point of view not yet accepted by all practitioners.

11. Trephining for hemorrhage of the middle meningeal artery; although, strange to say, after thus having reached the bleeding vessel, Larrey arrested the bleeding with the actual cautery.

12. Trephining for depressed fracture, comminuted fracture, or any condition that causes compression of the brain.

13. The value of drainage in preventing pressure in intracranial hemorrhage.

14. The recognition of discoloration over the mastoid process as a result of fracture of the base—the condition we now call Battle's sign, after Mr. Battle, of St. George's Hospital, London.

* J. G. Mumford.

15. A knowledge in advance of his time regarding the symptoms of cerebral injuries. He said that injuries of the cortex of the brain impair the intellect; that injuries of the ventricles and the base produce paralysis; and that the paralysis is on the side of the body opposite to the brain injury. Further, he stated that even in old cases of such paralysis, good results sometimes follow trephining the opposite side of the head, to relieve pressure.

16. The view that a fungus cerebri should not be cut off, and that no effort should be made to reduce it; because the cause is actual swelling of the brain, and the only treatment that promises good results is equable compression.

17. In hemorrhage from the lung into the pleural cavity he made a large incision. Le Conte has recently recalled to us that a large incision arrests bleeding by producing pneumothorax. Larrey stated that when drainage was thus inserted, bleeding stopped and the person was safe from subsequent dangerous empyema.

18. The belief that empyemata should be operated on, and that this is a very successful operation.

19. On several occasions, in gunshot wounds of the head, he explored the track of the bullet with a soft catheter; and, finding that the missile was on the opposite side of the cranium, he trephined on the side opposite the wound and extracted the bullet.

20. The belief in the great superiority of immediate amputation over the secondary operation so long in vogue.

21. The introduction of the flying ambulances into warfare. This method was soon imitated by every nation. It has saved countless thousands from death and from horrible agony, and may be regarded as one of the greatest of Larrey's achievements.

22. A description of adynamic ataxic fever, the typhoid of our own time; and the fact that gangrene may occur during its existence.

23. The inauguration of the custom of carefully attending to the wounded men, as well as to the wounded officers; the prisoners, as well as the surgeons own people.

24. Finally, his ideas as to reaching, removing, and caring for the wounded after the battle constitute the foundation stones of military surgery today.

The name of this eminent man is on the Arch of Triumph. His statue is at the Val-de-Grace. His body lies in the Cemetery of Père-la-Chaise, where his monument can be seen at the present time. Near him are a number of scientists; and about him are many of those soldier-comrades with whom he marched into most of the capitals of Europe. Near him is Saint Hilaire, the naturalist; Arago, the physicist; Monge, the mathematician; Laplace, the astronomer; and Gay-Lussac, the chemist. Around him we note a group of soldiers; Marshal Masséna, who held Genoa in the great siege, who fought Wellington, and who was one of the best strategists and grimmest fighters in the army; Marshal Lefebvre, who was the first man made a noble by Napoleon, and who commanded in his will that he be buried near Masséna, adding: "We lived together in camps and combats; our ashes ought to have the same asylum"; Marshal Kellermann, one of the first generals under whom Larrey served, and the man that won Valmy; Marshal Grouchy, who had had a great reputation as a strategist, and whose inexplicable hesitation lost Waterloo; Marshal Ney, "the bravest of the brave," who commanded the rear-guard in the retreat from Russia and who was shot as a traitor by the treacherous and wretched Bourbon king; Colonel Labédoyère, who, with Baron Marbot, was the first over the walls of Ratisbon; Marshal Macdonald, who won Wagram, and was made a Marshal on the field of battle, a man who was a gallant and loyal gentleman all his days; Marshal Suchet, who had been a junior officer in Napoleon's company, when the latter was a captain; Marshal Davout, the hero of Auerstadt; General Junot, whose wife Napoleon wished to marry, when she was a young girl—Junot, of reckless gallantry, who resembled Mad Anthony Wayne of our Revolutionary struggle; and General Foy, who was sent to Turkey to fight the Russians and the English, and was wounded fifteen times in his various arduous campaigns. It seems a pity that Larrey's old friend and patient, Lannes, is not near him. This celebrated Marshal's body lies in the Cemetery of Montmartre.

Those of us that go to Paris and look at the tomb of Baron Larrey can feel with justice that there is buried a soldier, a patriot; a great, learned, and brilliant surgeon; a brave, truthful, and loyal man; a gentleman; and a benefactor of the human race.

THE OLD BLOCKLEY HOSPITAL; ITS CHARACTERS AND CHARACTERISTICS*

I HESITATE to address this audience today. I can honestly affirm that I was loath to accept the invitation. I have spoken to you so frequently in the past that my views must have grown threadbare by repeated application. The few damaged goods that the show window contains today are familiar to you all. You will be justified in regarding me as like Tennyson's brook—not that "I come from shady spots," not that "I bring the sweet forget-me-nots that bloom for happy lovers," and certainly not that "I bicker down a valley," but that I do "go on forever." You have heard it all before, and just as the frightened jockey, spoken of by Holmes, "breathed a prayer, from scraps of oaths he used to swear," so I must formulate an address from scraps of speeches I used to make.

I would note in passing that it was scarcely fair on the part of my good friend, Doctor Stahl, to call public attention to my increasing years by scheduling my personal reminiscences of Blockley as "Historical Remarks." First getting me to speak, and then advertising me in this remarkable way, bears a strong resemblance to the conduct of the liquor known as gin, which, you will recall, Josh Billings says "has a heap of resolution and cussed little judgment." I am, therefore, driven to be, for a brief time, a historian.

THE BUILDING OF BLOCKLEY

Seventy-three years ago this same Blockley Almshouse was completed and ready for occupancy. It then stood on a tract of 187 acres. In 1834 the almshouse was moved from Eleventh

---

* Address delivered on the twenty-first anniversary of the Association of the Residents and Ex-Residents of the Philadelphia Hospital, November 12, 1907. Reprinted from *The Journal of the American Medical Association*, April 11, 1908. Copyright, 1908, American Medical Association.

and Spruce Streets to its present site, and in that year the institution was first called Blockley, from the township in which it was placed. Blockley was in Philadelphia County, but not within the limits of the city of Philadelphia. The term "city" did not signify the entire county until the consolidation of all the districts was effected in 1854, the year in which Robert T. Conrad, poet, statesman, patriot, jurist, playwright, and orator, was elected mayor—an office that in those days was highly honorable, and was highly honored among men.

The region west of the Schuylkill got its name long before William Penn crossed the Atlantic. This name was given it by Captain Warner, a soldier of the army of the grim old protector, Oliver Cromwell. When Richard Cromwell fell from power Captain Warner fled from England, came to America, and settled on the western bank of the Schuylkill, near what is now the western end of Girard Avenue bridge. The only other inhabitants of what is at present the city of Philadelphia were a few Swedes, in Weccacoe. Warner named the region he inhabitated Blockley, after his old home in England.

In 1834 the hospital was supposed to accommodate 400 sick; and to be able to care for 200 more, if necessary. The change of location from Eleventh and Spruce Streets to the western bank of the Schuylkill was much opposed by many medical men, on the ground that the great distance of Blockley from the medical schools would make it difficult of access to students, and would seriously interfere with clinical instruction. A portion of the answer made to this objection by a committee of the Guardians of the Poor is a splendid masterpiece of colossal stupidity, and proves that among the governors of the institution there must have been then, as there usually have been since, individuals who had attained the last possible degree in the way of being asses. The guardians did not think that clinical lectures on medical cases could be of any use whatever. They said: "But, except that the lecture is made more imposing by the subject of it being present, and possibly the students' attention to the case being fastened by the display, we know of no benefit

which can accrue from it which would not equally result from
the case being lectured on in the absence of the patient, from the
notes of the physician, which form, in reality, the basis of the lecture." Think of it! Clinical teaching of no value, when among
the teachers were Samuel Jackson, Hugh L. Hodge, William H.
Gerhard, Samuel George Morton, Jacob Randolph, William E.
Horner, and Richard Harland! The audacity of a nonmedical
board in settling a medical question offhand, and with *ex-cathedra*
authority is not the calm impressiveness of profundity, but is
rather the complacency of a hog in his wash, a complacency by
no means unusual even at the present time, in city officials of
all grades.

When the hospital was first opened it was far out, and it
certainly was difficult of access. Encompassing it was a high
board fence; and the gate of entrance was at the northeast corner
of the grounds, on Darby Road. One who wished to reach Blockley from the city could cross over Market Street bridge in a
lumbering bus (neither the Chestnut Street nor the South Street
bridge was then built), or he could take a rowboat at South Street
and be ferried over to the almshouse wharf.

All along the river front were meadows, which were protected
from the river by a bank containing sluice gates. It was the
custom to open these gates in winter, flood the meadows and let
them freeze. From the frozen meadows, ice, richly endowed with
bacteria, was cut for the use of the patients. Over in the region
of the Franklin Field of the present day, was the Potter's Field
of that day. Those of us who recall the opening of Thirty-third
Street to Spruce will remember the finding of many skulls and
other ghastly osseous reminders. The stone barn that stood until
such a recent period on Thirty-fourth Street was erected in the
same year as was the almshouse. It was not, as many used to
think and say, an ancient building of an old estate.

How we got here and when we came here, however, really
matter little. Here we are; and surely this institution, whatever
it may or may not be, is one of the most interesting places in the
world.

FEATURES OF PROGRESS

The most obvious feature of progress is the growth of the great centers of population; and, year by year, a larger percentage of our population live in cities. This tendency excited apprehension as long ago as the time of Henry VIII; for Hugh Latimer complains, in one of his sermons: "Now we have taken up whoring in towns, instead of shooting in the fields." The chief reason for the growth of cities is stern necessity. Men must work to live, and must live near their work, if they would have employment; and the remarkable counterfeit of public service furnished by the misnamed Rapid Transit Company, and by other common carriers, does not encourage people to live far away from their work. All of us, in modern life, have the disease from which Cortez said that his followers suffered. He told the Mexicans, "I and my followers have a certain disease of the heart, and gold helpeth it." The majority of the people in the city are there to seek the remedy of Cortez, and comparatively few of them find it. If a person dwells in a city long, he gets what might be called the city habit, a craving for the excitements of city life, which in its intensity resembles the craving for drink. If he leaves the city, it calls to him an imperious mandate to return. Doctor Johnson felt this craving, for he said he loved the very smoke and dust and mud and roar of London, and hated to be away from them.

As the shadow accompanies the substance, so poverty accompanies progress; and in a city, poverty assumes its deepest dye and most certainly gives birth to its deformed children—vice and crime. A city is a vast laboratory. Human beings are the chemicals. Nature makes daring experiments, finds strange affinities, and repulsions from chance juxtapositions; and obtains products, sometimes beautiful, occasionally useful, but more commonly useless or injurious or even terrible.

THE VICTIMS OF PROGRESS

Blockley is the microcosm of the city. Within these gray old walls we find all sorts of physical and mental diseases; and

11

also a multitude of specimens of those social maladies that degrade manhood, undermine national strength and threaten civilization itself. The sufferers from social maladies are often the helpless victims of progress. Here is drunkenness; here is pauperism; here is illegitimacy; here is madness; here are the eternal priestesses of prostitution, "who sacrifice for the sins of man" (Lecky); here is crime in all its protean aspects; and here is vice in all its monstrous forms.

And what a multitude of strange characters, of eccentric persons, of interesting individuals, reside here! What differences of disposition! What a clash of rival interests! What a conflict of motives! What contrasts of conduct are to be observed! Here are legends without number, and ghost stories without end. How many high ambitions must have dissolved here! What a multitude of souls must have passed into infinity to the tolling of the Blockley clock! How many persons, once prosperous and prominent, who had once loved their illusions and cherished their enthusiasms have come here sad and disillusioned, to die! Some of you will, perhaps, remember the son of a great American admiral; the German baroness; the ex-professor of Trinity College, Dublin; the soldier of Napoleon; and the snuff-taking, shriveled old hag, who had once been the charming sweetheart of a great American statesman, and had had her famous salon in the city of Washington—a salon in which had gathered the leaders of the Senate-house in the days just before the Civil War.

Here are some actually crushed by misery; some grown patient under continued misfortune; some fierce and resentful under Fate's injustice; some acquiescent and even well satisfied with a pauperism that means a warm bed at night, tobacco, a full belly, and conversation with agreeable companions on a sunshiny bench. Each one of the last named class believes that the world owes him a living and he comes here to collect it. Even here are rival ambitions; for some covet the captaincy of the slop buckets, and some the captaincy of the clothes room. Each petty official has his little court with its busy courtiers, who flatter, intrigue, and caress. Here we see in full, rank development the talebearer, the scandal-monger, the back-biter, the slanderer, and the liar. Here are some who seek health, and some who wish for death. Here comes the physician, to treat and to teach, and the student, to observe and to learn. Here come charity, to relieve, and religion, to console, and the foul blight of municipal politics, to annoy, to hamper, and to curse; and here, among some of the most unfortunate and some of the worst men living, comes woman, white capped and cheerful, to comfort and to bless.

BLOCKLEY POLITICS

In my days as a resident physician, something over twenty years ago, there were several features of the place that attracted my particular interest and have remained graven in my memory. One of the chief of them was Blockley politics, as applied by Blockley politicians.

Blockley, in those days at least, was a striking example of the errors, the stupidities and the villainies of municipal politics. In Blockley politics come and go, sometimes better, sometimes worse. At present, having had a succession of four excellent medical directors, we are reasonably respectable; but some time in the future we shall probably relapse, go off on another debauch of corruption, and see the institution, as of old, reeling down the editorial pages of the newspapers. When the naked arm of public theft is again permitted to plunge to the shoulder, unchecked, into the coffers of the treasury, then will return in full strength the genuine Blockley politician, in all his foulness, stupidity, and arrogance. Then, once more, we shall see the old-time spectacle, the struggle between the rival forces of light and darkness, between the Ormuzd and the Ahriman of Persian tradition. Then once more we shall see on one side the miserable, suffering poor, and on the other the spoilsman and the boss. In such a contest there is no doubt where we belong.

Politics was once referred to as a noble occupation. Our modern city legislators (many of them are law sellers rather than law givers) would doubtless be surprised to learn that the object of government, according to Aristotle, is to make a small city great and a great city greater. Themistocles knew this long before Aristotle had founded the science of politics. The present idea, however, among many is, that rulers should strive to make a great city small by perverting its resources and diverting its energies from things noble to things base; and that the proper instinct of a politician is not patriotism, but is to sail for a "divvy" as a bee for a buckwheat patch. I do not delve among dusty records simply to find globules of poison or cakes of gall. I know politics is not an occupation for a lotus-eater; I know that leaders must and should exist; but I am so old-fashioned as to wish that leaders would not have written legibly over the portals of their houses the motto that is still seen on the floor of a Pompeian house: "Lucrum Gaudium," which is to say, "Gain is pure joy."

Many of the Blockley politicians of former days acted on this saying as an unbreakable rule of life. The time has been when the foulest politics dominated here, and did it often in murderous form. Then medical appointments were always made purely for personal and political reasons. In those days epidemics raged in these wards, and the grim specter of sepsis was a haunting terror to those who performed the operations of surgery. Here were patients actually hungry. Here was scurvy, which should never arise, except in a beleaguered town or among a castaway crew. Here was puerperal sepsis, claiming its horrible contribution. Here the unfortunate insane were placed on weekly exhibition in a public hall, to which sad festivity, visitors with cards of admission, from guardians and councilmen, came to satisfy morbid curiosity. At the very time that the sick poor were lodged without blankets, so that they had, in the words of Job, "no covering in the cold," the steam yacht of the "boss," would be drawn up to the almshouse wharf, to be stocked with coal, provisions, liquors, and cigars, preliminary to a wild bacchanalian cruise.

To such things did politics bring us in the past. We all of us think with affectionate remembrances of that brave and good and great man, then a physician in this hospital—one who is a member of this association now—who dared to protest publicly against those whom he designated as the "board of buzzards," and who called this institution "a whited sepulcher filled with dead men's bones." We all remember how he defied authority, and how he was removed from office for daring to tell the truth. We can learn from these few facts what will become of this place if the politician ever succeeds in again getting the upper hand here, particularly if no one proves as brave as H. C. Wood.

The Blockley Politician

The Blockley politician of those days was well worth a study. He almost commanded affection, for the same reason that animals commanded the affection of Walt Whitman, "for not one of them is respectable or industrious throughout the whole earth." Let me sketch for you the Blockley politician as I knew him, and as some of us may know him in the future, if he is ever again permitted to dominate here.

He was strictly practical. He never chased any rainbows. He had no ideals. He regarded reform as the maunderings of the imbecile or the obsession of the wicked. He liked to speak of "snivel" service reform. He was a true Bourbon, who learned nothing and forgot nothing. There was never the remotest chance that he would undergo a change for the better. He was like a canal-boat horse, so used to walking on the level lowlands that you could never teach him to mount a hill.

The views of these persons were well voiced, on one occasion, by the superintendent. I referred him to Scripture for the statement that a good name is better than great riches, and he said: "That may be all true, but it does not carry so many divisions." The Blockley politician was as utterly insensible to all criticism as a stone dog would be to a vote of thanks. The only thing he was afraid of was the anger of the great boss; and he would fly from that like an ignorant savage frightened by a comet, and might fall into a hole as he ran. He always had a great deal of improper pull, and never enough reasonable and judicious push. He was always puffed up by deceit, but not propped up by it. He resembled a corkscrew in the fact that the more crooked he was, the more pull he had. You could no more expect a really good thing from him than you could expect to get peaches from a gate post or beefsteak from a nightmare. He was from 5 feet 6 to 5 feet 10 high, and from 10,000 to 20,000 dollars short. As a rule he could consume a considerable amount of liquor. He was apt to boast that whisky never gave him a head, which only goes to prove that whisky is not more powerful than the Almighty.

If he had possessed a coat-of-arms it would have been a plain, ordinary crook. He was called a "Poor Guardian," probably because he did some of the poorest guarding on record. He was always liable to take a trip to Canada on the advice of his lawyer, and not of his physician; for he was prone to have a leg in the board room and one in the Eastern Penitentiary. Like Leonidas, he held a pass; but it was a railroad pass, and even his pulse beat with a dead beat. He never wore gloves, and I do not know why his critics should do so. He seldom wore cuffs, and his wrists always presented a neglected and undecorated appearance without handcuffs. He was apt to boast that he was self-made, and I always regarded it as noble of him to assume the responsibility. He kept his party faith, and everything else he could get his hands on. His parents were poor, but Irish. He was skilled in the fundamental branches of addition, subtraction, division, and silence, and in the gentle domestic arts of perjury and blackmail. When he saw a "divvy" going on in the neighborhood he could cry out as did Hotspur:

> "I am on fire
> To hear this rich reprisal is so nigh, and yet not mine."

RESULTS OF MISRULE

Let me give you some examples of what the result of such rule was. I fancy most of you remember the dreadful fire in the Insane Asylum in February, 1885—a fire in which twenty-two persons were burned to death. I suppose that many of you know why it happened; for that fire was caused by the politicians of the Board of Guardians of the Poor, as truly as was every other calamity that affected this institution. When I became chief resident physician of the insane department I was able to gather this story from the minute book of the committee on the insane department. I found that on a certain date an attendant had been discharged for brutally beating a patient; and that at the very next meeting of the committee he had been restored, uncensured, by a motion of a politician in the board. Again, after a few weeks, he had been a second time discharged for brutally beating a patient; and again, at the next meeting, he had been reinstated, on a motion of the same politician in the board. Then he was thanked by the board for having discovered a fire and extinguished it; and then the other fire, which he did not extinguish, happened. From it he ran, like the miserable cur and coward that he was. The story of that poor insane colored boy, Nadine, was the truth; and that attendant had lighted those fires or had had them lighted for him, intending to extinguish them and gain credit with his political lords and masters, and also to destroy officially the able and kindly gentleman who was then physician-in-chief of the insane department, and who lately died while chief of the Norristown asylum. When the politicians responsible for this dreadful crime wake in the night "and see the dying night-lamp flicker and the shadows rise and fall," even they, at times, must hear those twenty-two dead men knocking at their doors.

I can relate another incident to show the tendency of some of these agreeable personages. I was called from my bed one midnight. In the hall I found a member of the Board of Guardians of the Poor, accompanied by a female, not of doubtful character, and both of them under the influence of liquor. He said to me: "Open the cell doors and let the lady see the lunatics." I replied: "I do not see any lady." and he said: "There she is." I remarked: "She is there now, and so are you; but you are both going to leave, or I will have you put out. I do not open a door to display a lunatic to you or your drunken companion." He said: "I will have your job in the morning," and I replied, "All right, come out and get it." When morning came he was there, but not after the job. The wish that was preeminent in his mind was that I should have no interviews with the newspaper men.

I was asked by a guardian to discharge a most decent attendant on the charge of drunkenness. The man never drank, but that made no difference. He had voted "wrong" at a primary. I was expected to discharge him because the guardian had voted for me. But, gentlemen, he was not discharged while I remained in the institution.

SOME GOOD POLITICIANS

I want to make some exceptions to this general condemnation of members of the Board of Guardians of the Poor. I wish to mention one of them who was a politician, but a politician of a different breed from these men—a man who never in his life had any connection with a dirty dollar; a man who was kindly, charitable, generous and warm-hearted; one who was always touched by a tale of distress; and one who made every effort, while he was in this institution, to benefit the unfortunate patients and to aid the medical staff. He went from here to the state Senate at Harrisburg, and from there to Washington to fill in Congress the seat of Samuel J. Randall; and he is still living, a respected business man, in the city of Philadelphia. I refer to the Hon. William McAleer.

Another whom I would mention with kindly affection was that prince of good fellows, the late John Huggard; and then I must come to that most interesting, eccentric and lovable personality, Mr. McMurtrie, the distinguished lawyer. He had been elected during a temporary attack of mental aberration on the part of the city, when it got under the charge of the reform element. He hated hospitals and was rendered unhappy by the sight of sick people; but he took the appointment as a call to duty, and he obeyed it rigidly. I can recall with amusement the time when the Committee on the Insane Department appointed Mr. McMurtrie to receive the Joint Committee of Councils, which once a year visited this institution. This committee would come out and be alcoholically entertained by the superintendent. They

would then aimlessly wander about, here and there; and afterward write a report as favorable as though they owned the place
and wanted to sell it.   Mr. McMurtrie was entirely childlike as
to the nature of this committee.   He came out to meet them with
dignity and solemnity; but when he saw them in the hall, he
took a single look, and then burst forth in rage.   He said: "I
came out here as an official of the city of Philadelphia to receive
other officials of the city of Philadelphia; but I did not come out
here to receive, speak to, or mingle with a damned set of drunken
blackguards."   Thereon, in a furious passion, he clapped his hat on
his head and departed, leaving the denounced councilmen speechless with astonishment.   A highly interesting, an honest and a
redoubtable personality.

Some of the facts related above show us where our duty lies.
We must always strive to keep the political "old man of the sea"
from hanging about our neck.   If I had my way I would strike
the whole accursed system dead.

The Nonmedical Superintendent

In the days of which I speak the superintendent was the
mouthpiece of the board, and was in charge of the entire institution and everyone in it.   The physicians were as completely under
his orders as were the gate-keepers and the watchmen.   To have
medical men, performing medical duties, under the charge of a
nonmedical man always works badly, and is provocative of endless trouble and manifold misunderstandings; for how can one
who knows no more of medicine or of the needs of the sick than
a dog does of the pons asinorum, a Hottentot of the Westminster
Confession, a mule of geometry, or a ward boss of the true and
the good and the beautiful, be expected to reach proper conclusions on medical matters of the first importance?

As a matter of fact, the superintendent never did reach wise
conclusions.   On one occasion, after ruminating for some time on
greatness, he decided to personally make the transfers and discharges in all the departments, including the insane department.
He butted into the diet question, with lamentable results.   His

views about ventilation, or, rather, lack of ventilation, were archaic and peculiar; and, as a result, the men's out-wards were as foul and ill-ventilated as the ark must have been. He personally selected the brand of whisky to be given the sick; and it was not the same brand, by long odds, that was given the visiting councilmanic committees and other political lights. He apportioned the amount of bedclothes with the same liberality with which certain bigoted Christian sects deal out salvation. He stimulated difficulties in the medical staff, and a complaint against a doctor was a badge of favor for the one that made it. He undertook, with wondrous enthusiasm, the arduous and well-nigh hopeless task of regulating the morals, pruning the language, controlling the views, and abolishing the late hours of unregenerate resident physicians. He was distinctly not a hospitable man, and it took an interview and a derrick to extract from him permission to let a guest stay in the doctors' dining room for a meal.

The meals that were served in that dining room were very far from appetizing or attractive. The coffee was gloomy, the vegetables were genuine antiques, the eggs had seen better days; when you tried the butter you always found it guilty; cold meat was hurriedly served by hot waitresses. This lack of hospitality arose from a perverted sense of economy. The superintendent was economical of hospitality, just as he was economical of the truth. He was liberal in promises and mendacities alone, and most of his promises were mendacities.

As a rule, the average superintendent of those days was addicted to the free and unlimited coinage of mendacities, without the consent of any other nation. His official court of doorkeepers, panhandlers, hall men, runners, gatekeepers, and understrappers was a hotbed of gossip and scandal. It was filled with flying rumors. Once in a while one of the rumors might be regarded as religious; for it would, perhaps, be confirmed. The nighs watchmen were argus-eyed for residential derelictions; and one't condition on mounting the high steps at night was guessed at and reported on by a groggy old reprobate, who possessed a red nose, a watery eye, and smelled like a distillery. Yet these poor, miserable, abject creatures were made masters of and presumed to think themselves superior to such men as the younger Gross, Ludlow, Tyson, Pepper, White, Horatio Wood, and all the visiting staff. Why, Dr. Horatio C. Wood, standing on the wooden floor of the old arena of the clinic room, was a better and greater man a thousand times over, than all the politicians combined that ever misruled a municipality.

I have known many former superintendents, and in the foregoing remarks have sketched a type rather than an individual. They were apt to become infected, more or less, with that petty spirit of tyranny which so often grows in ignoble breasts, when given absolute power over other persons. Their most distinguishing characteristics were poverty of heart, meanness of motive, and feebleness of understanding. The one that went to jail was by no means the worst of the lot.

Going to church used to be a favorite amusement with many of the patients. The venereal patients attended religiously. As iodoform was then a popular drug, you could smell these patients a long time before they appeared. As I have said on a former occasion, I used to wonder whether this was the far-famed "odor of sanctity."

I was once the recipient of many attacks from members of a sanctified society, who used to come here to regenerate the patients. These attacks alleged that I did not send enough insane patients to church on Sunday. I was ordered to send more; and the superintendent, exercising his profound knowledge of insanity, picked out the ones that were to go. The custom was for the attendants to place the patients in the room and then loaf around the doors, smoking, chewing, swearing, and telling stories, while waiting for those that were to conduct the services to arrive. The superintendent's selections were not fortunate, the services were of necessity abandoned, and ever afterward I was permitted to indicate those suited to receive religious consolation.

The clergy of the house were of some interest. One of them was of an affectionate nature, and was observed administering the kiss of peace in the kitchen of the women's nervous ward.

One of them would not enter the venereal ward, even if the patient were dying there. One of them dined at the doctors' table, where he would eat like Mr. Shadband.

> "Some love the matin chimes which tell
>   The hour of prayer to sinner,"

but he found much more to his taste

> "The midday bell
>   Which marks the hour of dinner."

I pause for a moment in recalling one of them who was here then and, I am glad to say, is with the institution still. I pause at the consideration of him because I realize that I have never known in life a kinder or more charitable man. He is of the very best type of the good priest. He has no thought but for the duties of his charge; and he has such a generous amount of warm human blood in his veins that his personality is a cordial, and his greeting a charm against the blues. I take off my hat with respect and affection to our old friend, Father McIlhone. Long may he live!

A Few Notable Characters in Blockley

A few characters of that day I would particularly mention. One was the strange personage who kept the gate between the men's out-wards and the hospital. He was so fat that he could scarcely move, even with the aid of a cane; and when he sat down in his little house he completely filled it. He had been quite a notable character in his day in the southern part of Philadelphia, and still retained the cordial friendship of Bill McMullin and other illustrious lights. He liked to talk about the old times when he kept a saloon near the old Navy Yard; when he was a leader in the festivities of the first of the year, down in the Neck; and when he played remarkable practical jokes on all his friends. He went out but twice a year, New Year's and the Fourth of July, and after each outing he returned in a condition wonderful to behold. It required the united efforts of all the hall men to get him up the front steps. He and I were on the best of terms; and when I left here he said: "I am going to send you lots of practice." I asked: "Pete, how do you propose to do it?" He replied: "I will do it by sending you my friends; for there is not a thief, there is not a gambler, there is not a thug, there is not a street walker in the whole district of Southwark as isn't my warm personal friend."

I should like to pause to speak of the man who kept the clinic gate, and kept it with the rigid loyalty with which Horatius kept the bridge. He would not have admitted his own grandmother, had she been dropping from exhaustion; and many were the conflicts he had with residents who sought to elude his vigilance in order to escape a critical inspection in the front office.

When I became physician in the insane department I had the good fortune to find a panel gate through the fence on Thirty-fourth Street—a gate that I alone used. It was a source of unending conflict between the superintendent and myself; for he used to nail it up at intervals, and I always kept a convenient axe with which to break it open.

Another interesting personage was the old gambler whose political friends had secured for him quarters on the medical floor, with permission to go out whenever he pleased. He was full of reminiscences of the newspaper men, politicians, and business men with whom he had cast the dice and for whom he had turned the wheel. He used to tell interesting stories of how the money that was taken from the beneficial saving fund by Big Frank and Ned McGee was used to establish a gambling room at Fifth and Library Streets; how all the police officials knew it; and how many of them used to go to this room to play.

Another interesting personage was the old man who, as a mere boy, had fought in the armies of the Great Napoleon. He had been on the march to Russia; he had been in the Battle of the Nations at Leipsic; he had been in that frightful series of battles when the emperor was driven back to his capital, and had fought finally on the disastrous field of Waterloo. When I knew him his mind had gone down in the wreck and ruin of dementia.

It was hard to extract anything from him, but he still had gleams of remembrance and love for the remarkable personality that passed from among men on the island of St. Helena in 1821.

A man I was fond of then and am fond of now was dear old "Tom" Owens, who always had a $5 to loan a resident in difficulties. I love still to shake him by the hand.

The institution, at the time of which I speak, contained, as it doubtless contains now, some of the most talented drinkers and ablest bacchanalian artists in the community. The barbers got drunk whenever possible, the carpenters were drunk at every opportunity, the tailor was always drunk, and the painter was never sober. The man who had charge of the dead-house had illuminating episodes of alcoholic exaltation, which were among the most remarkable that I had ever witnessed, and presented strong suggestions of the alcohol from broken specimen bottles.

The insane department, after the fire, was a dreadful place. There were no open wards; the crowding was fearful and insanitary in the extreme; and it was necessary to have two patients to a cell. Frequently they would fight during the night; and I got to regard it as an ordinary, everyday occurrence to get out of bed at midnight, put on a pair of trousers, and wade into a terrific combat. It was a dangerous place. People threw things over the walls and lunatics picked them up. We had to search each patient every night; and we frequently found on them matches or pointed pieces of iron, with which they could do great mischief. On one occasion a man attempted to kill me with a bill-file that he had found and secreted.

One of the interesting lunatics was Melchizedek, the prophet of the Lord—the blind man, who used to pass his time reading large books for the blind, and whose favorite amusement was to locate a visitor by his voice and then heave a huge folio in the hope of hitting him.

Another interesting character was a man who believed he was the savior of mankind. He endeavored to cultivate the appearance that he thought appropriate to the part. One day he issued an edict that no one should wear a hat in his presence.

He wrote this out on a piece of paper, signed it with the name that he regarded as his, and nailed it on the wall. A few minutes later another patient with the same delusion, and with a hat on his head, came in and stood directly beneath the edict. The writer of the notice called the attention of the other lunatic to it. The second one slowly and carefully read it, and then said that he had issued no such order. The first one told him that of course he had issued no such order because he would have had no right to do so. Thereupon they flew at each other like wild beasts. We separated them with difficulty, and it was never afterward possible to let these two apostles of peace and good will loose in the yard at the same time, for fear they would tear each other apart.

In those days I labored under a permanent financial stringency. There was an individual of the tailor persuasion who was unduly anxious to collect a bill, and he wrote me that he was coming to the institution the following morning at nine o'clock to collect it. At that time the office opened directly into the corridor of a ward, and this ward was used as an exercise ground for a number of violent patients. I directed the gate-keeper that when the tailor arrived, the door was to be opened; he was to be ushered into the corridor, and the door was then to be immediately closed. I heard the bell ring; I heard it close. In a few seconds the tailor, absolutely breathless and at full speed, appeared in my office, with no single ambition in life except to get out again at the first possible moment.

We had a man who used to have fits. He became much attached to me, and made me a Christmas present of a complete list of his fits for an entire year. We had another man who had been appointed an attendant at ten o'clock in the morning and had become a raving maniac by six o'clock the same evening. We had a woman who would break up glass with her foot and seek an opportunity to throw it in your eyes. We had the pope of Rome; we had the first case of katatonia reported in the United States; we had a notable clerk, with a famous bulbous nose, who was addicted to inebriating himself by drinking the compound tincture of cardamom. In the laundry were noninsane women who got drunk on every occasion, and fought one another indiscriminately. In the kitchen was the traditional ill-tempered cook, who was a blazing terror when in liquor, which was frequently.

An interesting character was a man who had been brought here with his memory a blank. He did not even remember his childhood. His memory gradually and slowly filled in from two points: From the time when he had shot himself with a pistol, backward; and from childhood, forward. He got back to the fact that he had been a locomotive engineer on a great railroad: he got forward to the fact that he had left school and become a wiper on the railroad; but he never filled up the intervening gap.

A BRILLIANT INSANE INVENTOR

Among the patients was a man to whom I became much attached. I took him out of the hospital, after I left there, and made him clinic orderly at Jefferson. He was closely connected with me for a number of years, and was one of the finest characters I have ever come in contact with. He remained insane to the last, but this had no effect whatever on the practical conduct of his affairs. He was the only productive lunatic I have ever encountered. He devised the method of making catgut that we still use in the Jefferson Hospital. He taught himself chemistry until he became a skilled chemist. I am satisfied that he discovered argon a year before Lord Rayleigh did, and by the same method that the latter followed. He had succeeded in treating cotton seed oil so that an expert could not differentiate it from olive oil—a process that must have been worth millions—and that died with him. He devised what is known as ethereal soap, which is largely used by medical men and by veterinarians. He had a method for soldering aluminum, and a multitude of other processes that he declined to write down.

This man's birthplace was Ireland. He obtained a good common school education in Birmingham, England; became a gun-ner in the British Navy; passed some time in Egypt, during the rising under Arabi Bey, and went to India, where he was station master at Bundelcohr, on the Trans-Indian Railroad. There he became completely imbued with the most curious Indian mysticism. He came to America as an agent for a sewing machine company, and was finally brought to Blockley suffering from an attack of maniacal excitement that terminated in paranoia. There have been few men in life whom I have learned to love so well.

All these things, all these people, and all these incidents come back to me now, as I stand in this clinic room and think of those days, more than twenty years ago, when I was a resident physician; of "those brave days, when I was twenty-one." There is something indescribably sad in looking back to this time, the time when I was young and brave and gay and full of hope; when responsibility sat lightly; when genuine black care was unknown; when the future seemed rich in promise; when I still believed that the race went to the swift and the battle to the strong; and when the pathway, even though domed by the stormy cloud, was spanned by the rainbow.

To turn back to those days is to turn back to good companions, loyal friends, honest efforts, generous impulses, convivial gatherings, and happy meetings; to song and story; to jest and laughter; to evenings that were all too short, and to mornings that were bright with joyful anticipations. A wave of tenderness and regret sweeps over me as I look back on myself and my colleagues. Each of us hugged to his breast some dear delusion. Then we had the courage to fight, the chivalry to make another's cause our own, and the hope that made the future rich in golden hues. Then we could catch the reflection of the skies, even in the stagnant pool of Blockley. Then we could hear real music, in the trees which were playmates of the wind and were ever singing beneath the silent stars. Then our eyes were princely with courage; our foreheads were royal with truth. Honor was an instinct, and enthusiasm ran hot in the blood.

In retrospection there is tenderness for what we were; there is regret for what we have lost: for in losing generous and un-

12

selfish youth, we have lost more than we can ever gain. Look
at us now! As Carlyle says: "It is a sad sight." We have gained
some substantial things, but we have lost the glory that once was
ours, and will never come to us again. We are stained by worldly
contact; we deliberately correct generous impulses by cynical analysis; we shrink from the conflicts and the knight-errantry of
old. The world disenchants us after we know it. The prizes of
life too often prove the Dead Sea apples which turn to dust in
the hand. The idols that we thought to worship are all too often
made of gilded clay. As we stand on the heights of middle age
and look about us on the world many of us will be disposed to cry:

> Here meanness wins; here vice comes from her hiding;
> Here profit is the teaching of each school;
> In pulpit, market, senate-house, abiding,
> We hear the jingling cap-bells of the fool.

Our own views of our own work have undergone mighty changes.

> "Once I compared it with the world's neglect,
>   And proudly said—it is better than they see.
> Now! I observe it tainted with defect
>   In the broad light of what it ought to be."

As I drift down the river and look backward toward the
spring of life, and think of the cheerful alacrity with which the
crystal water flowed when near its source, I cry out:

> "Give me the old enthusiasms back;
>   Give me the ardent longings that I lack;
>   The glorious dreams that fooled me in my youth;
>   The sweet mirage that lured me on its track;
>   And take away the bitter, barren truth."

THEN AND NOW*

WE meet this evening for the purpose of commemorating in an appropriate manner the fiftieth birthday of the Medical Society of the County of Philadelphia, and I rise to speak in answer to an instinct well-nigh universal, which bids nations, institutions, and individuals pause from time to time and contemplate their past.

The Chinese are a peculiar and an interesting people, and in many of their customs the pathetic is strangely blended with the ludicrous, and the practical is curiously linked with the absurd. But one custom they have which seems almost wholly admirable. Once every year a mandarin puts aside his usual daily occupations, visits the tombs of his ancestors, reflects upon their careers, contemplates their achievements, endeavors to draw lessons from their experiences, and in so doing mingles celebration with worship, two distinct yet colleagued acts, which enhance each other's beauty, as do snow and moonlight, or as rock and river. To look back in such a spirit is to have impressive lessons sink into the soul. It is to appreciate the inevitable succession of cause and effect and to know the vast and far-reaching influence of things apparently trivial. It is to recognize that man is not a mere isolated point in an ocean of immensity, but that he is a link in the chain between two infinities, that he is the child of Yesterday and the parent of Tomorrow, that he is born with privileges and with responsibilities, and that both privileges and responsibilities are transmitted to his descendants. To thus look back soothes the mind and rests the brain—it is as the cooling draught to the parched pilgrim of the desert—as the gentle sleep to eyes weary

* Oration delivered at the celebration of the fiftieth anniversary of the founding of the Philadelphia County Medical Society, January 14, 1899. Reprinted from the *Transactions of the Philadelphia County Medical Society*, May, 1899.

of the pageantry of commerce and to ears tired of the turmoil of
money-getting.

Tonight we will imitate the mandarin, will view the records
of our ancestors, will light the page of the present with sunbeams
of the past, as we sit at the feet of Clio the muse of history, the
famous daughter of Jupiter and Mnemosyne. I shall not attempt
to present a consecutive record, nor will I try to give a detailed
account, but will deal with many things besides the County
Society and with much besides medicine, will here set forth a
hint and there trace a line, will here relate an episode and there
sketch a fact, and will construct of things in general an address
made up of shreds and patches.

The Philadelphia County Medical Society was founded January 16, 1849—fifty years ago. Not so long ago, if measured merely
by the process of the suns, a period within the memory of many
who are still living, but an infinite distance into the past if gauged
by revolutionary changes and great events. The real way to
measure time is by changes and events. As Festus has it:

Faustus

> "We live in deeds, not words,
>   In thoughts, not breaths,
>   In feelings, not in figures on a dial."

Fifty years! What a multitude of things have come to pass
in this busy half century of time! Beliefs, once thought immutable, principles then held to be eternal, have been brushed
aside as so much dross. The iconoclastic and ruthless hand of
time has cast down many statues once niched high in the world's
esteem. Names once great have been forgotten, and other names,
then unknown, have replaced them on the blood-warm lips of
men. Tens of thousands of marvelous inventions have abridged
distance, economized time, increased production, facilitated exchange, subdivided labor and stilled pain. These inventions, and
the spirit which produced them, have wrought more wonders
than were ever conjured by the seal of Solomon or by the lamp
of Aladdin. We see resulting from them modifications, changes
or absolute alterations in business methods, financial ideas, po-

litical beliefs, scientific tendencies, religious tenets, moral views, modes of thought, tastes, habits, customs, and amusements. Some of these inventions, for instance, that one which enables us to imprison the sun's heat and force it to draw our chariots, and that one which permits us to harness the lightning and make it illuminate our streets, have destroyed ancient callings and given rise to new vocations. Every one of these forward steps has brought good to some and harm to others. The absolute good of Progress is not always obvious. The glorious chariot of Progress casts a shadow, and in this shadow crawls every noisome reptile and springs every noxious plant, and the dust from the wheels of this chariot is composed of perished hopes and of dead ambitions. It seems as if wealth must cast the shadow which we call poverty, and as if additions to the house of Dives mean subtractions from the den of Lazarus. The world is not quite purified, and progress is far from complete. There is much to do in the future, there are still giants to conquer, there are still dragons to slay. We have more homes than had our ancestors, but also more prisons— more libraries, but more almshouses—more philanthropists, but more lawyers—more school-children, but more tramps. We have among us still in fearful intensity those problems which have in the past excited the anxious and apprehensive interest of the sage, the statesman and the philosopher, those Sphinx's riddles to fail to answer which is to be destroyed. Here is drunkenness, here is pauperism, here is prostitution, here is madness, here is Vice with her bared talons, here is Crime with her gleaming fangs. When we contemplate the gains and losses, the sorrows and pleasures, the griefs and joys of fifty years of time, we are inclined to cry with the poet—

> "Are God and Nature, then, at strife
> That Nature lends such evil dreams,
> So careful of the type she seems,
> So careless of the single life?"

The year 1848 has been called "the year of revolutions." In that year the streets of many continental capitals ran with blood, thrones swayed or crumbled and scepters shook in palsied hands. Violent revolutionary outbreaks occurred in Italy, Germany, and Austria. In Ireland fierce mobs clamored for the repeal of the union. The angry flame of Chartism swept over England. Louis Philippe was driven into exile by the raging brutal mob of Paris.

In 1849 the flames of revolt had largely burnt into embers of discontent, although a practically united Hungary, bent on throwing off the Austrian yoke, followed with mad enthusiasm the banner of Kossuth.

What of things in general in 1849?

Victoria had been upon the throne of Great Britain almost twelve years. William Ewart Gladstone, the grand old man of Liberalism, who was so lately laid to rest in England's "temple of reconciliation and silence," was then a Tory in opposition to the Liberal ministry of Lord John Russell. The Duke of Wellington was still living in Walmer Castle. Thomas Carlyle was in Chelsea, viewing with jaundiced eye the "30,000,000 of people mostly fools," and writing the life of Irving. Macaulay was finishing the third volume of his wonderful history. Thackeray, fresh from the triumph of *Vanity Fair*, was writing the adventurers of *Arthur Pendennis*. Dickens, after dazzling the world with *Dombey & Son*, was writing *David Copperfield*.

Francis Joseph had ascended the Austrian throne a few weeks before and had taken on himself the burden of sorrows, calamities, and misfortunes without end.

Louis Napoleon was the Prince-President of France, and even then was revolving in the depths of his melancholy mind the details of the coming plebiscite and the coup d'état. Thiers, accepting the Republic, was immured in his library, finishing *The History of the Consulate and Empire*. Count Cavour, with persistence that nothing checked, with courage which never faltered, and with ability both subtle and daring, was striving to make a united Italy. Otto von Bismarck was already dreaming of blood and iron, of treaties made but to be broken, of a splendid German Empire with a puppet Hohenzollern at the head and Bismarck at the helm.

There were thirty states in the American Union, Wisconsin having been admitted a few months before. The contending political parties were the Democratic and the Whig. The great territories known as California and New Mexico had been added to the Union by the Mexican War, and then, as now, there were angry recrimination and fierce dispute as to the deaths of our soldiers in camp and battle, and as to the necessity or advisability of territorial acquisition. The curse of slavery was on the Republic, and threatened to split the nation asunder, and the Wilmot Proviso was producing the most bitter controversy. Manufacturing industries were developing with amazing rapidity, the Democrats said because of, and the Whigs asserted in spite of, the Walker revenue tariff. Gold had been discovered in California, the papers were filled with stories of wonderful strikes, and 200,000 Argonauts were facing all kinds of hardships and perils as they slowly moved toward the land of splendid hopes. A vast expansion in the area of operations for mining coal and a great improvement in mining methods was taking place because of the enormous growth in the use of machinery. The first oil well was not bored in Venango County until 1858, and the whale fishery was still an important calling, although the extensive use of gas was greatly affecting it. Every year scores of ships sailed from Nantucket and New Bedford, Salem and Falmouth for the Arctic regions, the coast of Africa, the coast of Brazil, and the Pacific in search of the right whale and the spermaceti whale. The great trades-union movement was becoming formidable and organized labor was assuming a peremptory attitude in its demands. The famine in Ireland and the political discontent in all European countries drove tens of thousands of emigrants to our shores. Electricity was ceasing to be a toy of the scientist, and the silent heralds of Morse were beginning to fly along the wires. The sewing machine had been invented by Howe in 1841, but had not yet been accepted by the public. McCormick had invented the reaper in 1831, but it had not yet driven out the scythe. The iron-footed messenger, whose breath is steam, was beginning to link cities, to cross rivers, deserts, and mountain ranges and to penetrate virgin forests; but still in many sections of our vast country travelers went on foot, or considered themselves fortunate to be able to ride in an emigrant wagon, in a 'bus, in a stage, or on a canal boat.

The locomotive of 1849 differed greatly from the iron horse of the present day. It often had no cab. It usually had but two driving-wheels, whose diameter was about $4\frac{1}{2}$ feet. It burnt wood, had a slow-working slide-valve throttle, a huge funnel-shaped stack, and was destitute of a cow-catcher, air-brakes, injectors, automatic oil cups, a spark arrester, and a thousand ingenious contrivances which are familiar to all who understand that marvel of mechanism, the modern locomotive engine.

The Senate of the United States was at this period never called a club of millionaires. It was not regarded as a collection of corporation attorneys and office brokers, it was composed of law-givers not law-sellers; it numbered among its members some of the ablest and purest orators and statesmen of the Republic. The roll of the Senate bore the names of Daniel Webster, Henry Clay, Thomas H. Benton, John C. Calhoun, John M. Clayton, Thomas Corwin, John J. Crittenden, Lewis Cass, and Stephen A. Douglas. James K. Polk was President of the United States, and was soon to give place to Zachary Taylor, "old rough and ready," as he was affectionately called, who was crowned with the laurels of Buena Vista, where he had defeated Santa Anna. Geo. M. Dallas was Vice-president and was about to give way to Millard Fillmore. James Buchanan was Secretary of State. William M. Marcy was Secretary of War. Robert J. Walker was Secretary of the Treasury. Robert C. Winthrop, of Massachusetts, was Speaker of the House of Representatives, and in that house sat Abraham Lincoln, Andrew Johnson, and Horace Greeley. Winfield Scott, "old fuss and feathers," was one of the martial heroes of the nation and was particularly dear to the people because it was rumored that he had refused the chief magistracy of Mexico.

Henry Wadsworth Longfellow had written *Evangeline* two years before. Oliver Wendell Holmes had recently become Professor of Anatomy in Harvard. James Russell Lowell was writing the *Bigelow Papers*. Nathaniel Hawthorne was plotting out the *Scarlet Letter*. Edwin Forrest was being acclaimed as the first tragedian of the day. Washington Irving had just published *Mahomet*. Prescott had been crowned with the honor of election to the French Academy. Motley was being scored by the critics because of his novel *Merry Mount*. Whittier was attacking slavery in burning lyrics. Emerson was visiting his great contemporary and friend, Carlyle. Cooper was actively engaged in literary work. William Cullen Bryant was editing the New York *Evening Post*. Edgar Allen Poe was going to his grave, a grave which was to cover so much sorrow and so much greatness. Edison was but two years old. Andrew Jackson had been dead but four years, and was the St. Andrew the First of Democratic tradition. Percussion caps had recently been thought of, the screw propeller had recently been devised, negro minstrel entertainments were novelties, and a glass of lager beer had not yet been drunk in Philadelphia. Blotting pads were not used and letters were dried with sand. Houses did not have furnaces; sleeping rooms in winter were icy cold and beds were warmed by warming pans before retiring. The apprentice system existed. Junior clerks always swept out the office. Sneak-thieves were few and bank counters had no wire netting. Newspapers did not publish extras. Children, as a rule, made their own toys and baseball bats. Tobacco chewing was very common, but gentlemen never smoked in the streets. Negroes were rigidly suppressed. Quill pens and gold pens were generally employed. Church-going was far more common then than now. Cigarettes were never used. It was vulgar to wear a mustache (see Haswell's *Reminiscences of New York*). Mrs. A. J. Bloomer, of Homer, New York, in this year invented bloomers.

Philadelphia in 1849 differed greatly from the Philadelphia of today, although names familiar then are often met with still, and some few of the good old traditions have not entirely perished.

The city was not showy, was quiet; visitors considered it dull and its inhabitants distant and unsocial. But it was a most comfortable city to live in, and there was no more cultured society in the country. The hospitality of a Philadelphia gentleman was proverbial, and often alcoholic, for it was the day of Santa Cruz rum, high-flavored port, Oliviera Madeira and punch sweetened with guava jelly. Its inhabitants boasted that it was a true American city, for it contained fewer foreigners than either New York or Boston. The traditions of the Revolution were by no means dead. There were men living who, as children, had heard the Liberty Bell toll out the message that rang throughout the world, and who, some years later, had jumped from their beds and run to the windows as the watchmen called out "Half-past three, and Cornwallis surrendered." There were great numbers living whose fathers had crossed the Delaware with Washington, had wintered at Valley Forge, had been in the fight at Germantown, and had seen the surrender at Yorktown. The ideas and beliefs of the Revolution were active still. The deeds of the heroes of the Revolution were known to every citizen. The people were patriotic before anything else. They loved their country, and were proud of it. The Fourth of July was the greatest day of the year, and Christmas and New Year's were nothing to it. The broad-brimmed hat and the sugar-scoop bonnet were more commonly seen in 1849 than in 1899, and the old Quaker ideas permeated society, and influenced, if they did not direct, tastes, habits, business methods, and official ideas.

This influence tended to ultra-conservatism, to narrow-minded views in many things, to a suppression of the softer emotions and the finer feelings, to an inordinate respect for money, but also to moral purity, personal dignity, rigid personal and business honor, political integrity, truthfulness, and love of justice, if not of mercy.

Fifty years ago the city had not been consolidated, and the area now known as Philadelphia consisted of the city proper and of various districts and townships (the Northern Liberties, Frankford, Kensington, Kingsessing, Southwark, Moyamensing, Weccaco, West Philadelphia, etc.).

The city proper lay between the Delaware and the Schuylkill and Vine and South Streets, and its population was 120,000. The population of the entire county was about 400,000.

John Swift was Mayor of the city. City Council was composed
of very different material from that extraordinary and infamous
pirate crew which legislates for us today. The foremost citizens
of Philadelphia were once proud to serve the people, and the
people were proud to have them as city fathers. Such men as
Horace Binney, John Rodman Paul, Theodore Cuyler, Geo. M.
Wharton, W. Heyward Drayton, A. J. Lewis, and John Price
Wetherill were Councilmen. The Philadelphia bench was widely
known for its ability and purity, and the Philadelphia bar was
celebrated throughout the continent. Pleading or presiding in our
courts were William M. Meredith, Horace Binney, David Paul
Brown, George Sharswood, James Thompson, George M. Dallas,
John Cadwallader, William J. Duane, and John Sergeant.

This city was the medical center of the country, its medical
authorities were revered far and wide, and every ambitious
medical man in the United States looked toward a chair in a
Philadelphia college as the crowning point of his career. Philadelphia still possesses great schools and eminent teachers, and is
still a medical center, but she has rivals in New York, Baltimore,
and Chicago. It is the narrow-minded policy of some public
officials which gives aid and comfort to our rivals. Hospital
teaching should be encouraged in all institutions, and not discouraged in any. Postmortem examinations should be permitted
far more often than is the rule. The coroner's physicians should
invariably be men of the highest scientific standing, students
should attend the official examinations and the necropsy classes
should be what they are in Paris. It is true that we have more
medical students than we had in 1849, but rival cities have gained
more than we. We educate a smaller proportion of American
students than we used to. In 1849 the University of Pennsylvania
had 508 students, the Jefferson Medical College had 480 students,
the Pennsylvania Medical College had 90 students, the Philadelphia College of Medicine had 91 students, the Franklin Medical
College had about 40.

One of the most influential physicians in the country was
Dr. Geo. B. Wood. He was a famous teacher, a celebrated author

and practitioner, the founder, with Dr. Franklin Bache, of the National Dispensatory. He was tall, broad-shouldered, and slender, his skin was almost olive, his nose was prominent, his face was wrinkled, he had scanty eyebrows, wore a wig, and always dressed in somber black. At this time he was fifty-two years of age, and was physician to the Pennsylvania Hospital and the Professor of Therapeutics in the University, and had not yet succeeded Chapman as Professor of Physic.

His life was an unending round of labor, and if we agreed with Carlyle that genius is an infinite capacity for labor, we would say he had genius, but great originality he did not have.

John K. Mitchell, the Professor of Practice in Jefferson College, was a medical philosopher and a famous man. No man was ever loved more by his patients and his students. He was tall, portly, and handsome. His face was manly and genial, and his smile warmed the heart to see. At this time his hair was black, lightly touched with gray. He dressed in black, with the exception of his vest, which was white. He was a versifier of no mean power, a very eloquent public speaker, a chemist, a physiologist, a scientific author, and a most successful practitioner. In his essay on the Cryptogamous Origin of Malarial Fever, with the inspiration of the poet and the prescience of the philosopher, he anticipated many of our present views regarding the action of fungi in producing disease. This remarkable essay is to be found in the *American Journal of Medical Sciences* for 1849. He was one of the first to point out the value of rest in spinal troubles and to suggest the nervous origin of rheumatism.

Nathaniel Chapman, the Professor of Practice in the University, was a learned, brilliant, and eccentric man. His witty sayings were celebrated, and to listen to a conversation between Chapman and his particular friends, Godey and Judge Conrad, was a privilege to be sought for. His mouth was large, and while his eyes were remarkably keen, his face was strangely wrinkled. His voice was peculiar, because he had a cleft palate. He, too, dressed in black. He had been a private pupil of Rush, and had also studied under Abernethy in London. He held the chair of

practice in the University for thirty-four years. He was physician
to the Philadelphia Hospital, the first President of the American
Medical Association, and the first editor of the *American Journal
of Medical Sciences*. He wrote a work on *therapeutics* and
materia medica, and many of his lectures were published in book
form.

Charles D. Meigs was Professor of Obstetrics in Jefferson. His
versatility was wonderful. He was a learned man and a scholar,
a wise man; in spite of his squeaky voice, a speaker and teacher
of remarkable power. He was dramatic, eccentric, witty, lovable,
much given to interesting stories and odd remarks, and even
toward the end of his life was as enthusiastic as a boy. He was
of medium height, stood erect, and was rather thin. His thin
and sallow face was fringed with brown whiskers. His head was
large, but his forehead was narrow. Nature made him a great
actor, and his lecture upon postpartum hemorrhage was a dramatic
masterpiece. He taught so as students could not forget. In postpartum bleeding he believed in turning out the clot, and he would
stop before a student, peer into his face, and say: "What would
you do in postpartum hemorrhage, turn out the clot?" would
pass to the next student and repeat this, and so on. No one
forgot who heard him even once. He had a famous controversy
with Holmes regarding the contagiousness of puerperal fever, and
maintained that chloroform was a very dangerous agent. A most
kindly, conscientious, lovable, and redoubtable man.

Wm. Gibson was the Professor of Surgery in the University.
He was an able surgeon, a classical scholar, a learned man, but
of a violent and passionate temperament, which led him into innumerable quarrels. He was the first surgeon to tie the internal
iliac artery.

Robley Dunglison was the Professor of Physiology in Jefferson.
He was not original, but was considered the most learned man in
the medical profession of America. His knowledge was encyclo-
pedic. He wrote a library of successful works. His *Medical
Dictionary* and his *History of Medicine* are still frequently consulted. He was born in England, and had begun practice in

London as an obstetrician, when Thomas Jefferson brought him
to the University of Virginia in 1824. He came to Philadelphia
in 1834.

Thomas D. Mütter, then only thirty-eight years old, was Professor of Surgery in Jefferson. Gross says: "He was of medium
height, slender, and graceful in form, with bright eyes and a
handsome forehead. His voice was remarkably clear and distinct,
and had unusual strength and compass." His manners were
charming. He was a follower of the French school of surgery,
and was particularly noted for plastic and orthopedic operations.
He was not an original man; he wrote but little, and in operating
was prone to lean somewhat on the strong arm of Joseph Pancoast.

Joseph Pancoast, the Professor of Anatomy in Jefferson, was
one of the most remarkable surgeons of the day. It was as an
operative surgeon that he was at his best, rather than in the
library or the lecture room, and Keen has said that he shared with
Bernard von Langenbeck the distinction of being the greatest
operator of the time. He was bold, brilliant, resourceful, his anatomical knowledge was perfect, his steadiness of hand and keen-
ness of eye were proverbial, and he was a successful clinical teacher.
His book on operative surgery was fiercely attacked by the critics,
but it was a success.

Hugh L. Hodge was Professor of Obstetrics in the University.
He was a man of wide and growing celebrity. His nose was long,
his hair was curly and brushed up high, he wore gold spectacles,
his walk was solemn, his face was broad, but was occasionally
illuminated by a sweet smile.

Dr. Samuel Jackson was a man of great intellect and learning.
He was not only learned, but was wise. He was more than a
practitioner; he was a medical philosopher. He was a delightful
lecturer, and a very eloquent speaker. He was for many years
Professor of the Institutes of Medicine in the University.

Among other eminent medical men we may mention Drs. Paul
Goddard, Wm. E. Horner, Robert Hare, Franklin Bache, René La
Roche, Isaac Hays, John Rhea Barton, George Fox, George W.
Norris, Samuel G. Morton, James McClintock, D. Francis Condie,

W. P. Dewees, Isaac Parrish, W. W. Gerhard, and Washington
L. Atlee.

At the time of which we write the ships of all nations entered
the Delaware, and boats sometimes lay four deep at our wharves.
American ships, manned by American sailors, sailed from Philadelphia for all parts of the globe—to Rio, to the West Indies, to the
East Indies, to the Isthmus, to California, to Liverpool, to London,
to Londonderry, to Amsterdam, to Havre, to Malaga, to Portugal,
to Calcutta, to China, to Manila, and to the Guinea coast. Philadelphia merchants were widely celebrated for their probity and
enterprise; the word of one of them was as good as his bond, and
any man who broke his word became a business outcast and a
social Pariah.

Among the best known merchants of the period from 1829 to
1849 were the Welsh family, John McCrea, Lewis Clapier, Isaac
Norris, Henry Pratt, Samuel Archer, William D. Lewis, Chas.
Ritchie, and John C. Da Costa.

The methods of business were very different then from now,
when cable communication brings us next door to the most distant nations, and steam reduces a voyage to days which then
occupied weeks. In 1837 the first steamboat had crossed the
Atlantic, and several lines of steamers had since been organized.
The Cunard line began to run steamers in 1839, and the first mail
to cross the Atlantic in a steamer was taken over in 1840. In
1849 most transportation was still effected by swift sailing boats,
the American packets and clipper ships being especially famous.
The captain navigated the boat and a supercargo took charge of
the cargo out and the return cargo. The cruises were often very
lengthy. There was danger from the elements, and in Chinese
and West Indian waters danger from pirates. Insurance rates
were very high. A boat might leave this city loaded with manu-
factured goods for Rio, sail from Rio to Liverpool with hides,
tallow, and coffee, from Liverpool to Havre with shoes and woolens,
and from Havre home with light wines, brandy, silks, and laces.
A trusty supercargo was given large discretion, and on his judgment and intelligence success largely depended. Stephen Girard

did not believe in giving them discretion; he gave them orders and insisted they should follow them even if unexpected events made such a course lead to inevitable loss. He said: "Obey orders if you break owners." John C. DaCosta pleased Henry Pratt by disobeying an order, and he was wont to say that "every sensible man knew there are times when he must disobey orders to save owners," and "only a sensible man should be a supercargo." The position was a training school for merchants, and a few successful voyages were apt to make a supercargo either a junior partner or a merchant on his own account.

Fifty years ago the houses of the well-to-do were rarely more than three stories high. They were broad and roomy, and were built of red brick, with white marble facings. Back of each one was a large grassy yard. The shutters were closed promptly at sundown. The steps and pavements were washed every day, summer and winter, with an almost religious zeal, an observance which greatly excited the surprise of strangers and the wrath of pedestrians. Houses contained no furnaces, no bathrooms, no water pipes, and the room doors were not locked. The front door contained a plate with the owner's name upon it. Many of the poorer houses were of frame, and fires were frequent and disastrous. Very high buildings and iron buildings were unknown. The pavements were of brick. The streets were paved with the resentful and enduring cobble. Trees were numerous and large. The chief thoroughfares were illuminated with gas, but the jets were not lighted on nights when the moon was out. The police were called watchmen, wore no uniforms, and could shelter themselves in watch-boxes, which houses were frequently attacked by Bacchanalian revellers. The water works had been moved from Penn Square, and this area was ragged and unfenced. Duck ponds could be found on Broad Street. There were woods on Poplar Street; there were open fields on Frankford Road. Knockers were often seen. There were no letterboxes, newsstands, messenger boys, cabs, photographs, or eyeglasses; oranges and bananas were luxuries. There were no canned fruits or foods. The use of ice was much less common than now.

St. Joseph's Hospital, recently opened to patients, was considered especially salubrious because of the wide expanse of open fields around it. South Street was called Cedar; Locust Street was Prune; Sansom Street was George; Arch Street was often called Mulberry; Race Street was Sassafras. The streets west of Broad Street were called Schuylkill Eighth, Schuylkill Seventh, etc. The omnipresent and pugnacious English sparrow had not been imported, and the squares were inhabited by friendly squirrels. There were no street cars, and passengers were conveyed about in lumbering 'buses, which seemed to run according to the taste and fancy of the drivers. No omnibus came in from west of Broad Street after 10 P. M. There was no bridge at either South Street, Walnut Street, Chestnut Street, or Girard Avenue. The wire bridge at Fairmount was considered a wonderful masterpiece of engineering skill. The first telegraph office had been opened five years before. The Pennsylvania Railroad was being built. There were three trains a day for Norristown and three trains a day for Germantown. Passengers for Germantown took the 'bus at the Commercial Exchange, Third and Walnut Streets, and were carried to the depot. Cope's packets sailed for Liverpool from Walnut Street wharf. These celebrated boats often crossed in three weeks. Every old Philadelphian will remember the "Tuscarora," the "Tonawanda," the "Susquehanna," the "Wyoming," and Captain Dunleavy's "Saranac." Street market houses were common, identical with the one still standing at Second and Pine Streets, which was built in 1745.

The city contained many good hotels and comfortable old-time inns. Among them we may name the United States Hotel, opposite the Custom House; Jones', on Chestnut Street, above Sixth; Washington, on Chestnut Street, above Seventh; the Merchants', on Fourth Street, below Arch; the Eagle, on Third Street, above Race; the Red Lion, on Market Street, above Sixth; the White Swan, on Race Street, above Third; Bloodgood's, at Chestnut Street wharf; the Ridgway, at Market Street wharf; the Bull's Head, on Sixth Street, above Callowhill; the Black Horse, on Second Street, below Callowhill, and the Barley Sheaf, on Second

Street, below Vine. The Black Horse, the Barley Sheaf, and the Ridgway still stand.

Fairmount Park had been opened to the public five years before. Many of the foremost citizens still lived on Front Street, New Market Street, Second Street, and the lower portions of Race, Vine, Callowhill, Spruce, and Pine Streets, and continued to live in these localities until the emigration westward was precipitated by the great fire which started in Brock's wholesale grocery store, July 9, 1850.

There were only a few competent dentists, and the Pennsylvania Dental College was not opened until 1850.

There was not a single female physician, and the Woman's Medical College was not opened until 1850.

The Volunteer Fire Department was in full blast, and contained some of the most promising pugilists and politicians of the day. Some companies were very respectable and others were the reverse. At any large fire you would be certain to meet with Paul Goddard and Jakey Tripler, Richard Vaux, and Bill McMullin. The more humble and gentle the name of the company, the more apt was it to be pugnacious. For instance, the Good Will would fight anybody at any time. We have observed the same tendency in certain religious sects.

The electric fire alarm was not introduced until after the consolidation. When a fire occurred and was discovered by a watcher in the State House tower, the direction was signaled by taps on the bell. When there was a fire, hand engines and hose carriages were dragged by men, a shrieking crowd ran along the pavements, and quiet citizens got out of the way, as there was often a fight which would have brought joy to the heart of a Comanche or Pawnee. Great disorders and riotous demonstrations were frequent. Fires were often of incendiary origin, and the firemen fought citizens, policemen, and other firemen with scrupulous impartiality. In June of this year a fight in the neighborhood of Eighth and Fitzwater Streets lasted all day, and two weeks later the carriage of the Franklin Hose was thrown into the Delaware by a rival company. Organized gangs of thugs and robbers were numerous and rampant, gangs bearing such refined names as the Rats, and Schuylkill Rangers, the Blood Tubs, and the Killers.

Among the chief buildings were the Arcade, at Seventh and Chestnut Streets; the Athenaeum, the Girard Bank, the Custom House and the Mint. The Academy of Natural Sciences was at Broad and Sansom; the Academy of Fine Arts was at Tenth and Chestnut; the College of Pharmacy was at Seventh and Filbert; the Chinese Museum was where the Continental stands today; the University of Pennsylvania was at Ninth and Chestnut; the Jefferson College was on its present site; the Pennsylvania Medical College was on Ninth, below Locust; the Franklin Medical College was on Locust, near Eleventh; the Philadelphia College of Medicine was at the northwest corner of Fifth and Adelphi.

One of the chief daily papers of the country was the *North American and U. S. Gazette*, edited by R. T. Conrad. Among other papers we should mention the *Pennsylvania Inquirer*, *Saturday Evening Post*, the *Pennsylvanian*, edited by John W. Forney; *Public Ledger*, published by Swain, Abell and Simmons; *Philadelphia Democrat*, the *Dollar Newspaper*, in which Poe had published the *Gold Bug*, in 1843; the *Daily Sun*, the *Evening Bulletin*, and *The Item*, edited by Thomas Fitzgerald. It is interesting to note that *The Item* was a weekly and was largely devoted to literature, art, the drama, and the home. The chief scientific periodicals were the *American Journal of Medical Sciences*, which had been founded in 1820; the *Journal of the Franklin Institute*, the *American Journal of Pharmacy*, the *Medical Examiner*, edited by Biddle, Clymer and Gerhard; the *Medical News*, founded in 1843, and the *Dental News Letter*. *Godey's Lady's Book*, *Graham's Magazine* and *Peterson's Magazine* were popular publications.

The numbering of the houses was carried out on a different principle from that now employed, and the number gave no information as to the street the house was nearest. Number 183 Callowhill Street would now be found below Second; then it was a boarding-house above Fifth. Number 219 North Second Street would now be above Race; it was then above Vine.

Postmen brought mail to houses, but if you wanted to post a letter you took it to the post office, or else to some designated drug store, where you could entrust it to the uncertain mercies of Blood's Penny Delivery.

It is interesting to look at the *Ledger* for January 16, 1848. It was published at the northwest corner of Third and Chestnut, and cost one cent. It consisted of four pages, and about one-quarter of it was taken up with quack advertisements, testimonials and striking cases, although they had not got to the point of publishing pictures of the saved. We see many old acquaintances here: Wistar's Balsam of Wild Cherry, Jayne's Alterative and Jayne's Expectorant, Swaim's Compound Syrup of Wild Cherry, Schenck's Pulmonic Syrup and Townsend's Compound Syrup of Sarsaparilla; and it is affecting to note that the old philosopher of St. Petersburg is curing venereal disease with a purely vegetable remedy, and that an eminent scientist has removed a tape-worm sixty feet long, with three black heads.

The following notice appears on the first page:

NOTICE.—A meeting of the Philadelphia County Medical Society will be held this (Tuesday) afternoon, January 16th, at half-past three o'clock, at the hall of the College of Pharmacy. The regular physicians of the city and county are invited to attend. The Committee on Constitution will meet at 11 o'clock.

D. FRANCIS CONDIE,
Secretary.

During the meeting there was a fire at Crown and Race Streets, and the "Osceola," loaded with emigrants for California, was being towed down the river by the city ice boat.

There were many advertisements of California goods, whale oil, sperm oil, burning fluid, and camphene.

We find that the best daguerrotypes were to be gotten at Peale's rooms; that Donnelly sold safety-glazed capsuled blue matches; that Amos Briggs, attorney-at-law, attended expeditiously to all law business at No. 6 Spring Garden Street; that

Dr. William Mayberry had removed to the northwest corner of Franklin and Vine; that Cyrus Horne, who had learned undertaking with William H. Moore, had a large stock of lead coffins on hand; that corns could be speedily and easily removed by Doctor Caywood's salve; that tinsel headdresses were popular; that evening schools were held for married and single ladies; that an eating house at No. 26 Market Street had rabbit pie three times a week; that Spanish cigars were 50 cents a hundred; and that an employer wanted to hire a single man who could loan him $200.

At the Walnut Street Theater there was a new burlesque by Thomas Dunn English. It began at 7 P. M., and the cost of admission to the parquet was 50 cents. At the Athenaeum and National Museum (Seventh and Chestnut Streets) there was a benefit to Mr. Joseph Jefferson, the comedian, who was to play the "Cricket on the Hearth." At the Museum Building, at Ninth and George Streets, Signor Blitz was to perform.

Many names known in business now were known then. You could buy guns from Krider, surgical instruments from Gemrig, watches from Bailey, safes from Farrel, tickets for New York steamers from Thomas Clyde, clothing from Jacob Reed, books from Blakiston, seeds from Buist, paper from Megargee, drugs from Blair, chemicals from Powers & Weightman, malt from Perot, ale from Smith, optical instruments from McAllister, oils from Wetherill. Baldwin built engines, Lea published medical books, Adams expressed goods, and Peterson published novels.

Some famous public buildings which then existed have been destroyed. Penn's cottage still stands, but has been moved from Letitia Street, where it always should have remained.

In 1849 there were still standing the London Coffee House, at Front and Market; the Hultsheimer House, at Seventh and Market, in which the Declaration was written; the Indian Queen Hotel, on Fourth Street below Market, where Jefferson had lived, and the Slate Roof House, in which Adams, Hancock and Baron De Kalb had lived, in which John Penn had been born, and in which General Forbes had died.

1849 is further to be remembered as a year in which Asiatic cholera again visited Philadelphia.

The story of the foundation of the County Medical Society is known to you all. The American Medical Association was organized in 1847. December 11, 1848, a number of physicians of the city and county met in the hall of the College of Pharmacy to arrange for the foundation of the County Medical Society. The first regular meeting of this society was held January 16, 1849. Dr. Samuel Jackson was the first President.

The constitution declared that the objects of the society are "the advancement of knowledge upon all subjects connected with the healing art; the elevation of the character and the protection of the proper rights and interests of those engaged in the practice of medicine, and of the study of the means calculated to render the medical profession most useful to the public, and subservient to the great interests of humanity."

A man to be eligible for membership "must be a citizen of Philadelphia, a graduate of a respectable school, of good moral and professional standing and a regular practitioner."

No man can become a member who has "patented a remedy or surgical instrument, who deals in patented remedies or nostrums, who prescribes a remedy without knowing its composition or who shall give a certificate in favor of a nostrum, a patented remedy or instrument."

It was aimed to make the society a forum where all respectable physicians could meet and debate, and exchange experiences. It was hoped that association would bind them together, so that the rules of gentlemanly conduct and honorable dealing would be observed, and each would feel he owed a duty to the other and to the public. The society was a success. It grew year by year. In 1853 it had 220 members. At present it has over 700. It was not incorporated until 1877. The Mutual Aid Society was initiated and incorporated in 1878.

An enormous number of valuable papers have been read, and excellent debates, not always free from acrimony, have been frequent. Some of the most eminent men in the city have been

presidents of this organization, and we may mention Samuel
Jackson, D. Francis Condie, Alfred Stillé, Samuel D. Gross, James
A. Meigs, D. Hayes Agnew, Washington L. Atlee, William Goodell,
Henry H. Smith, Albert H. Smith, R. J. Levis, J. Solis-Cohen,
and W. W. Keen.

The profession was long violently opposed to the female doctor.
After the foundation of the Woman's Medical College, the censors
of the County Medical Society recommended that physicians
should not consult with females. Much controversial literature
was published. One excited individual pointed out the fact that
when the Duchess of Devonshire got into politics, she obtained a
butcher's vote by kissing him, and he expressed great fear that if
women got into medical societies they would try to carry elections
in the same way. In 1867 the State Society issued a pronuncia-
mento against women practitioners. This declares that women
cannot stand the strain of practice, that their physiologic necessities forbid the attempt, that if married they will neglect home
duties, that they will not consent to only attend women, and
that their nerves are too delicate for the work. In 1868 the County
Society decided that members should not consult with women,
and that if any member accepted a chair in the Woman's College
he should forfeit his membership. In 1871, so strong was the
prejudice, that Doctor Agnew resigned from the Pennsylvania
Hospital rather than lecture to mixed classes. But woman, as
usual, finally had her way. In 1882 the names of five women
passed the censors, but were rejected by the society. In 1888 the
first woman was elected. And yet the earth did not rock, the sea
did not overflow its banks, the stars did not fall.

> "The moving finger writes, and having writ,
> Moves on, nor all your piety and wit
> Shall lure it back to cancel half a line,
> Nor all your tears wash out one word of it."

In June of 1857 the County Medical Society took a positive
stand against the appointment of an irregular practitioner as chief
physician of Blockley. Henry Hartshorne attacked the policy of

political appointments to medical positions as a fearful evil. But since that day political powers have again and again made medical appointments for personal or political reasons. It is the curse of our government. It is a system which would send out our country to fare like a prostitute in the slums—our country which seemed born to be, and which should be, the morning star amongst all the nations of the earth. Oh, if I had my way, I would strike that thrice accursed system dead!

The science of medicine has been profoundly altered in the last fifty years. A recent graduate today knows more than George B. Wood or John K. Mitchell knew after half a century of thought and study; but in spite of his knowledge, he would not of necessity be so useful in a case as Wood or Mitchell. Much has been gained; something has been lost. The successful physician of 1849 was apt to be a practical man. The absence of many aids on which we moderns rely forced him to cultivate to the highest degree the powers of observation. Specialties were few, and the practitioner was apt to be broad, self-reliant and many sided. The growth of specialism has been in a sense a confession of failure. It resulted from an appreciation of the fact that it is impossible to correlate all medicine by a few general rules, and that the only possibility of progress is in the accumulation of great numbers of apparently isolated facts, which can be weighed, analyzed, and compared. Specialism has done much good; it has led to important improvements, it has distinctly benefited humanity, but its place should be recognized. No man should be able to come forth and proclaim himself a specialist any more than Wilkins Micawber, Jr., could go forth and proclaim himself a lawyer. A man should not be primarily the narrow man of one idea. He should be first the physician, and out of the abundance of knowledge he should gradually become the specialist, because of special liking, particular aptitude or peculiarly favorable circumstances. Again, medical colleges should not try to make graduates specialists in all branches, but they should teach them thoroughly the great fundamentals of medical science and not encourage them to become specialists until time and experience fit them to be.

The physician of 1849 did not possess the ophthalmoscope, a practical laryngoscope, the endoscope, the cystoscope, and the x-rays. Electrical illumination as a diagnostic aid or an operative adjunct was not employed. The therapeutic uses of electricity had not been placed on a scientific basis and the value of the same agent in diagnosis was not understood. Ether and chloroform were novelties distrusted by many. Local anesthesia was not employed. Nitrous oxide gas was not given for surgical purposes. Hypodermatic medication had not been devised. The microscope of that day stood on an erect frame, and the achromatic glass was not employed. Therapeutics was a purely empirical science and was long to remain so. Bacteriology was unknown. Blood studies were rarely attempted. The study of the urine was in its infancy. Cerebral localization was undreamt of, and it was supposed that the brain, like the liver, functionated as a whole, and had no special centers. The infectiousness of puerperal fever was still disputed. Appendicitis was practically unknown, although Hancock, of London, in this very year claimed that abscesses in the right iliac fossa arose from the appendix (*American Journal of Medical Sciences*, 1849). Delirium tremens was treated with opium. Venesection was still frequently employed. Huge doses of purgatives were given by the most conservative men. In most asylums mechanical restraint was extensively employed, although in the Pennsylvania Hospital for the Insane, under the influence of Doctor Kirkbride, it was being largely abolished, along with the tranquillizing chair and the centrifugal machine. Tetanus was thought to be due to reflex irritation. The bromides had not been used in epilepsy. Nitrite of amyl was unknown. Digitalis was thought to be a heart depressant. Strychnine and atropine were not employed in shock. Drugs were often bulky and nauseous, and the elegant pharmaceutic preparations of today were not obtainable. Calomel was given for most conditions. The salicylates were not given in rheumatism.

The injection of saline fluid into the veins, the rectum or the subcutaneous tissues had not been devised. The remarkable products of coal tar had not yet been discovered in Pennsylvania petroleum by the French chemist, Chevreul. The cold-bath treatment of fevers would have been regarded as murder. Goiter was not operated upon. Brain surgery and lung surgery were not attempted, except in accident cases. Intubation had not been invented. Cases of appendicitis were called peritonitis, and were left to die. The battle for abdominal surgery was being opened by Lizars, John L. Atlee, Washington L. Atlee and a few others who were operating for ovarian tumors. The intra-abdominal organs other than the ovary were not attacked surgically. The bladder was only opened for stone, and Bigelow's operation had not been devised. The catgut ligature was not used. The grim specter of sepsis was ever present where there were wounded men or men who had been subjected to surgical operations, and the world was to wait for twenty years before Lister's article on the prevention of sepsis in compound fractures was to be published. Almost all wounds suppurated. Erysipelas was very usual, hospital gangrene and pyemia were common, the mortality of compound fractures was from 60 to 80 per cent, it required from three to six months for a case of amputation of the breast to heal, and several months for the healing of a major amputation. Cancer of the breast was never cured. The Esmarch apparatus and hemostatic forceps were not used, and bleeding in operations was profuse and not unusually fatal. The nurse of the period was very generally ignorant, often dirty and sometimes drunk, and the modern trained nurse, the right hand of the surgeon, was just beginning to be thought of. Surgery consisted chiefly in the removal of tumors, amputation of limbs, correction of deformities, cutting for stone, trephining the skull, performing tracheotomy, and dressing wounds.

How different the picture now. An anesthetic is given without fear, and the patient passes through the dreadful drama of the operation without knowledge and without pain. The abdomen is opened unhesitatingly and surgical operations performed on any organ or viscus which may demand it. Fifty years ago Liston, in opposing ovariotomy, said the diagnosis is impossible without opening the abdomen; he scoffed at the idea of opening the abdomen to discover what was wrong and quoted Hudibras:

"As if a man should be dissected
To see what part is disaffected."

Today we open the abdomen or skull by exploratory incision. The surgeon is like a bride arrayed in purity, and the teachings of Lister and Pasteur have revolutionized the world. Sepsis has been practically banished, hospital gangrene is never heard of. The mortality from compound fractures is extremely small. An amputation of the breast or of a limb is healed in a week. The patient suffers very little pain, and a pauper in an almshouse is now rendered more comfortable and is cared for better after an operation than was a king but fifty years ago.

Men come and men go, but science lives and advances. Individual discoveries are glorious and worthy, but we must give due meed of praise to the hard-working, obscure practitioners who, regardless of fame and wealth, apply them. Too often in this modern world even the scientist has been touched by the love of notoriety or the joy of gain, emotions which will mar his usefulness, will cloud the agar in his test-tube and blur the glass of his microscope. Such men there have been, but not many. Better than such a man the dulness of inanimate dust! Better the roadside pond which at least reflects in its stagnant bosom the glories of the firmament! Better the pine trees singing 'neath the stars! Our fathers did wonders with the resources they could command. The lesson of their lives is largely one of dignity, self-sacrifice, devotion to science and regard for the bonds of professional conduct and duty, and carelessness as to wealth or fame.

This is our heritage. Let us prize it justly. To be always retained if we are worthy. To be ours until we weigh the precious gold of the star-light, draw to earth the serene azure of the skies, take the heat from flame, steal the beauty from the rose, capture the glory from the sunset or strip the splendor from the radiant brow of morning.

THE OLD JEFFERSON HOSPITAL*

WE meet today to dignify with appropriate ceremonies an event of the first importance in the history of this school—an event long hoped for, long despaired of, but which has finally come to pass. The dream of a multitude of yesterdays is realized today, and this splendid new hospital is a monument, not to public vanity, not to private gain, but to unselfish effort for humanity and science. Those who tracked the toilsome pathway, those who bore the heavy burden, may well be pardoned a feeling of exultation and a sense of triumph.

My first and most agreeable duty is to turn to the Hon. William Potter and his associates of the board of trustees, and, in the name of the great alumni of this school and of my colleagues of the faculty, tender our heartfelt and most grateful thanks.

This event is of the first importance to the Jefferson Medical College, but its influence is of far wider significance. It is of importance to medical science that a corps of the army of healing, a corps in the front of the battle against Death, has been strengthened and enthused. It is of economic importance to the city and the state. When a man is saved from death or rescued from sickness he returns to the support of a family which might otherwise be a public charge, and he becomes again an industrial unit, a factor in the production of wealth, a factor which adds its share to the power and greatness of the commonwealth. From the economic view alone, to say nothing of the humane aspect, it actually pays the state to aid hospitals financially. It particularly pays it to aid teaching hospitals, in which the lessons learned from a single sick or injured man may save valuable lives and cure hundreds in distant places. The event is also of importance to the diseased and hurt of the state and city, for more of them than

* Address at the opening of the new Jefferson Medical College Hospital, June 7–8, 1907.

204

formerly can come to us for help. The need of hospital accommodation is every year becoming more and more pressing. This is an age when dangerous occupations multiply. The streets are filled with rapidly moving and death-dealing vehicles; every few stories of a great modern building mean one man dead and many injured; every twenty miles of railroad in the country mean a man killed, and every three miles mean a man injured, each year; great machine shops and factories crush and mutilate, and deadly electric currents are on all sides of us. Closely adjacent to the hospital are the slums, the inhabitants of which, when injured or diseased, know no resource but the hospital; the people of the slums pour into the wards and throng in the out-patient departments. The very situation of the building means a wealth of clinical material, because it is placed where it is most needed. In the slums the slime of humanity gathers; there plagues are ever lurking, ready to burst forth and overwhelm us; there is drunkenness; there is madness; there is pauperism; there is illegitimacy; there is "Vice with her naked talons"; there is "Crime with her dripping fangs." Truly the slum is the shadow of civilization itself, and in that shadow crawls every noisome reptile and springs every noxious plant. The slum is the interrogation to civilization; it is the problem that excites the anxious and apprehensive interest of the scientist, the philanthropist, the statesman and the philosopher; it is the Sphinx's riddle, and to fail to answer it means destruction.

We depart from the old hospital, and truly it is time w did; yet even in going to better quarters there is reminiscent regret at leaving the old home. We leave much besides a building that has outlived its highest usefulness. We leave memories of good work done, of progress inaugurated, of great men and of high achievements. In the arena of that building voices have spoken in tones so authoritative as to sound through this hemisphere and to echo beyond the sea, and the spirits of absent or departed great ones seem to stand beside me as I speak.

In that arena the Grosses and the two Pancoasts operated, and Bartholow and J. M. DaCosta taught. There spoke Levis,

Parvin, Wallace, Biddle, Brinton, Maury and others. There, as guests, have stood Esmarch, of Kiel; Mikulicz, of Breslau; Faure, of Paris; Lorenz, of Vienna; Bryant, Durham, Horsley, Ballance and MacCormac, of London; Macewen, of Glasgow; Lawson Tait, of Birmingham; Annandale and Chien, of Edinburgh; Emmett, Weir and Thomas, of New York; Senn, of Chicago; our own Marion-Sims, and a host of others. There, until yesterday, one fortunately still living was a tower of strength. I refer to our distinguished Emeritus Professor of Surgery, my well-loved master, Keen. I find in these memories strength and inspiration, and I will hold them and cherish them as long as memory remains a portion of my intellect, and until my body becomes again a part of the dreamless dust.

Thirty years ago, in May, 1877, the hospital that we now leave was opened for patients. Our college was, I believe, the second institution in the country to have its own hospital for teaching purposes. When opened it was modern, well equipped, amply satisfactory, an ornament to the city and the pride of the school. In only thirty years it has become completely antiquated, so quickly do conditions change. Thirty years! A comparatively short time, if measured merely by the figures on the calendar, but an infinite period if estimated by multitudinous and revolutionary changes. Thirty years ago vivid chromos, the product of lithography, were immensely popular; they have entirely given place to really beautiful Christmas and New Year cards. Typesetters and compositors were not being pushed aside then by composing machines. Men wrote letters by laborious effort with pen and ink and did not have typewriters. The newspapers did not publish pictures, and the pictures in the magazines were wood cuts, not half-tones. In the entire country there were only four establishments for making artificial ice; there are now over eight hundred. The preservation of food by canning was just beginning to become a great industry. Numbers of persons were reading Jules Verne's recently published book, *Twenty Thousand Leagues Under the Sea*, but navigation under the water was then but a poet's dream; it is now realized in the submarine boat. The United States Navy was almost extinct, thanks to some of the ablest political engineers of destruction that ever wrought evil deeds. The Philippine Islands were known to but few in this country, and then only in connection with hemp and peculiar-looking cigars, and the man did not live that could forecast the message of progress that Dewey was to write in iron hail on the battlements of Manila, and out of which was to spring that new island empire in the very portals of the distant sunset. The United States Army numbered but 20,000 men, some of whom were being used to carry elections in the southern states, and some of whom, under General Miles, were fighting Chief Joseph and his Nez Percés in Northern Montana. The small-caliber, long-range rifle and smokeless powder were unknown—the combination that has revolutionized warfare, made cavalry an almost insignificant arm of the service in actual battle and rendered the taking of fortified places by assault almost impossible to any except the "little brown men" of the land of the Mikado. The largest locomotive in general use weighed 35 tons; the latest type of freight engine built by the Baldwin Locomotive Works weighs over 152 tons. Express trains, as a rule, ran at a rate of 30 miles an hour; they now run more than 50, and often over 60 miles an hour for long distances. The largest ocean steamboat was under 500 feet in length; the Baltic, of the present day, is 726 feet in length. The record passage across the Atlantic was over seven days; it is now under five days, seven hours. There was not a building in Philadelphia above eight stories in height; there are bulidings now in the city twenty-three stories high. Yellow brick and terra cotta were seldom used in building, steel and cement were never employed, and our present Babylonian towers with ribs of steel would have seemed to the people of that day as marvelous as Aladdin's palace. There were no hansom cabs on the streets. The bicycle with the huge front wheel was just appearing, and twenty years were to pass before the advent of the automobile. Hand organs were of small size, and there were no huge breweries of din pushed about in carts or drawn around by dejected donkeys. The street cars were dragged slowly by bony and wretched horses. The public squares were enclosed with iron railings. The streets were paved with Belgian blocks and cobblestones. The wizard, Edison, was at Menlo Park, deep in perfecting the incandescent electric light and in inventing the phonograph. Our streets were illuminated by flickering gas jets. The telephone had been exhibited the previous year at the Centennial Exhibition and was regarded as a marvel, but a toy; few guessed that it would soon become a necessity of life—a perplexing and harassing necessity, breeding wrath and bad language. Marconi had not yet beckoned the mystic symbol out of the fogs of the North Atlantic across 1800 miles of lonely sea. Unjustifiable and maddening street noises were less common than now; the trolley with flat wheels, the huge hand organ, the riveting machine and other sin-breeding infamies were not, every minute of the twenty-four hours, producing profanity, insomnia and neurasthenia. Color photography, safety matches, the underground railroad, the elevated railroad, the steel trust, benevolent assimilation and the big stick were unknown. The country was just recovering from the fierce electoral struggle between Tilden and Hayes, and there was no such thing as an eastern question known to the policy of the United States.

A man could be graduated in medicine after two years of study; only the crudest preliminary education was required; the college professors divided the fees and made enormous incomes by it, and most medical schools were private institutions run for private gain just as truly as groceries and tobacco shops. There was not a genuine trained nurse in any hospital in Philadelphia. Surgery was narrow and limited compared to what it is today: It consisted chiefly in ligating for aneurysm, performing tracheotomy, amputation and resection; operating for empyema, strangulated hernia, bone disease and stone in the bladder; reducing dislocations; setting and dressing fractures; trephining for head injuries; caring for wounds; removing foreign bodies and extirpating tumors. A few surgeons—notably the Atlees—were doing ovariotomy. Comparatively few operations were done, and most ignorant persons were afraid of hospitals, would go to one only in the last extremity, and then went in deadly terror of the black bottle and the fatal potion.

Year by year there has been a growing confidence in hospitals. During the year ending September 30, 1880, there was 890 in-patients treated in the hospital. During the year ending June 1, 1906, there were 6118 treated—nearly seven times as many—with the same accommodations. During the year ending September 30, 1880, 483 new patients were recorded in the Surgical Out-patient Department, and these included genito-urinary and orthopedic cases. Last year there were 4043 new cases, excluding genito-urinary and orthopedic cases. During the year ending September 30, 1880, only 267 operations were done, including general, orthopedic, ophthalmic, and genito-urinary surgery, as well as gynecology. During one day a short time ago 20 operations were done—nearly 10 per cent of the number performed in an entire year twenty-seven years ago. In other words, at the present time as many operations are performed in two weeks as were done in a year in 1880.

In 1877 the great wave of surgical progress, which is one of the most notable events of a notable age, was beginning to form a moving billow. Appendicitis was unknown and was to remain so until Reginald Fitz, of Boston, published his epoch-making paper in 1886. Mellier had guessed the truth in 1827, but he was suppressed by authority, and thousands died because Dupuytren wrong was believed and Mellier right was doubted. In 1877 drugs producing local anesthesia had not been discovered. Bodies for dissection were difficult to obtain and great abuses sometimes arose in attempting to obtain them. The essential importance of embryology in solving many problems of deviation and of disease was beginning to be appreciated. Pathology, chemistry, physiology were becoming fruitful of marvels.

It was just dawning on teachers that students must not only see and hear but must also do, and that, as anatomy is learned in the dissecting-room, many other branches must be learned in the laboratory. We have had the dissecting-room—that is, the laboratory of anatomy—for centuries; we now must have labora-

14

tories for at least a dozen other subjects. A few progressive and able men had grasped the full importance of the recent discoveries of Pasteur, had realized that infectious diseases were probably due to bacteria, and that preventive medicine was destined to become one of the highest callings to which man could devote his brain and consecrate his life. Professor John K. Mitchell, with the intuition of the poet, had claimed, away back in the forties, that fungi caused infectious diseases, but he was unable to prove it. The evidence of the existence and power of minute fungi was furnished by Pasteur, but the germs of suppuration were not discovered by Ogston until 1881, and the bacilli of tubercle were not discovered by Koch until 1882.

One reason that operations have become notably more frequent since 1877 is found in a great discovery made but a few years before that time. In 1876 a modest, unassuming Scotch surgeon attended the International Medical Congress in Philadelphia, and from that visit dates the beginning of a radical change and an enormous advance in surgery. That surgeon, a few years before, had made a study of the views of Pasteur and had come to the conclusion that microscopical fungi were responsible for many unfavorable changes in wounds, and he sought to prevent the entrance of bacteria into wounds by what he called antisepsis. The profession was slow to believe. In 1877 only two surgeons in Philadelphia employed antisepsis. Those surgeons were W. W. Keen and J. Ewing Mears.

Antisepsis has wrought marvels as mighty as were ever conjured by the seal of Solomon. It made really possible most of the surgery of the brain, the chest, the abdomen and the abdominal viscera. It has practically abolished the so-called "blood poisoning" as a sequel of surgical operations; it has enormously mitigated postoperative pain and fever; it has lessened the mortality of major amputations from over 50 per cent to under 5 per cent, of compound fractures of the long bones from over 60 per cent to under 1 per cent, of ovariotomy from at least 50 per cent to about 5 per cent. Truly the life of Lord Lister has been a greater boon to the human race than the lives of a hundred military heroes or a score of kings. I would be prouder to be Lord Lister than to be any potentate that lives and reigns.

For fifty-two years Jefferson College was without a regular hospital. During those years many notable things were done, in spite of cramped quarters, inadequate means and makeshift appliances. This indicates that able and enthusiastic men can often obtain great results with very imperfect instruments. Fine buildings and ample equipments are of great value, but men are of even greater value. It has been well said that the laboratory in which the x-rays were discovered contained little but a Crookes tube, a Ruhmkorff coil and Roentgen himself. Back of every appliance must stand a man able and anxious to use it to the best advantage. Sound college policy seeks to obtain able men as well as costly buildings, and to develop teachers, operators, writers, and experimenters, as well as to found laboratories. Let us not be so "charmed with the shell" that we "cast away the pearl"!

Although until 1877 we had no building especially devoted to hospital purposes, we had a sort of hospital from the very beginning, and dispensary patients were cared for and operations were regularly performed before the class in our original college building. That building, the precursor of our present college and hospital, was our home for three years and still stands. It is 518 and 520 Locust Street. It is an old building. From the side driveway iron tiebeams are visible in the walls. It is three stories in height. The front door and windows are arched, and access to the interior is obtained by mounting several well-worn stone steps. The front, except for the sign of a business firm, is practically as it was eighty-two years ago. Around it are many modern structures and also some houses that stood in 1825. It was built for a cotton factory, then became the Winter Tivoli Theater, then the Jefferson Medical College and is now a bottling establishment. In 1825 Locust Street was called Prune. Directly opposite the college was the Walnut Street Prison for criminals and debtors, one of the rules of which was that the yard must be "kept free from cows, hogs, dogs, and fowls." On the east the college looked out directly on the burial ground of the Free Quakers, those

apostles of peace whose combative instincts had grown so strong
that they had fought under Washington in the War of the Revolution, and had been expelled from meeting for doing so. To the
west, across Sixth Street, was the potter's field, now Washington
Square. Directly back of the college was an ale house, and a
block or two away were several churches. Crime and misery
in front, death on either hand, and manifold consolations in the
rear!

Every teacher wore a swallowtail coat, even in the daytime,
and drove a chaise. If a student were hungry he could go forth
into Fifth Street and purchase hot corn or pepper-pot from colored
venders in the street. If he felt convivial his wants could be satisfied in the Goose and Gridiron or in the Robinson Crusoe. If he
wished to see a play he chose between the Olympic Theater, at
Ninth and Walnut Streets, and the Chestnut Street Theater, on
Chestnut Street above Sixth. If he wished to read he went to the
Philadelphia Library on Fifth Street above Walnut. If the thirst
for combat filled his youthful veins he wandered up to Ninth and
Chestnut Streets, where he was sure to be promptly accommodated by a university man.

The Philadelphia Dispensary, Christ Church, St. Peter's
Church and the Pennsylvania Hospital were where they stand
today. The law courts were at Sixth and Chestnut Streets. The
mayor's office was at Fifth and Chestnut Streets. The United
States Bank, which once was a political institution and a national
issue, was in the building that is now the Custom House. The
almshouse was between Tenth and Eleventh, Spruce and Pine
Streets.

There were no policemen, only watchmen, who were also
lamplighters, and a favorite nocturnal amusement was beating the
watch. At this time revolutionary traditions were still active and
influential, and many men were living who had crossed the Delaware with Washington, had wintered at Valley Forge, had known
Benjamin Franklin, and had gone out in the streets to cheer and
build bonfires when Colonel Tilghman rode in with the news from
Yorktown.

The year of our college opening was in 1825, the year Lafayette completed his final tour in America, that John Quincy Adams became president, that Henry Clay assumed the office of secretary of state, that Oliver Wendell Holmes went up to Harvard, that Poe prepared for the University of Virginia, that Washington Irving started for Spain, that Longfellow celebrated his eighteenth birthday, that Fitz-Green Halleck traveled in Europe, that Hawthorne was graduated from Bowdoin, that Daniel Webster cast aside his free trade views and that Andrew Jackson really became the St. Andrew of Democratic adoration.

In that old building of the Jefferson College the elder Gross studied as a pupil of McClellan, the professor of surgery, Washington L. Atlee was a student, Nathan R. Smith taught anatomy, John Eberle taught practice of medicine, and W. C. P. Barton taught materia medica. In it George McClellan invented teaching by public clinics and the first operation was performed in it May 9, 1825.

Teaching from actual cases in collegiate clinics, a plan invented by McClellan and first applied in the school he founded, came to be the greatest strength of the institution. Teaching by college clinics was long opposed by many conservatives. It was held by them to be misleading, ineffectual and superficial. but nevertheless, after much controversy, it came to be adopted as the most prominent feature of the curriculum by the famous faculty of '41, the faculty that contained Pancoast, Dunglison, John K. Mitchell, Huston, Bache, Mütter and Charles D. Meigs—a group that was unbroken until 1856. But we learn as we advance. "The thoughts of men are widened with the process of the suns." The large clinics have played an infinitely valuable part in medical teaching, but the days when they could constitute the sole method of clinical instruction have forever passed away. Accurate and intimate knowledge can be obtained only by close observation, and close observation is possible only to small sections; and the students now personally examine cases, assist in operations and give anesthetics—of course, guided and controlled by a teacher.

A new building was erected in 1828, and the last lecture was delivered in the original college building in March, 1828. The new building was on Tenth Street above Walnut. This building was twice enlarged and was finally succeeded by the present structure on the corner of Tenth and Walnut Streets. The ground once occupied by the college is covered by the new hospital. Up to the year 1844 patients on whom serious operations had been performed were taken to their homes in carriages and were cared for at home by the professor of surgery and his assistants. In 1844 two rooms were rented over a store at the southwest corner of Tenth and Sansom Streets and a miniature surgical hospital was established. December 23, 1846, a patient in this little hospital was operated on by Mütter for tumor of the cheek, and ether was given to him—the first time an anesthetic was used in Philadelphia. In 1850 two floors were rented over a bottling establishment, which stood next door to the college, and were fitted up for a hospital. In 1852 these rooms were opened directly into the college. Fifteen patients could be accommodated. On clinic days a patient was carried into the arena of the upper lecture room of the college, the room in which the professor of anatomy taught, and the room that is shown in Eakins's famous oil painting of Professor Gross operating, which now hangs in the college. The operation was performed and then the patient was carried back to the little hospital. The meals for the patients were cooked by the family below. Those rooms constituted the hospital until 1877, and were the hospital of Mütter, the elder Pancoast and the elder Gross. There was no resident physician in this hospital; the clinical assistants took turns in acting as residents.

My late colleague and old teacher, Doctor Brinton, in his address on *The Faculty of 1841*, says:

Hard-worked, these latter were, too. For my part, I can remember many a night of waking and bedside watching within those narrow, cramped and musty walls. I have sat, since then, at many a well-ordered table; but never have I relished dainties as I did then the savory oyster and steaming midnight cup of coffee, served by the order of a crafty faculty to insure the watchfulness of the fagged-out watcher.

The school and its hospital had, from the start, a surgical bent. A surgeon created it. It was born of genius, for McClellan was its founder. He was not a Philadelphian, but came here and made his fame. His ancestry was distinguished and the blood of fighting Highlanders and Revolutionary patriots ran hot in his veins. He was born in Woodstock, Conn., in 1796. He was graduated from Yale in 1815. During his boyhood he was called "Little Mac," but he could not have dreamed that a son of his, another "Little Mac," was to come to the command of great armies, to direct titanic battles, to stand on the flaming brow of Malvern Hill, and to ride between the lines at Antietam.

Doctor McClellan studied medicine at the University of Pennsylvania, was an office student of Dorsey, and was graduated in 1819. During his student days he was a resident student in the almshouse (they then had resident students instead of resident physicians). He became almost immediately successful in practice. All his interest was for surgery, and shortly after his graduation he couched for cataract, extracted the lens for the same disease and did many formidable operations. He organized a private class in anatomy and surgery and started a dispensary for the instruction of its members. This class and this dispensary were the germs of our school and hospital. The class became extremely large, numbering 180 men. McClellan knew and loved his subjects and taught them with captivating vim and enthusiasm. By the time he was twenty-seven years of age he was regarded as one of the inevitable men of the future.

He removed the lower jaw for sarcoma; he devised a method to extirpate the parotid gland; he amputated the entire upper extremity; he advocated tearing out certain tumors, instead of dissecting them loose, in order to limit hemorrhage. He was anxious to teach; and, a place in the existing institution being denied him, he founded a new school, and took to it 150 men of his private class. He was energetic, intrepid, rapid in movement, quick in comprehension, positive in conclusion, emphatic in utterance, enthusiastic in everything he undertook. He had a wonderfully retentive memory, a steady hand, and a quick eye.

He fought for what he believed to be right, but always in the open, and he never lurked in a dark alley and stabbed the passer by with innuendo or calumny. He was in the thick of all controversies, sure of the justice of his contentions and inspired by the fire of his genius. If an enemy was in the open, he attacked him; if a foe was in disguise, he unmasked him; if something was needed at Harrisburg, he rode there and got it done—all the time lecturing, operating, practicing, writing, arguing in a perfect fury of amazing and keenly directed energy—an eccentric, lovable, brilliant, formidable and redoubtable man! Troubles came in the faculty, led by small and narrow men. Efforts were made to control, to direct, to suppress the professor of surgery, but the lash of official coercion struck unfelt on the stout shoulders of George McClellan. He resigned his professorship. We lost the name from the school; we were without it for sixty-eight years; but it has, I am proud to say, been restored to us again in the person of the founder's grandson, my distinguished colleague, the professor of applied anatomy. We have done the founder scant justice in the past, and it is with a feeling of peculiar retrospective affection that the least of all his successors pays this tardy tribute to his name.

I wish that time permitted me to speak of some of his successors—of Joseph Pancoast, one of the greatest operating surgeons of his time; a man so celebrated that Sir William Ferguson, then the head of English surgery, referred to him the daughter of a great Lord Chancellor for a plastic operation; Pancoast, the dexterous, the dramatic, with a hand as steady as a rock, but as light as a floating perfume; with a heart that was a stranger to fear, and with an eye as quick as a flashing sunbeam.

Of Mütter, he of the musical voice and charming personality: Mütter, the debonaire, the eloquent, the enthusiastic, the beloved of the class; the man that brought to America the views of the great French school of Velpeau, Dupuytren, Roux, and Lisfranc; who developed in America plastic surgery and orthopedic surgery, then recently founded by Dieffenbach and Stromeyer; Mütter, who had wished the institution to build a hospital

in 1841, but was defeated by the stupidity against which Richter
tells us even the gods fight in vain.

Of Samuel D. Gross, the greatest of them all, with whose life
and services we are all familiar; Gross, who had fought his way to
greatness from humble beginnings, who was graduated from our
school in the class of '28, who founded surgical pathology in
America, and who came to the foremost position ever occupied
by a surgeon in this country; Gross, the author, the operator, the
scholar, the teacher, the organizer, the scientist—LL.D. of Cambridge and Edinburgh, D.C.L. of Oxford; the founder of the
American Surgical Association; the Emperor of Surgery in the
United States, beloved and respected by all medical men. Whenever I had the privilege of listening to him I felt that fifty years of
American surgery were speaking through his lips.

I would like to dwell on the younger Gross—brilliant, positive,
emphatic; a teacher of wonderful force; a diagnostician of marvelous power; a determined, impressive and most courageous man
—the man that, first of all in America, insisted on the necessity
of radical operations in cancer cases. We stood by the corpse
of a dead lion when we went to the tomb of the younger Gross!

I would I could speak of Brinton, so lately gone out into the
great beyond, my former teacher and late colleague, my father's
friend and mine; the trained military surgeon, one of the founders
of the Army Medical Museum and one of the originators of the
"Medical and Surgical History of the War of the Rebellion."
And Keen, the master of us all, fortunately living still and kept
from being with us today only by the interposition of the ocean—
Keen, whose name is written broad and clear on most of the
pages of surgical progress during the last twenty-five years.
McClellan, Pancoast, Mütter, S. D. Gross, S. W. Gross, Brinton,
and Keen were the seven men that controlled surgery in Jefferson
College for eighty-two years.

They obtained triumphs and made mistakes, but their triumphs
were many and their mistakes were few. Let us learn from both.
We have had a great instrument for good placed in our hands;
let us see to it that it is used to the best advantage. Let us be

earnest and energetic; let us have the highest ideals; let us strive for unity of action and harmony of thought; let us suppress as a venomous reptile any one who would breed contention, conflict and hate, and, above all, let us have enthusiasm.

Enthusiasm is the motive-force of progress. No really great deed was ever done in arts or arms, in literature or science, that was not the product of enthusiasm. It took Cook to the southern seas; it lured Gama around the Cape; it called De Haven to seek for Franklin in the awful solitude of the frozen North, and it beckoned Columbus across the ocean, from Palos to the Indies. Because of it the explorer tracks the dusky canon and the miner "bleeds the veins" of the mountains, the navigator seeks the northern pole, and the student prints on his face the unobliterable lines of thought. It carved the Belvidere Apollo and it painted the Sistine Madonna. It struck fire from cold flint; it gave the wheel to the wagon; it invented the alphabet, and it saw in the steam wreaths from a tea kettle a force greater than that of all the men in the world united. It reared the pyramids; it built St. Peter's; it bridged the Hudson, and it laid the gleaming rails of civilization on the summits of the mighty Rockies. It took signals under the ocean; it carried messages through the air; it stored up speech in reservoirs, and it harnessed the lightning to drag the vehicles of man. It discovered the circulation; it invented the ligature; it introduced vaccination and anesthesia, and it laid the gentle hand of healing on the wounds of humanity through antiseptic surgery.

We note its presence in the aphorisms of Hippocrates; in the orations of Demosthenes; in the demonstrations of Newton, and in the discourses of Pasteur. It was with Alexander in the field as he conquered the world; it was with Plato in the grove as he founded philosophy. It was by the lonely lamp of Celsus and behind the sightless eyes of Galileo. It was on the battlefield with Paré and with Larrey and in the laboratory with Welch and with Leidy. It was in the hospital with Sydenham and Boerhaave, with Agnew and Samuel David Gross. It filled the lion heart of Abernethy, and it stirred the lordly soul of Hunter. It stimulated the labors of Washington and Cromwell, of Shakespeare and of Franklin, and it lit the councils of Cesar and of Lincoln, of the great Napoleon and of England's "Grand Old Man." May we feel it; may we realize it; may we be animated by this immortal principle; may we be driven by this divine fire! If we are, we shall take our college through higher aims to broader destinies, and make of her what she ought to be, the morning star among all the institutions of the land.

> "I hold it truth, with him who sings
> To one clear harp in divers tones,
> That men may rise on stepping stones
> Of their dead selves to higher things."

CHARACTER SKETCH OF
PROFESSOR SAMUEL W. GROSS, M. D., LL. D.

ONE of the ablest men ever connected with the Jefferson Medical College was the late Professor Samuel W. Gross, and only a singularly notable man could have escaped being dwarfed into insignificance by his father's transcendent reputation. During the several years before I became a medical student, I used to attend the Saturday clinics at the Philadelphia Hospital. The younger Gross was then surgeon to Blockley, and it was at Blockley that I first saw him. He made a most forcible impression upon my mind. His positive character, his clean-cut sentences, his readiness to accept responsibility, his scorn of clap-trap and hatred of boasting, his diagnostic skill and operative ability, all captivated my youthful imagination.

I graduated from the Chemical Department of the University of Pennsylvania in 1882, and it was at about the same period that Samuel W. Gross became Professor of the Principles of Surgery in Jefferson College. Admiring him and respecting Jefferson as I did, I had no difficulty in coming to the conclusion that I would take my medical course in the Tenth Street school. The elder Gross, the Emperor of American Surgery, full of years and honors, had been made Emeritus Professor in the spring of 1882. He was succeeded by his son, the subject of this sketch, and by Dr. John H. Brinton. As the latter said in the introductory address the following fall, it required "two pegs to fill one hole."

It was less than twenty years ago that the younger Gross became a Jefferson professor, but where are now his former colleagues? Death has claimed both the Grosses, both the Pancoasts, Wallace, Rogers, Parvin, and J. M. DaCosta. Bartholow, the celebrated therapeutist, one of the greatest original thinkers with whom I have ever been brought into contact, is now an

Samuel W. Gross, M. D., LL. D.

emeritus professor; but three of that notable faculty remain actively in our service, Dean Holland, Dr. John H. Brinton, and Dr. Henry C. Chapman.

The first didactic lecture that I ever heard the younger Gross deliver in Jefferson was on what was at that time a novel subject—surgical bacteriology. To thus open the course was regarded as a radical innovation, and many elderly conservatives, swathed round and round with mummy-cloth, regarded it despondently as destructive radicalism. There was not a fragment of doubt in Gross's mind, however. He laid down to the class the basic principles of the science, insisted that they were eternally true, persuaded every one of us that the world of the infinitely little is as much a reality as the world of the infinitely great, and made us to a man enthusiastic followers of the doctrines of Pasteur and Lister. He also applied rigid surgical cleanliness in the hospital clinics; and it was a revelation to the students, after visiting an adjacent hospital and seeing wounds reeking with pus, to go to Gross's clinic and see wound union in a week, without a trace of infection. I never once, even for a moment, doubted the reality of infectious micro-organisms after Gross delivered his first lecture.

His lecture on the arrest of hemorrhage was a masterpiece, and, had it ever been accurately reported, would, I am sure, have become a medical classic. I have never forgotten it, and again and again, when confronted with some serious emergency, the expedients he taught us in that lecture have come to my aid. Every word of it was practical, and every word of it is true today.

From the students' standpoint, Gross was a formidable personage. His tongue did not shed "honeyed dew"; neither did his lips "drip gentle words." Tall, with an erect carriage, he had a stern countenance, a firm jaw, and eyes which seemed to pierce one. His short, sharp, "Well, sir?" when a student approached him, was like the question of a general on the field of battle. No one ever went to him with a proper inquiry, but that it was most fully and lucidly answered; in fact, it pleased him to be questioned about his lectures—but heaven help the dunce who propounded an imbecile interrogation!

I thought then, and I think now, that no man ever was a better teacher. He threw himself into his subject to the degree of complete self-absorption. His voice was high pitched, and would not have been considered pleasing in an orator; but no one ever thought of his voice—only of the lecture. He used plain Anglo-Saxon words; short words, whenever possible. He believed in calling a spade a spade, and not an agricultural implement. He reasoned out every proposition from several different standpoints, and reached a conclusion which seemed to his hearers irrefutable. He was fond of homely similies to illustrate his meaning, and described actual occurrences to emphasize his points. His splendid memory was stocked with thousands of observations from the library, the sick-room, the battlefield, and the hospital, all pigeon-holed in his brain, and every one accessible and capable of production at a moment's notice. He never dealt in subtle distinctions, elusive refinements, or exaggerated theories; and his most prominent characteristic was good common sense.

All the students heartily respected him, but many rather feared him, awed by his demeanor, and unaware that a kind heart was beating beneath the cloak of apparent harshness. In 1887 I became a junior assistant in the Out-patient Surgical Department, of which department Dr. Orville Horwitz was then the chief. From that time on I was brought into daily relationship with the younger Gross, and came to know him thoroughly. I had always admired and respected him, but as one of his assistants I grew to love him. Our first meeting in the hospital, however, was not altogether encouraging. He strode into the Out-patient Department with a baleful gleam in his eyes which was truly terrifying, and with evidences that he had been pulling the right side of his mustache (an action which those who knew him well regarded as of evil import to the tranquillity of residents and assistants). He said: "Where did you put that bottle of juniper catgut which I gave you?" I replied: "You never gave me any catgut." At this denial he almost pulverized me with a glance, and cried in peremptory tones, "I gave it to you yesterday." Then I became angry; all prudence disappeared. I felt that I was casting the appointment overboard and definitely losing my job; but I was not willing to stand any more, and told him that I would be blessed—at least, as I recall the scene, it seems to me that it was a remark of that nature—if he ever gave me any catgut, and that I could not see why in the name of all that was inflammable he lighted on me—or something to that effect. A trace of amusement hovered about his mouth; his eyes softened, and he laid his right hand on my shoulder and said: "That's right, young man; if there is anything you believe, say it, and say it so that it can be understood," and from that moment he treated me in a friendly manner which was most agreeable.

He always stood by an assistant in difficulty if he thought that his conduct was justifiable. On one occasion an inebriated individual entered the Out-patient Surgical room and became involved in a quarrel with me, with the result that I succeeded in forcibly and violently ejecting him. It turned out that he was a physician. He reported me to the authorities and got me into all sorts of trouble. Gross had been away from the city for a few days, but on returning he heard about the occurrence, and instantly took means to save me, not only from a reprimand, but also from criticism. When the bibulous and irate physician went, as he presently did, to Gross's house, in order to protest against my conduct, he was violently seized and propelled with celerity into the street.

Gross's self-confidence was one of his noteworthy characteristics. In the '80's, when operations upon the kidney were still rare, he opened the loin and exposed a kidney in which it was thought that there was a stone. The method of procedure then in vogue was to puncture the organ in several places with a long pin; and, if no stone was detected by this means, to sew up the wound. The case was then abandoned to its fate. The pin failed to detect a stone in the case mentioned, and Gross's colleagues advised that he go no further; but he turned to the class and said: "From a careful study of the symptoms, I know that this man has a stone; and I know that I can find it." He thereupon opened the kidney, found the stone, removed it, and saved the patient. This plan has since come to be regarded as the proper surgical procedure.

Gross was extraordinarily calm in moments of great emergency. I once saw him unexpectedly break into the longitudinal sinus, with the result that immediately there was a most enormous hemorrhage. He instantly placed his finger on the bleeding point, and, looking quietly up to the benches, said: "This gives me an opportunity to show you that in my didactic lectures I told you the truth when I said that any bleeding could be temporarily arrested by the pressure of a finger if the wound were large enough, and that even bleeding from a sinus could be permanently arrested by the pressure of gauze packing." He then arrested the bleeding in that manner, and the patient recovered. The fact is that when he was in some vital surgical emergency he was usually good humored—far better humored than when everything was going well. In that he resembled the great General Picton, famous in the British Army during the Napoleonic wars, who was said to have been in a perfectly heavenly humor when every foot of the ground was mined.

Gross had certain mannerisms of expression. He was not a believer in a great many drugs; but those which he used were given in sufficient amounts to obtain results, and he constantly denounced what he called "piddling doses." Instead of telling an assistant to sponge a wound, he would say "touch" it; and it was always a joke with a new assistant to get him to accurately carry out this injunction, and to lay a single finger on the wound when told to touch it—a proceeding which would always provoke a burst of indignation from the Professor.

Professor Gross was not opinionated. He had the greatest respect for the views of others, and in his lectures he frankly mentioned adverse beliefs. In answers to examination questions he would accept opinions the reverse of his own, if he thought that the man who put them forth really understood what he was talking about. He did not think that his word, and his alone, must be right; and if he made a mistake in diagnosis, or if he taught a view which turned out to be erroneous, he would come before the class and frankly acknowledge his mistake.

He was capable of doing ample justice, even to an enemy. He sometimes quarreled, but never from pettiness or jealousy. In medical societies he always took a leading place, and he was so forceful in discussion that it was well for one to hesitate before stirring him up. On one occasion he had read a paper on Extensive Operations for Cancer of the Breast, and a gentleman of small experience had criticized the paper on the ground that such an operation left a large wound, which could not be closed, and that from the granulations cancer would again develop. Gross's answer was terse and to the point. He said: "When fireplugs produce whales, and oak trees polar bears, then will granulations produce cancer, and not until then."

He was essentially truthful. He told the truth, even when it was unpalatable. He was no actor. He said what he meant, and meant what he said. These tendencies frequently made him unpopular; but he believed, with Sophocles, that truth is the strongest argument. He hated hypocrites, hypocrisy, and cant. Like Randolph of Roanoke:

> "He mocking rent with ruthless hand
> The robe pretence was wearing."

If one went to ask a favor of him, he never shuffled or evaded. His "Yes, sir," or "No, sir" was final; and if he said "Yes," he would leave no stone unturned in carrying out his promise; but when this was accomplished, he would not listen to thanks.

He was an indefatigable worker, but his labors were scientific, and not merely for the making of money, for he constantly refused paying cases. He was jealous of his time, because he did not wish to be taken away from the work which he loved. A person who desired the services of the younger Gross had to obtain them on Gross's own conditions; that surgeon would have no other plan.

15

Gross kept copious notes of his cases, and his journal articles and society papers were masterpieces, written with the utmost care. When writing a paper, he would consult all authorities, and finally embody his own personal experience. He was a trained pathologist, and one of the few practical surgeons able to examine microscopically a tumor after its extirpation. He kept this habit up until he met Doctor Coplin, then a resident in the hospital. This man Gross took to his heart as a genuine scientific brother, and came to trust him to do this work. It was no small compliment.

It may sound strange to those who did not know Gross well, to hear that he was a deeply affectionate man. He was devotedly attached to his household gods and truly fond of his friends—particularly of his colleague, Doctor Brinton; Doctor Hearn, the surgeon to the hospital, whom he always called Joe, and Dr. Orville Horwitz, the chief of his clinic. He was also fond of some animals. He had a parrot to which he was attached, and he was frequently seen sitting at the Walnut Street window of his house with the parrot on his shoulder. On one occasion this unfortunate bird ate some strychnine pills; and Gross came over to the hospital, more agitated than most of us had ever seen him, and very indignant that no one could suggest to him a means of relief. The sorrows of horses always appealed to him. At Eleventh and Walnut Streets a brutal driver of a street car was once flogging a horse, when Gross ran up and pulled him over the dashboard, and was with difficulty prevented from signally chastising him.

He was a wonderful judge of fine porcelain and could discuss most learnedly upon ancient Oriental, Dresden, etc. His favorite relaxation was to attend auctions where he would buy works of art and curios, study character, and irritate unpleasant people by buying things they thought they wanted.

Gross did much for surgery. He pointed out to the profession that veins could with perfect safety be ligated, just as can arteries. He promulgated proper views upon the subject of impotence; he was the first American surgeon to advocate extensive operations for cancer of the breast, and was one of the greatest authorities of his day on tumors; he was a wonderful diagnostician, and used to love to call his assistants together and show them a strange or unusual case, and he would force each one of us to venture a diagnosis before giving his deciding opinion. As a writer, he was clear, direct, and positive, never ornate and never obscure. He wrote many valuable articles, especially a treatise on Tumors of the Breast and one on Diseases of the Male Sexual Organs. He was revising the book of his illustrious father when death overtook him. Had he lived, there is little doubt that he would have produced a masterpiece on cancer, which was the study of his life. He investigated it as a surgeon, as a microscopist, and as a sociologist. Few men of his day, I am convinced, understood this affection so well from so many points of view.

The death of Gross was a loss to humanity. He died too soon, for he was in the full possession of splendid powers, and was doing his best work; had he lived but a few years more, he would have left a mighty name.

Few knew him well; none, I fancy, but his family, his assistants, several loved colleagues, and some true friends. He was a man of strong likes and dislikes, of interesting mannerisms, and of some eccentricity. He was possessed of a somewhat harsh manner—a manner which veiled only from the hostile and nearsighted one of the most affectionate of natures. Brave, manly, modest, truthful, brilliant, learned, and forceful, he was a great teacher, a powerful writer, a gifted operator, a wonderful diagnostician, and an honorable man in every relation of life. "He was a man. Take him for all in all, I shall not look upon his like again."

THE SURGEON, THE PATIENT, AND THE CLINICAL DIAGNOSIS*

TECHNIC commands almost the undivided attention of the younger surgeons. It has been said that as the bride in Milton's *Comus* was arrayed in chastity so the modern surgeon is arrayed in purity; hence, postoperative infections have well-nigh disappeared.

The relative safety of operations, the dramatic features of a surgical procedure, the profound impression such a procedure has upon the patient's family and a portion of the community, and perhaps a lurking thought now and then among a few of a handsome fee, are luring younger surgeons into the exclusive path of technic.

In this age, technic and the laboratory are twins, dominant and insistent, and not unusually insolent. The bedside diagnostician must usually wait for the laboratory report and a favored diagnostic method without the laboratory study is surgical exploration. One who explores habitually is like Mr. Micawber seeking wealth and in momentary expectation of something turning up. Often, of course, exploration is demanded.

All emergencies are in the imperative mood and the present tense. To delay in order to obtain reports of the roentgenologist, who may not be accessible until some hour of the next day; of the hematologist and the bacteriologist, who may be on a journey, perhaps will mean an unnecessary fatality. I believe thoroughly in having *proper* laboratory studies made and by proper I mean when there is necessity and when there is time for them.

---

* A number of years ago I presented a paper on this topic which was published in the *Pennsylvania Medical Journal*. The two articles are similar but not identical. In this paper, I quote myself at times. Such quotations may mean scantiness of mental resource but may also be due to profound conviction. If one believes, he must preach and repeat. The great Carlyle did so often, surely an insect may. Reprint from *Surgery, Gynecology, and Obstetrics*, October, 1929. Copyright, 1929, by Surgical Pub. Co. of Chicago.

It is true that at times a certainly accurate diagnosis, that is to say a diagnosis as to details, may be impossible without exploration or laboratory aids. It is possible, for instance, to diagnose dislocations, most fractures, cerebral compression, and many other conditions without laboratory or x-ray help. It is very difficult today to force the younger hospital surgeons to submit a diagnosis of a fracture until they have x-ray pictures. In the abdomen it may be quite impossible for the surgeon to be certain as to the exact nature of the lesion but he can be certain if there is an acute abdominal calamity. Again the x-ray is not always certain. This is the case in some fractures of the vertebrae, in some cases of gallstones, in stone in the ureter (which may be confused with a phlebolith or a calcified gland), in brain tumor (which in some doubtful cases excites a suspicion of a mental thunderstorm), and various other conditions. Nor is exploratory incision always a certain revealer of the truth. Its value depends largely on the experienced mind and the trained fingers of the operator. An inexperienced man may find nothing. Even an experienced man may at times be disappointed and find nothing to explain the situation.

The late Prof. J. Greig Smith, of University College, Bristol, said many wise things, among them the following:

"There is no doubt that a good deal of rashness and a certain amount of incompetence is sought to be concealed by the practice of exploratory incision. No incision ought to be simply exploratory and at the utmost it ought to be ultimately diagnostic in a case of extreme doubt and difficulty. . . . The exploratory incision of the skilled surgeon is extremely different from that of the tyro. Where the former may make a correct diagnosis in 99 out of 100 cases, the latter will fail over his tenth case; but he may not conclude that the justification of exploration is assured simply because he is in doubt in this case. Perhaps surgeons of large experience are somewhat to blame for so freely speaking of this tentative procedure as being frequently justifiable and necessary. What is justifiable in their experienced hands may not be so in the hands of the less experienced men. Before submitting our patient to what after all is a serious operation and a trying illness we ought again and again to return to the examination of the disease, read and re-read the exhaustive history and decide only after having done this. At different examinations the mind focuses its attention on different points and in different directions and each examination may give us new information."*

It is true that at times a complete and accurate diagnosis is impossible without an exploratory incision, but even in such a case a diagnosis can be made of an acute condition requiring immediate operation or of a chronic lesion requiring exploration for complete elucidation and treatment. The diagnosis is, of course, in every case the foundation of prognosis and treatment.

In striving to identify the condition, the surgeon should grasp all the physiologic deviations and endeavor to visualize the anatomy of the region, the situation and extent of the lesion, and the picture of the pathologic process. The surgeon himself must do this. The investigation is not to be delegated. The moral responsibility is on the surgeon in charge and he must not be lazily or carelessly indifferent to his responsibility and must not shrink from it because of fear or try to evade it because of doubt of himself. If he doubts himself he has chosen the wrong calling in life. To operate simply and only because a pathologist recommends it or a colleague advises it is an evasion of personal surgical responsibility due to laziness, indifference, ignorance, or moral cowardice. All recommendations from consultants and all laboratory reports must be studied and judged by the surgeon without a trace of prejudice. Such a grave personal responsibility cannot be laid upon the shoulders of another, no matter how broad those shoulders may be. Needless hesitation and delay in rendering a decision as to the diagnosis and treatment is abandonment of duty by the general when the battle has begun. His decision should be prompt and final. He may be in entire agreement with the consultant but he should never go solely upon the opinion of any other person, however prominent or persuasive that person may be.

* *Abdominal Surgery* by Prof. J. Greig Smith.

The surgeon must see to it that his own shoulders bear the burden, for a surgeon's shoulders, by study and experience, in the words of the late Prof. Joseph Pancoast, must become broad enough to bear the burden. This is a peremptory mandate and in it is a proof of the dignity of our calling. If one cannot or will not assume the full responsibility cast upon him by the personal trust of the patient, he belongs in some other calling and the trials and triumphs of the surgeon are not for him.

Of course, I do not mean that the surgeon should disregard the opinions of consultants. He should give such opinions full and respectful attention particularly if they do not agree with his own opinions. In every case when necessary and when there is time to obtain them, the reports from the chemical, pathologic, and x-ray laboratories must be obtained; and these, with the opinion of consultations, will be studied and weighed before the final decision, which is and must be made by the surgeon in charge. A consultation is a great comfort and a decided support and it often furnishes extremely valuable suggestions. Responsibility is lessened when a colleague shares it. A family is soothed by a consultation and, should things go wrong, the acerbity of criticism is blunted. A surgical consultation resembles a council of war, but the surgeon may do as General Grant did after a council of war, proceed in accordance with his own opinions and against the advice of his consultants. In doing such a thing, however, remember Davy Crockett's words, "Be sure you are right and *then* go ahead."

A very young surgeon, laboring under mental growing pains, may oppose or actually resent a request for a consultation, believing that a family desire for one is an implied criticism of him or that a suggestion from him for a consultation would be regarded by the family as a confession of incompetence. A very ignorant man is apt to oppose a consultation because he fears exposure before a wise and learned man. Such a coward, it is true, guards himself but he does so by sacrificing his patient. A man dominated by vanity and obsessed by the conviction of his infallibility is sure to be contemptuous of the views of others and is certain to sacrifice patients to his obsessions and contempt. Such a man will not hear of a consultation. The more profound the knowledge and the greater the experience of a surgeon the stronger will be his conviction that often the best of men make mistakes and the gladder he will be to have a consultation. To insist on being the one to assume the responsibility and issue the final decision as to the diagnosis and treatment will at times bring embarrassing experiences. The surgeon may be obliged to disagree entirely with the attending physician as to the diagnosis, the treatment, or both. He may have traveled many miles expecting to operate and yet be obliged to decline to use the knife. Such a course may make medical enemies and lessen the number of referred cases, but it diminishes needless operations and saves lives. A surgeon should go to a case without any preconceived belief as to what the condition is. Preconception, prejudice, predominant ideas may prove fatal to accurate observation and reasoning, because the mind is all too apt to put the condition on the bed of Procrustes and stretch it to fit the ideas. It is all too easy to see the things we want to see or fear particularly to see. In order to make a diagnosis it is not enough to obtain from the patient one or two symptoms. The study should be complete. There should be a mental picture of the disease, a picture made up of the essential elements belonging to it. A clinical picture may be complete, it may lack one or two of the usual features or one or two elements may be exaggerated into seeming caricatures. The picture may be confused or blurred or something may be present which doesn't seem to belong there. Occasionally the picture consists only of a dim outline of a group of shadows.

Even the veriest tyro should comprehend those unusual cases in which the picture is complete. An exaggerated, blurred, or shadowy picture can be interpreted by no one but an expert and perhaps not by him. In not a few cases a positive diagnosis can be reached only by exploratory incision, by x-ray studies, by therapeutic tests, or by laboratory aids.

We have just pointed out that even an exploratory incision does not invariably make the diagnosis clear. Nevertheless, whereas comprehensive mathematical certainty as to the study of the entire organism is not possible, in most cases it is possible to make a correct diagnosis. It is seldom that a symptom could have but one possible cause, hence every possible cause of such a symptom must be thought of and sought for. *Elevated temperature* may be due to bacterial infection, auto-intoxication, hyperthyroidism, gout, uremia, leukemia, poisoning by illuminating gas or belladonna, sunstroke, malignant disease, Hodgkin's disease, syphilis or absorption of aseptic pyrogenous material from an area of traumatism, injury of the brain or cervical cord, iodoform poisoning, or other things. As a solitary symptom, elevated temperature does not suffice for a diagnosis. The mode of onset, the conduct, the course, and the associations of the fever may be conclusive. In doubtful surgical cases, the rectal temperature is the only one upon which reliance is to be placed. In many cases of severe peritonitis, the axillary temperature may be found normal or subnormal and the rectal temperature much elevated. The wider the difference between these two records the worse the situation.

A question always to be asked is this: Did the disease begin with chilly sensations, a chill, or chills? Did a chill or chills arise without other symptoms? Were chills slight or severe, regular or irregular, and were they followed by sweats? In a multitude of diseases *pain* is a striking symptom. It is necessary to know its exact situation and if it has shifted from one region to another; if it developed with or as an addition to pain in another region. Its character (is it aching, lancinating, pulsating, shooting, or dull); if it came on suddenly or gradually; if it was at first trivial and became progressively worse. We ask if it is intense or moderate. Is it continuous and steady, continuous with exacerbations or remissions, or is it intermittent? Is its position fixed or shifting? Does it follow a nerve trajectory? Does it arise only on motion or pressure or is it present even when at rest? Is it accompanied by tenderness or rigidity? Is there nausea and does vomiting take place? Is the temperature elevated? Is the pulse accelerated and what is its character? In determining the exact situation of pain, have the patient place his hand or a finger upon the spot so as to avoid a mistake. Make every effort to determine which organ, viscus, or structure is the cause of pain. The sudden cessation of violent pain, if not obtained by opiates, may mean the relief of a pathologic condition, for instance, the release of strangulated hernia or a twist of the sigmoid, but it may be a most ominous sign, significant of gangrene, as in certain cases of appendicitis or intestinal obstruction.

In estimating the reality, persistence, and intensity of pain, study the *face*. For instance, in acute peritonitis, the face is set and contorted. The upper lip is raised, exposing some of the teeth. There is an expression of the greatest anxiety, the tips of the ears, the lips, and even the rest of the face may be cyanosed. Fothergill pointed out that in pain, not due to peritonitis, there is a marked twitching of the muscles about the eyes and the upper lip. When a person has been a long sufferer from pain there is a heaviness and fulness about the eyes, the brows are contracted, the angles of the mouth droop, and the expression is utterly weary and hopeless. The expression of the face in children is extremely important. Professor Hobart A. Hare* says: "It is not uncommon for an expression to pass over the face of a child while sleeping when suffering from pain, which begins with a smile and ends with a drawing-in of the corners of the mouth, an expression somewhat like that seen on the face of a waking child when it seems to be in doubt as whether to laugh or cry. Whether asleep or awake a child in pain, if not crying, has a pinched look about its nose and mouth and sometimes some idea of the seat of pain may be gained by the part of the face which is drawn. When pain is in the head, the forehead is apt to be wrinkled into a frown; if the nose is pinched and drawn, it is said to show that the pain is in the chest; and if the upper lip is raised, the pain is probably felt in the belly."

The face, of course, may indicate many things besides pain, for instance, alcoholism, the opium habit, tetanus, strychnine poisoning, tic douloureux, jaundice (the white of the eye and skin being yellow), anemia, cachexia of cancer, hyperthyroidism,

* *Symptoms in the Diagnosis of Diseases.*

hypothyroidism, menstruation, edema, Bright's disease, mouth-breathing from adenoids, acromegaly, paralysis of the facial nerve, etc. In shock, there is deadly pallor; in most cases of advancing peritonitis, cyanosis—in poisoning by coal tar products, cyanosis—in exhausting diseases, pallor and emaciation. Cancer imparts a straw-yellow color to the skin, contrasting with the pearly white conjunctivae. This contrast at once indicates the diagnosis from jaundice. In lobar pneumonia the face is flushed and the flush is usually accentuated on one cheek. In cardiac disease there may be pallor or cyanosis with distended nostrils and gasping respiration. In advanced sepsis the dull and apathetic face is ashy pale or dusky, the lips mutter in delirium, and the teeth are covered with sordes. Bodily weakness, marked loss of flesh, rapid pulse, polyuria, hematuria, disorder of the reflexes, diarrhea, spitting of blood, cough, melena, constipation, ascites, indigestion, nausea, vomiting, headache, motor paralysis, analgesia, hemorrhoids, may be due to various causes.

The mode of onset, character, severity, duration of the disease, and the apparent cause help us to mark the significance of any of the above symptoms.

An isolated symptom is very seldom as valuable diagnostically as a symptom group. Pathognomonic symptoms are extremely unusual. The disease may fail to exhibit some symptoms regarded as belonging to it. Such an absence constitutes a negative symptom.

A victim of brain tumor may not have choking of the optic disks (for instance in glioma, in slow growing tumor, and, for a considerable time, in tumor of the pituitary gland). A patient with cancer of the stomach may have no pain. An individual laboring under pyogenic infection may have no elevation of temperature, and a man with peritonitis may have a slow pulse. Leukocytosis may be absent when pus is present (if the defenses of the system are failing or if the pus is encompassed by adhesions). A negative Wassermann reaction is not uncommon in tertiary syphilis and a positive reaction may only be developed after the inauguration of specific treatment. In appendicitis, if the appendix is in the pelvis, there may be for a time no abdominal tenderness or ridigity. Abdominal rigidity may be absent if the appendix is tucked up back of or outside of the cecum, a condition the late Dr. Joseph Price compared to a dog with his tail between his legs. Rigidity will be absent in appendicitis if the belly is much relaxed from repeated pregnancies, if considerable morphine has been given, and perhaps if an ice-bag has been employed.

Hare points out that valvular heart disease may produce no symptoms until the circulation is failing and that in a lung that is engorged there may be no râles. A negative symptom is often very important and may suggest failure of physiologic reaction, acquired immunity, a complication, the previous administration of a drug, or the simultaneous existence of another disease.

Grave myocardial failure may cause the disappearance of heart murmurs. Morphine may arrest pain. The ice-bag lessens abdominal inflammatory pain. Gangrene halts pain. Sometimes a clinical picture contains more than seems to belong to it and perhaps something thought to belong to a different disease. Such a condition is due to a complication, a predisposition, a drug habit, the previous administration of a drug by a physician, or the simultaneous existence of another disease. When an inflamed appendix is adherent to the ureter, there may be hematuria and pain like that of renal colic, although, of course, hematuria in a case of appendicitis may be due purely to nephritis. In the first form of hematuria the blood comes from only one ureter, in the second form it comes from both. Such determination can be made only by means of the cystoscope. A patient who has been anesthetized by ether or chloroform, but particularly by chloroform, may develop jaundice and acid intoxication. Abdominal operation even when carried out in a region well away from the stomach may be followed by vomiting of blood. When a man with piles develops intestinal obstruction, we know that the obstruction is not due to the piles but is due to some lesion, probably cancer, higher up in the intestinal canal. Obstinate insomnia during the course of a disease or an injury, if not due to pain or a psychoneurosis, demands an inquiry as to whether the patient is an alcoholic, or a habitué of morphia or heroin who has been deprived of his usual doses. Some persons are so strongly predisposed to delirium that it arises from very trivial elevations of temperature. Delirium from slight fever is common in children and in the aged.

Just as certain persons resemble each other, so may certain diseases. Typhoid fever with severe abdominal pain may resemble acute appendicitis. Chronic appendicitis, duodenal ulcer, gallbladder disease, gastric ulcer, chronic pancreatitis may resemble each other. Acute hemorrhagic pancreatitis has been mistaken for intestinal obstruction, although the horrible pain of the former condition, as pointed out by Lord Moynihan, should prevent the mistake. The resemblance may be a mere suggestion of a likeness. It may be first more definite but on investigation will be found to lack certain features. The resemblance may be very strong, in fact, it may be so close as to lead to the gravest diagnostic uncertainty. A disease unfortunately without any usual resemblance to another disease may take on such a resemblance for a brief time. Pleural pneumonia does not usually bear any resemblance to acute appendicitis, but pleural pneumonia of the right lower lobe may be thought for a time in the beginning to be appendicitis because of the abdominal pain, tenderness, and rigidity which may occur for a time in pneumonia and may lead to a diagnosis being made of acute appendicitis.

Sometimes a disease acts like an ingenious criminal and disguises itself so as to imitate another disease or at least so as to escape recognition entirely. Just as a person may have a different appearance at different times, so may a disease at different times and also in different persons. Unfortunately, there is no Bertillon system of measurements and there are no finger prints to aid us in recognizing disease. Nevertheless, despite complications, disguises, and resemblances, it is usually possible to identify the nature and seat of the disease.

Sometimes a doubtful diagnosis may be cleared up by the state of the consciousness, the occurrence of fits and their character, the posture of the patient in bed, or his gait while walking. Even the odor of the breath may help.

Failure in diagnosis makes symptomatic treatment the only resource and symptomatic treatment is haphazard, indefinite, and frequently hazardous. In fever from an infection, what good could possibly come from lowering the temperature with anti-pyretic drugs? Who can deny that fever is beneficial by destroying the bacteria or toxins? By lowering temperature great harm may be done. It is as true of sepsis as it is of scarlet fever that the most dangerous cases are those with a low temperature.

A correct diagnosis is essential for correct treatment. Diagnosis is in part a science and in part an art. As science it employs all known facts and accepted principles in the solution of a problem. It is in part an art because the surgeon must know how to observe, how to examine, how to utilize facts, and how to employ principles. Diagnosis possesses enormous interest and is of vital importance. It is the greatest and most serious of all games, a game in which limb or life is frequently the stake. Its problems absorb the trained seeker for surgical truth as the problems of an obscure crime absorb the trained criminal investigator. On the proper solution of the puzzle the future or even the life of the patient may depend. Diagnosis is no job for a dull, callous, or lazy man.

In the making of a diagnosis the history must be developed and all morbid phenomena must be observed with accuracy. The history includes the history of the family, of the person, and of the disease. Heredity may be of interest and importance—as in developmental defects, suspected syphilis of early life, neoplasms, tuberculous disease, hemophilia, hereditary telangiectasis, mental disease, spontaneous fractures, etc. The personal history is of extreme importance. Is there a history of syphilis, tuberculosis, cancer, antecedent febrile trouble, etc.? What are the habits of the patient as to drugs, tobacco, alcohol, etc.? In what way did the disease begin and where did it seem to be located? What were the symptoms and what has been its course? To what does the patient attribute the condition? Is it continuous, remittent, or intermittent? Is it getting better or worse? What has been done for it and by whom? The latter is decidedly an important query.

It is wise to check up on the patient's statements by obtaining a statement, if possible, from the family physician, but if that is impossible, from a member of the family or a friend. In a young child our only source of information is the physician, a nurse, or a member of the family. If the patient is mentally affected, we must rely for his history on others rather than on himself.

The occupation of the patient may be the key to the diagnosis. For instance, in the keratoses of a radiologist; housemaid's knee; miner's elbow; arsenic workers' neuritis; phosphorus workers' necrosis; painter's paralysis; chauffeur's fracture; mercury workers' salivation; anthrax as seen in the woolsorter, the worker in hides or the junk dealer; the chrome sores of leather workers, etc. Even his sport should be considered. For instance, in the buttock bursa of the rower, lawn tennis arm, rider's knee, etc.

If a surgeon would question a patient well he must use as much skill as a lawyer requires to question a witness. Truths may have to be fished from floods of loquacity or dragged from depths of taciturnity. To listen for a moment or two when a patient is being questioned, will enable us to determine not only the caliber and equipment of the patient, but also of the questioner. Haphazard questions are useless and often harmful. Questioning must be purposive, systematic, and logical. Repetitions are needless and often irritating to the patient. Sometimes it is well to be alone with the patient and to be very tactful when asking certain questions, for instance, as to a drug habit, masturbation, sexual perversion, alcoholism, or venereal disease. A sudden fool question stupidly propounded may result in violent rage, sullen silence, evasion, or a lie. One should not ask a clergyman when he last had gonorrhea, or an unmarried girl how long since she has been pregnant. The clergyman may be guilty and the girl unfortunate but a gentler examination would have been more apt to have elicited truth. Lies are common. As Prince Hal says: "Some lies are as gross as mountains, open, palpable," but even the ablest diagnostician may be deceived by lies.

A paranoiac, a melancholiac, a paretic, or a victim of cerebral syphilis may make absurd statements, varying them and altering them under questioning. Such fabrications are delusional. A man who has had a head injury perhaps long before may be deliberately untruthful or he may exaggerate unconsciously, mistaking his imaginings for realities, as in Korsakoff's psychosis. At times lies are difficult to detect and at times detection is impossible. Litigants often lie, so do the victims of venereal disease, so do pregnant girls, so do masturbators, so do menstruating women and women going through the menopause. Hysterical women, opium eaters, cocaine users, heroin addicts, alcoholic inebriates, and epileptics lie freely and often needlessly. Habitual criminals are habitual liars and even in illness are prone to exaggerate and pervert. Some lies are prompted by the wish to become important or by the desire for sympathy. For instance, those of hysterical women who lie from an egotism which leads to the assumption of a leading heroic or a martyr's rôle. A not uncommon cause of falsehood, particularly among women, is the desire to worry or injure a person. A man pretended desperate sickness in order to punish a wife for nagging him. Another man pretended to have received an internal injury in order to provoke the wrath of a hated foreman. Children are apt to tell the most amazing untruths. An old man's statements are often unreliable particularly because his memory for recent events may be much confused. I would hardly go so far as Falstaff who said, "Old men are addicted to this vice of lying." Hypochondriacs invent diseases and morbidly magnify real phenomena. The hysterical patient imitates unconsciously and so deceives. The boaster lies about his condition and his case in expectation of receiving a reputation for fortitude and heroism. A man who fell down when drunk claimed to have been injured rescuing a child from in front of an automobile and stirred the police into searching for the child and the car. Neurotics are very apt to make false statements. They may misinterpret real sensations or invent pains and disabilities. A child may lie to avoid school or punishment and many persons lie to avoid work, domestic discord, jury duty, in order to get in a hospital to collect accident or disability insurance or to obtain money by a suit at law. The trained army surgeon and the experienced naval surgeon are always on the watch for shirkers and become remarkably skilful in detecting them. Some patients lie to avoid a subpoena in a court case or to cover up drunkenness. Sometimes the family lies. They may do so in an injury involving litigation. They are almost certain to do so to cover up domestic trouble. They will usually do so in regard to epilepsy and mental disease. The supposed disgrace of insanity and epilepsy leads to absurd or shadowy claims of causal head injury in the far past. A statement which is part a lie is even more confusing than a complete lie.

> "A lie which is all a lie may be met and fought with outright,
> But a lie which is part a truth is a harder matter to fight."

Observation, accurate and complete, is imperative. This requires a master's knowledge of disease and injuries, interest in the problem, close observation, knowing how to observe and question, and the ability to obtain clear registrations upon the memory. Accurate notes must be taken down at the time of the examination.

In Sterne's *Tristram Shandy* we find set forth a threefold cause for "obscurity and confusion" in a man's mind. "Dull organs, dear sir, in the first place. Secondly, a slight and transient impression made by the object and the said organs are dull, and thirdly, a memory like unto a sieve not able to retain what it has received." Dull organs in a patient or a doctor constitute formidable obstacles. "Against stupidity even the gods fight in vain."

Bedside notes constitute a record which is a lasting memory and may be most important in the scientific and at times in the medicolegal aspect of the case.

Some men have an aptitude for the art of observation. Some have not. But no man is an accurate observer by instinct. He can become an accurate observer only by long training. Maudsley, in his brilliant and learned *Pathology of Mind*, says: "True observation comes not by instinct but is gained painfully by training."

A person with an aptitude for observation can train the power more quickly and to a higher degree than can one whose observa-

16

tion reactions are dull. One observes most easily and accurately those things in which he is interested and which he knows best. Suppose a group of persons were thrown together by accident. Each one studies the other. The shoemaker at once notices the shoes, the tailor the clothes, the barber the hair, the dentist the teeth, and the hatter the hats. "Lazarus has rightly called to mind what is told by the pious Charles von Schmidt concerning the clever boy who lies under a tree and recognizes the condition of every passerby according to what he says, which means what he sees. 'What fine lumber,' 'Good morning, carpenter.' . . . 'What magnificent bark,' 'Good morning, tanner.' . . . 'What beautiful branches,' 'Good morning, painter.' " (See *Criminal Psychology* by Hans Gross.) This significant story shows how effective is observation.

A competent specialist will at once observe phenomena which are in his line, which a general practitioner or a specialist in another line may not note at all.

Few men are universal observers as was Joseph Bell, of Edinburgh. Because a man observes quickly things relating to his own calling is no sign that he will be adept in observing things relating to other callings.

A woman is greatly interested in dress and a glance of but a moment enables her to describe accurately every visible garment worn by another woman; and yet she may not be able to describe intelligently anything else in life. A woman will give a description of the guests at a wedding and of the dress each one wore so comprehensively and detailed as to seem uncanny but then a woman's real profession is matrimony, and dress is a powerful aid to matrimony, hence her interest in dress and her success in describing it.

A person not interested in diagnosis is certain to be a poor diagnostician. Many persons are devoid absolutely of the power of correct observation. They go through life seeing nothing fully, accurately, or in detail; they know things only by their salient features and many things they do not really see at all. Such a person is a very unreliable witness in court, is often sure that what did not happen did happen and uncertain as to what he did see. He would make a better copying clerk than he would a surgeon.

Many sensations are never registered or rather are faintly registered and do not become impressions in the brain. Slight impressions do not give rise to ideas and cannot be recalled as memories. We have really observed when impressions have been registered and have given rise to ideas.

During a long period a person may fail really to see things with which he is in daily contact. Edridge Green in his treatise on *Memory* gives an example of such failure. He passed to his students the leaf of a tree. Not one could identify it. It was the leaf of the common plane tree of the streets of London. Every student had passed plane trees hundreds of times but no student had truly observed them.

The surgeon must carefully train and cultivate the power of observation. In most men the power may be greatly enhanced by constant exercise. Robert Houdin, the famous French prestidigitateur, is an example of one who trained his powers of observation so highly that they came to constitute a faculty which acted with marvelous speed and precision. While walking in the street he could, after a simple passing glance into a show window, name and describe nearly everything exposed there for sale. In this we see a wonderful combination of close attention, rapid observation, vivid registration, and faultless memory.

Few men can become Houdins, but almost any man, unless absolutely stupid, utterly careless, or extremely lazy, may become a reasonably good observer. Every good diagnostician is a careful observer though some are better than others. A really good clinician sees at a glance the obvious things that a lesser man descries only after prolonged study or perhaps does not discover at all. A considerable part of the education of a child should be the development of the powers of observation. Children are natural observers but with the general idiocy which characterizes so many of the proceedings of modern life we carefully strive to take out of them this valuable faculty. In modern education observation should occupy a great place, even if so placing it makes necessary

the sacrifice of the teaching of many facts and of some of the
narrow specialties.

Our great aims should be how to observe, how to visualize the
disease and its seat, how to study, what to study, and how to
think. Most children visualize naturally. Tell them a story and
they see the gnomes and the giants, the fairies and the goblins.
We are doing our best to take this great faculty out of them.

The real method of observation was set forth by Huxley in
1880. He called it the method of Zadig. Zadig was Voltaire's
philosopher who observed many apparently trivial things and
from such indications reached conclusions so striking and unexpected as to cause his hearers to attribute them to supernatural
influence or to roguery.

In modern literature we find a similar method employed by
Edgar Allen Poe's *Dupin* and by Sir Arthur Conan Doyle's
Sherlock Holmes. Those who read Dumas will remember how
D'Artagnan searched the field in which the duel had been fought
and from a series of small indications gave to the King a descrip-
tion of exactly what happened there.

If one observes inaccurately or incompletely he will never
make a correct diagnosis unless he blunders on it or makes a successful guess.

Benjamin Franklin said: "Want of care does more damage
than want of knowledge." Sir William Gull said: "We make
more mistakes from not looking than from not knowing." A so-
called "diagnosis by intuition" is simply a jump to a conclusion
after observing a symptom or a symptom group. It is seldom
correct, and I pointed out years ago that it is usually only a rapid
method of reaching a wrong conclusion.

As Professor Stengel has said: "An occasional apparent hit
by this method may do great harm to a group of assistants or a
class of students by leading them to believe that the more toilsome method is not necessary. The latter plan is less dramatic
but far and away more certain and valuable."

Some intelligent men never become good diagnosticians. The
incapacity may be due to deficient training, lack of interest, lazi-

ness, the use of poor methods, unwillingness to take pains, dominance of a temperament, the riding of a hobby, chasing the elusive will o' the wisp of imperfect and unsound knowledge.

Men are prone to think they see the things which they expect to see, wish to see, or fear to see.

Predominant ideas may exclude or they blur the optical images which, were they admitted to consciousness, would give rise to ideas which would be registered as memories. Even the things seen may be seen incorrectly or incompletely, and things which are not there may be described. Similarities are recognized more certainly than differences unless the differences are very conspicuous.

Reid in *Principles of Heredity* says: "As is well known we are apt to overlook considerable differences especially in unfamiliar forms unless our powers of observation have been trained by experience. Thus we are able to detect most differences between people of our race, but Chinamen are much alike to us. The ordinary man hardly knows one sheep from another—the shepherd knows every member of his flock."

Fashion and custom in surgery may control a diagnostic decision. One is apt to find many instances of a disease which is the fashion. We know how often appendicitis is diagnosticated when it does not exist, and how commonly nephroptosis is pointed out as a cause of neurasthenia when in reality there is no movability of the kidney beyond normal.

Some who love paradoxes are prone to have contempt for the probable, they always seek for the improbable, the unusual, and the bizarre.

A neurotic surgeon is particularly prone to obsessions, and enthusiasm is as dangerous as prejudice. A good portion of skepticism plus reasonable accessibility to new impressions is the proper mental atmosphere which favors clear judgment. Some men labor under morbid doubt. Such a man says, "It may be this or it might be that." He brings little comfort to a family physician and none at all to a patient. A surgeon always strives to form a definite opinion (although to do so may be impossible) and if he forms one he will, of course, always have the moral courage to state it.

A diagnostician may fail because of ignorance, stupidity, inability to concentrate the attention, abject subservience to authority, love of new ways and new things, unreasonable worship of old ways and old things, inability to recognize differences and to reject apparent similarities, mental dishonesty, impairment of sight, smell, hearing, or touch, or the use of improper methods. A man who is usually an excellent observer may at times become a poor one. Such a failure may be due to illness, a sleepless night, tire, worry, carelessness which is a child of overconfidence, preoccupation, dropping into routine (as busy dispensary men sometimes do) or attempting to make a brilliant "intuitive diagnosis." Bodily tire and mental fatigue make close attention and observation all but impossible.

Logic is described by Sheil as the science of evidence. In order to reason correctly a logical mind is a necessary instrument. It is necessary for the diagnostician to reason correctly on the information furnished by the history and by the examination. The surgeon must analyze, measure, compare values, separate the casual from the causal, the transitory from the permanent, that which is guessed from that which is known. He must cast out absolutely what Junius called "false facts." Surgical sea serpents and base scientific coin are to be rejected. In reaching a conclusion the surgeon calls upon the memories of his reading and his personal experience in order to compare them, contrasting them with the case which is being studied. Even a good observer will make great mistakes if he is devoid of the logical faculty. Even the best of logicians will make miserable failures if he doesn't possess or doesn't use the faculty of observation.

James Berry in his admirable *Manual of Surgical Diagnosis* says: "Surgical diagnosis ought not to consist, as some students imagine that it does, in the mere fitting of a name to a diseased condition. It should be much more than this, it should aim in ascertaining as exactly as possible and in what respect and to what extent the patient's condition deviates from that of perfect health. In other words, it should comprise not only the nomenclature of the disease but also the degree and extent of that disease."

When one endeavors to practice surgery as advised in this article, he assumes a great responsibility, and how great a responsibility it is. Vast is the responsibility borne by a conscientious practitioner of medicine or surgery. A very great writer says: "One can fancy how awful the responsibility must be to a conscientious man, how cruel the feeling that he has given the wrong remedy or thought it may have been possible to do better, how harassing the sympathy of the survivors if the case is unfortunate, how immense the delight of victory." These solemn words, as the reader knows, were written by William Makepeace Thackeray.

BEHIND THE OFFICE DOORS. SURGICAL ORATION BEFORE THE OHIO STATE MEDICAL ASSOCIATION*

STANDING before this great audience as the recipient of a flattering invitation I am apprehensive of failure. I am afraid you have made a mistake. You are the victims of the poor judgment of the committee which has gone to Philadelphia for a speaker, forgetting that reputations, like glowworms, often seem brighter from afar. I am so afraid of being regarded as an impostor that I am as miserable as a man who takes at one time boils, a toothache, a bad cold, and religion. You are going to partake of a repast as unsubstantial as that of the moon men in Lucian's history, that is, you are to dine off the odor of a roast frog's leg and drink air squeezed into goblets.

In olden times, when theologians were wont to gather with great pomp and circumstance, it was the custom in such an assemblage to appoint a *filius terrae* (Andrew McPhail). It was his duty to suppress pride, vainglory, and vanity. To hold men down to a level of earthly truths and obligation. To keep all the dignitaries reminded that worldly greatness is transitory and deceptive; that human glory is trivial and brief; that the proper mental attitude combines humbleness, resignation, and hope; and that even the greatest ecclesiastic is only a man. Quoting Andrew McPhail I say that, "in assuming the congenial character of *filius terrae*, or child of the earth," to this distinguished audience, "I shall neither resent the taunt nor disclaim the credit that this self-election to the humble office of speaking as a fool has been done with perspicacity."

Being a child of the earth I shall not be expected to describe great scientific achievements, to point out epoch-making surgical discoveries, to tell of the marvels of this age of progress, or to

* The Address in Surgery before the Ohio State Medical Society, May 10, 1911. Reprint from the *Ohio State Medical Journal*, July, 1911.

prophesy of the wonders that are soon to be. Beyond doubt
wonders loom on the horizon. The first few hesitating words of
truth have, as yet, but scarce been lisped by the baby lips of
Science. But I must leave it to others to speak of these things;
to write the history and to cast the horoscope. I must *not* join
in the

> "Acclamation of self-praising, self-admiring,
> At every mile run faster, oh! the glorious, glorious age."

But shall ask instead,

> "If we work our soul as worthily as our iron,
> And if angels shall reward us at the goal of pilgrimage."

I am addicted to the luxury or, if you will, to the vice of
musing. In silent hours of isolation one may for a time fly on
wings of Memory and Fancy through an ampler heaven than that
"in which the Nations sun themselves." I am aware that the
habit of dreamy speculation is often an excuse for laziness; and
that, as a state of mind, it is regarded as most reprehensible
by all purely practical mortals. It excites vast indignation
among all who find the exalted end and aim of life, in buying
at five cents and selling at six. It stirs the antipathy of every
follower of what Carlyle calls the "full-belly philosophy." A follower of this faith devotes all his allotted earthly hours to eating, drinking, sleeping, pleasuring, and light muscular exercise.
Yet in spite of expected protests from the eminently respectable slaves of convention I dare to maintain that in such a mood
one may seize not only harmony and beauty, but strength and
truth, and may develop the flabby muscles of the mind and fit
them to swing the sledge of Thought! The purely practical man
deals only with the obvious, the inevitable, the evidently possible. The man who ponders and muses bodies forth conjectures
and dreams of what men regard as impossible. He, by the magic
alchemy of thought, may make probable, or at least possible,
the thing supposed to be impossible, and then the practical
mind forges the possibility of yesterday into the achieved cer-

tainty of today. Without winged thought the speculation could
not have come at all for test and trial, to the purely practical
man. He would never have speculated about anything. He
could not found a brilliant hypothesis or a striking theory, though
he were to slave in laboratory and library through half a century
of toil and study. The history of progress is the attainment of
the supposedly impossible. The instigation of every discovery
was first a hope, an aspiration, a fancy, a guess, a dream, in the
mind of a single man. The Baconian method clears up doubts,
exposes falsehoods, proves truths, but does not make discoveries.
Before a discovery can be made the scientific imagination of
someone must flash into Auroral hues. The progess of humanity
has come from the optimist and he is the dreamer of dreams.
In these days we are getting too busy to try to really think.
As a rule we only think we think.

> "Though many things and mighty are fathered in the West,
> The ancient peace has vanished before today's unrest,
> For how among their striving, their gold, their lust, their drink
> Shall men find space for dreaming or take the time to think?"

All over the world we are trying to teach men to be discoverers. We train them to investigate by the Baconian method. We
can so instruct men that they can carry out an indicated research, but we can never teach a man the imagination which
must picture conditions and found the hypothesis to be put to
the rigid test of experiment. You may easily educate a man to
test a hypothesis. You can never educate a man to *found* a brilliant one. A real discoverer is the poet of science and like the
poet he is born, not made. Who would think of making poets
by teaching men the mechanism of verse, and yet we try to
make men discoverers by teaching them the mechanism of test-
ing hypotheses. Out of 1000 graduates perhaps one is mentally
able to discover, and yet each one of the other 999 was educated
as though he were the man. The scientific imagination is a splendid faculty. Of those who have it few are able to regulate it,
control it, guide it and test its productions. Great and fortu-

nate is that man who has a scientific imagination linked with the knowledge, honesty, capacity, and ability to put his hypotheses to rigid tests. He is one of the greatest of men. He is an asset of science. He is a gracious gift to humanity. When we find him we should cherish him, endow him, give him every facility, and study all he puts forth. Claude Bernard was such a man, so was Pasteur, so is Lister. Right in this city you have a brilliant example of the investigator and discoverer in the person of the distinguished surgeon, Dr. George Crile.

I would not for a moment imply that my musings are important because those of Bernard were and those of Crile are. I know full well that I cannot be a discoverer. I have no illusions on that point. But at least my musings do no harm but to my own pocketbook, and surely I, too, may hop about and flap my little wings of fancy. I may even gaze into the distant land of Poetry, as a cat may look at a king. Please regard me as the disreputable alley cat looking longingly from afar into the imperial domain of Poetry. *There* feelings count more than dollars—emotions more than calculations—ideals are followed—conventions are repudiated—generosity is on a pedestal and avarice is in the gutter—some people and many things condemned by the world are honored—some people and many things honored by the world are condemned—there even the roadside puddle reflects the constellated glories of the firmament—there is heard but vaguely the roaring fremitus of selfish men—there even the somber pine trees sing anthems beneath the silent stars.

Sitting behind the closed doors of my office I am like a worm in a cocoon, wrapped in a web of thought, but alas! few, if any, of the threads are of silk. I am here to unravel before you a tangle of threads. The threads are numerous and my lens can get but two or three of them into focus.

Life used to be larger and simpler than now. It is now infinitely complex because it is composed of a legion of separate and often conflicting interests. We live in a mechanical age of narrow specialties. This is true of all trades and all professions. A man is trained highly in a few activities and the other possibilities of his nature wither from neglect. How many men do we see who exhibit

> "One too favored faculty or sense,
>   O'er fostered at the other's vast expense."

For instance, some surgeons are great operators, but neither diagnosticians nor therapeutists.

The work of the humblest individual helps to make up the sum total of the lifework of the world. He who devotes himself purely to a narrow part of a great subject may forget this. If he should forget it, then the human element goes out of his work and with it the high purpose which must instigate all *good* work. He becomes narrow, tends to settle into a rut, and magnifies his own branch to the level of the great subject of which it is a small part. The house built by such a man has only one good side. The medical specialist who is first of all a physician and after that a specialist, takes up his particular line of work because of special aptitude, unusual opportunity, or remarkable training. He is one of the broadest and most useful of men. The man who proclaims himself a specialist without special ability and training, and who enters the work purely for gain or position, becomes one of the narrowest of men, and would make his branch, which is a mere little finger, greater than the loins of the science of medicine. He dwells in a cave. All he sees of the universe is the small circle of sky visible through the little opening of his abode. But he thinks he sees the entire universe. He is like a car conductor who knows of no place off his own route. No man should dare to follow exclusively a specialty until he has had the broadest kind of training in general practice. Such training is particularly necessary to a surgeon. During his early years of study and effort he cultivates a knowledge of surgery, works in private and in the hospital, helps an older man in operations, but gets his income largely from general practice. A training in general practice is invaluable. It broadens a man immensely. It gives him knowledge he holds for life. It increases enormously his diagnostic ability, his prognostic accuracy, his therapeutical sense, his knowledge of foods, hygiene, and people, and his power to control and handle patients.

No man can begin professional life as a full-fledged surgeon. No conscientious man will try to. One can be properly equipped for a surgical career only by years of general practice, the broadest reading in all branches, a profound special study of surgery, and daily work as a surgical assistant. If a surgeon tries to start near the top he is sure to fail. He does not know and never learns the rudiments. You remember that during the war between the States many politicians were made generals. One of these generals had failed miserably and was the object of virulent criticism. General Grant said: "Don't be too hard on the poor fellow; it's not his fault. He began life as a brigadier-general." A man can't begin life as a hospital surgeon and a professor of surgery, any easier than as a brigadier-general.

When a man, determined to follow surgery, has really become well equipped for the duties and responsibilities of a surgical career, he should abandon general practice. No surgeon should continue to treat medical patients, when he is well launched as a surgeon. He lacks time and opportunity to keep thoroughly informed in both branches. He can't keep abreast of the times in both. If he is busy in general work he will always be so tired that he will not study enough surgery to be the man he ought to be, or he will be so occupied in surgery that he can't study medicine. It is unjust to patients and physicians that he should try to practice both. Should he do so he will certainly be a failure in one branch and probably in both. When a surgeon saves a patient's life by an operation the patient has confidence in him and may want him to become the medical attendant of the family. It is his bounden duty to refuse.

In the first place he is not nearly so fit to be the family doctor as is the regular attendant, and if he pretends to be he deceives the patient. In the second place, to do so is a gross breach of trust to the family physician.

The life of a surgeon is a very hard one. It is a life of ceaseless strain. During a large part of every day his faculties are tense to the breaking point. Physical tire goes hand-in-hand with mental exhaustion. He must learn to bear the heaviest responsibility. No matter how tired he may be his judgment must be clear and accurate, his hand steady, his eye quick, his knowledge always immediately accessible. He must be calm no matter what the peril and perplexity. He must expect harsh criticism and must make his shoulders broad enough to bear the burden of injustice. He must learn thorough self-surrender and must ever bear the iron yoke of duty. Worry is not a transient guest. Her somber garments ever trail the floor. To care-worn eyes the future often stares spectrally. Yes! it is a difficult life, a life of stress and strain, and it is small wonder that surgeons as a class are not long lived.

Pneumonia, angina pectoris, Bright's disease, vascular disease are the commonest agents of dissolution. As a rule a man is in the forties before he gains a large surgical practice. Few are successful and prosperous at twenty-five, as were Liston, the first McClellan, and Syme, or at thirty-two, as was Fergusson. D. Hayes Agnew was in the fifties before he had a fairly remunerative practice. A surgeon can continue as an operator only while he retains a keen eye and a steady hand. Usually hand and eye are failing in the sixties. Hence, as a rule, a surgeon has at best only twenty-five years to make enough money for his old age and for the decent support of his family. The period of remunerative work is probably shorter in surgery than in any other profession and during this period surgeons are obliged to charge fair fees, to those who can afford to pay them. Failure to do so will mean an old age of privation and a family left with scanty means.

A crippling injury of the hand at once wipes out the career of an operator, though of course a broadly trained man can continue to practice as a pure consultant. One who elects to be an operator and only an operator puts all of his eggs in one basket and then travels a road full of pitfalls.

A surgeon's life is full of tragedy. Sometimes, in spite of every care, disaster treads upon the heels of disaster, it seems as though some malign destiny were intervening in our affairs, and one finds himself thinking of Pirogoff's essay on "Luck in Surgery," and Velpeau's superstition as to the law of three. How often does a surgeon stand by, impotent to save, and watch "beauty and anguish, walking hand in hand, the downward road to death"?

But there are compensations. The many lives saved by surgery, lives otherwise inevitably lost. The mighty aid for service given us by scientific methods: by anesthesia, antiseptics, the modern hospital, the trained nurse, the x-ray, and therapy by serums and vaccines. The *occasional* gratitude of patients. The delight of working in such a magnificent, beneficial, and progressive science as surgery; and such a wonderful and advancing art as operative surgery. In the narrow gaps between our labors, poetry and romance may bloom as flowers spring into sunlight from the crevices of a somber city wall. Noble aspirations, palpitating with life, may rest in the midst of strife and worry, as swallows nest in the grimy old house eaves of my own city.

The dusty way of the beaten track lies before us all, a weary way if we see nothing but the road. But beside the road are hedge rows and violets—beyond it are green fields, nodding grain, rustling trees, and the gleam of laughing waters—and above it are the skies; vast, blue, glistening, and eternal.

How many hours of weary waiting a young practitioner must pass in his office! Those hours may serve to make him or to mar him. They always help to determine what sort of man he is going to be. Then he should persistently study languages and all branches of medical science. Then he should read deeply of general literature. Then he should teach himself a literary style in writing, one natural to himself, and one that clearly presents ideas. Then he should learn to think, and his thoughts should be many on the greatness, the responsibilities, the obligations, and the duties of his profession. Thus he becomes a real personality, with real ideas, with definite beliefs, and with high ideals, and not a mimic, an imitation, a simulacrum, a despicable pretense.

There is danger in those inevitable dark houses of a non-recognition. The sensitive soul shrinks, falters, and perhaps fails. Brooding discontent may come and it is full of peril. Jealousy may bud, bitterness may grow, selfishness and avarice may develop. Then come low ideals, the desire for unworthy objects, mean admiration for mean things, improper professional conduct, the erection of the dollar mark into the conception of the flowing curve of faultless beauty.

Those early years of poverty drive many men out of the profession—take the highest elements out of many others—but forge the real man into greater strength and usefulness, and show him truths "as night discloses stars." There is only one thing more dangerous than early poverty and that is early wealth. The ill-effects of the first are common. The evil results of the second are almost unavoidable.

In my days of waiting for the practice that was most reluctant to come and in my later and far busier times, I reached numerous conclusions about the profession, its duties, its cares, and its rewards, few of which have had to be repudiated. Perhaps you will bear with me as I cite some of those opinions.

1. Everybody maintains that you should paddle your own canoe. In order to do this, a man will now and then be found who begs, borrows or steals, both the paddle and the canoe. A tow now and then gives a useful and most welcome rest and may save a career.

2. It is mentally profitable to burn the midnight oil, but it is a great deal more profitable financially to sell it than to burn it. You good people of Cleveland know this truth. If one seeks only wealth he had better go into business than into medicine.

3. One of the earliest discoveries made by a recent graduate is that some members of the medical profession possess marvelous powers in dealing out personal detraction and great versatility in selecting subjects for it. In a public lecture, Lisfranc referred to Dupuytren as "l'infâme du bord de l'eau," and Dupuytren spoke as follows of Lisfranc, "Que sous une enveloppe de sanglier on portrait parfois un coeur de chien couchant."

4. Many patients are as oblivious to all sense of gratitude as is a cast-iron dog to a resolution of censure, or the Sublime Porte to a demand for an indemnity. When asked to pay a bill they exhibit what Sir Thomas Browne called "four-footed manners."

5. A sensitive man, conscious of worth, finds one of his hardest trials in seeing preference given to the ignorant and unscrupulous pretender. A victim of this common tendency may find some comfort in a story of Mr. Abernethy. I will paraphrase the anecdote. John Abernethy on one occasion spoke to a wealthy quack, and said: "I am John Abernethy, surgeon, of London. I work and study constantly to know my profession, yet I must walk on my daily rounds. You, an utterly ignorant pretender, ride in a chariot and dwell in a palace: pray tell me why are these things?" And the quack said: "Mr. Abernethy, yonder is London bridge, how many people think you, cross it in a day?" Mr. Abernethy said he had no idea, "perhaps a hundred thousand." And the quack said, "And how many of them are fools? You attend the wise men and I attend the fools."

6. When a man begins practice he believes for a few months that his medical neighbors and acquaintances are all the most generous of men, because they send him to visit patients. Later, when in a thorny mood, he changes his views, because he finds out that such patients often live at the jumping-off place, or are addicted to sudden complaints demanding medical attendance at unearthly hours, or are apt to acquire delirium tremens at frequent intervals, or are complaining and censorious, or liable to sue a doctor, or have babies as frequently as is lawful, and that it never dimly dawns upon one of them to pay a single cent. He must gain comfort in such cases from Boerhaave's saying: "The poor are my best patients, for God Almighty is their paymaster." In spite of the great Dutchman's predeliction for poor patients, he somehow or other accumulated a huge fortune.

7. As one mounts in years he is apt to specialize less and less upon the purely ideal side of life. He may not be quite sure that the good die young, but he becomes entirely certain that only the young die good.

17

8. A good many men we meet in life are not trying to leave footprints in the sands of time, but instead are devoting precious energy to covering up their tracks.

9. While a young man is trying to climb up the ladder of Fame, his chief difficulty is to avoid being knocked off by older men engaged in coming down.

10. It is just as important for a man to learn what he can't do as what he can do. Each one should try to get a just estimate of his own abilities in various directions. When he does a thing badly he should learn to do it well or give it up. This applies notably to teaching and operating.

11. Jealousy of a colleague or rival is one of the meanest and most foolish of vices. Everyone has strengths and weaknesses. A colleague can certainly do some things better than I. Why hesitate to acknowledge it? Surely I can do some things better than he. The account is even. If it is not, and I acknowledge complete inferiority by jealousy, I have no business in the profession.

12. I have seen as grave infractions of medical ethics by older men who knew better than by younger men who did not know. If the abbot plays cards, what can you expect of the monks?

13. There is no system of communication so rapid as the wireless telegraphy of defamation.

14. No man, except perhaps the resident physician, so grossly overestimates his own value as one who sues a corporation for damages.

15. When a man has never climbed, but has loafed easily along through the levels of life, he can't climb if the need comes. He is like the canal horse of former days, so accustomed to the level that he don't know how to mount a hill.

16. When I was a young doctor without patients, my sign used to look to me like an epitaph on a stillborn business. The first patient I ever had stole my only umbrella.

17. One of the hardest things about the profession is the requirement that its members shall be always conventionally

respectable. The world is pleased by subservience to its dicta. Artists and literary men are not required to be respectable. Lawyers don't have to be. Politicians are not expected to be. Doctors often don't want to be conventional, but must be unless they have personality. One who is bold enough to defy this public sentiment does so at his mortal peril. Only a real man can defy it successfully, and such a man does not care a continental what people think of him or what they will try to do to him. The man who is always showing the world his fear of its growls is sure to be bitten. The world is a snarling dog, leaves alone the real man who defies it, but fawns at the feet of one who "flings it a bone."

18. To elect a man to a faculty or to a hospital staff simply because he has influence (family, financial, religious or political) is a crime against humanity and the medical profession. That foul system, when once fixed in an institution or a community, clings like the asp to Cleopatra's breast and instils poison into the veins. If I had the power as I have the will, I would strike that thrice accursed system dead.

19. A man who becomes an embodied grievance may perhaps be a victim of persecution, but the chances are that he is lazy, incapable, or generally impossible. To have been turned down for every position he wanted is no real claim upon us to elect him to something.

20. A surgeon has great opportunities to do good, particularly if he does not care who gets the credit for it. To fight for credit is a dreadful waste of energy. As Joseph Leidy said: "It does not make any real difference who discovered something, the important thing is that it has been discovered."

21. "The meek shall inherit the earth," but my experience is that in spite of inheriting it, they seldom get it. It is true that it rains upon the just and the unjust, but when it does, the unjust are usually possessed of the umbrellas of the just.

22. It does not matter how sure you are that the world owes you a living, you won't get paid until work identifies you. In surgery the imperative *must* is work. The top will continue to spin only while you whip it. The law, in the monastery conceived

of by Rabelais, was "do what thou wilt." The law which governs the surgeon is "do all the things that you should do to be worthy of your title and place."

23. Follow Paget's suggestion and note to what direction a surgeon looks for reputation. The dignified surgeon looks only to his own profession. The newspapers may make a man's name familiar to thousands, give him a large practice and help him to get rich, but they can't make him a great surgeon. The Commonwealth of Science is and ever will be a Democracy. It selects its own leaders and does not consent to receive them. Distinction in surgery comes from a mightier ordination than that by the newspaper press, that is, ordination by the medical profession itself. The profession knows its own great men and they are by no means always the ones puffed by the newspapers.

24. A medical certificate of the value of a proprietary medicine is only straw bail. It may be regarded as testimony to character by one who badly needs such testimony for himself. Such a certificate does not teach us much about the drug, but does give us a lot of information about the writer.

25. A great surgeon who does mean things is like the thunder, mighty and majestic, which nevertheless stoops to sour the milk in a poor man's larder.

26. Very rich men are apt to be the victims of neurasthenia. Some of them have to work too hard. They may get an occupation neurosis which we will call coupon-cutters' palsy, and they are liable to be severely strained trying to get daughters off their hands and to set noble sons-in-law on their feet. There is nothing a millionaire is apt to resent so much as a large bill for medical services. He will cheerfully pay a lawyer thousands for doing something to protect his money or to enable him to get more. He usually hates to pay a doctor a few hundred for saving his life. He evidently makes a true estimate of the real value of his life.

27. One who is a slave to numerous office hours is kept by them from steady study and from doing his best work. Office hours may hang upon a man as a millstone about the neck. A surgeon is far better off to see patients by appointment.

28. Nothing is so efficient in clubbing the enthusiasm out of a man as the discovery that his best qualities are counted as detriments. Many a man has been surprised to find out that if he *thinks*, the world calls him a dreamer. If he *studies*, a book surgeon. If he *stands on principles*, an obstinate individual. If he is *tenacious for a cause*, a pugnacious personality. If he *tells the truth*, a rude, blunt and unpleasant mortal. If he *joins no faction*, one unwilling to act or constitutionally incapable of acting with his colleagues.

29. The complete radical is wrong. The complete conservative is wrong. Burke's conception of a statesman applies to a surgeon. He must have a keen disposition to improve *and* a notable ability to preserve. Surgical fashions change as rapidly as fashions in battleships or woman's headgear.

30. When you know the direction to which a man looks for reputation—how he acts to and speaks of brother practitioners—what his relations are with the newspapers—to what degree his lips are sealed about the affairs of his patients—how he makes and uses statistics—what is his attitude regarding splitting fees, receiving commissions, and furnishing certificates for proprietary medicines—you know exactly what kind of man he is.

31. Temptations are apt to come to us disguised as opportunities.

32. Surgical sea serpents are discovered several times a year.

33. One who operates for statistics declines to save some lives.

34. A kindly word of commendation from a distinguished man is long remembered by a young man. It is one of the best of instigations to and rewards for good work. Words of commendation at the right time, evidences of confidence, expressions of medical brotherhood, save many a beginner from despair. A helping hand is of the greatest value, not only because it materially aids a man in rising, but also because the warm clasp of sympathy gives him strength and desire to fight his own way upward.

35. Objectionable people are numerous. They have one trait in common, that is, a most unfortunate tendency to longevity.

Few die and none resign. They haunt physicians' offices. Among them I would mention: That breathing outrage, the fierce female who glares petrifaction on all who enter the private office ahead of her.

The human disaster who constantly borrows trouble and pays some of it off to you whenever he calls.

That unescapable calamity, the doctor who has a row on his hands and wants to get you into it.

The lawyer whose client has traumatic neurasthenia and wants to sue a street car company. Some of these lawyers remind us of Milton's description: "Men allured to the trade of law, who ground their purposes not on the heavenly contemplation of justice and equity, but on the promising and pleasing thoughts of litigious terms, fat contentions, and flowing fees."

The undertaker who leaves his wagon in front of your door while he comes in to get a death certificate signed.

The life insurance agent who proves that without insurance your family will be reduced to begging bread from door to door.

The religious beggar who has a mission, and a peculiar hat, who snuffles grievously in conversation, who serves a good cause, and would persuade you that a small contribution will be to you a sort of fire insurance against an inextinguishable spiritual conflagration. Such a man is a true philanthropist, that is, he tries to get you to give your money to somebody else, although he gives none himself.

The friend with nothing to do, who just drops in when you are busiest to have a little talk. He forgets that a doctor's time is exchangeable for other people's money. Every caller of this description picks the doctor's pocket, and is an embodied pestilence.

The patient who is always late and catches you just as you are ready to leave.

The fellow who *will* come too early and disturb the tranquillity engendered by the morning cigar.

The agent who is an M. D., and sends in his doctor's card.

The sexual hypochondriac loaded down with specimens. The drug agent who desires to describe it all. The patient who does not know when to leave and is as hard to get out of the office as an ocean liner off the stocks. The book agent who points out the names of subscribers, must have your name to complete the list, and is convinced that failure on your part to sign will cause a blight to settle on you and your remotest posterity for duty unfulfilled.

The man who wants to sell mining stock.

I am sitting writing among my medical books. Every doctor's office should be rich in books. One must have at hand books of literature, books for study, books for diverting reading, and books for immediate reference. Unless things are looked up at once, they are seldom looked up at all. When in the mood for a certain sort of book the mind is receptive to what that sort of book contains. We read with the greatest benefit when receptive and we must have the book then, not tomorrow or next day. By tomorrow a mood may be gone, or the desire to look up a fact, an article or a view may be forgotten. No distant library, however large and complete it may be, is a perfect substitute for even a small library in the house.

Around me are many books clad respectably in cloth and a number arrayed soberly in sheepskin. A few are dressed in all the glory of Russian leather and here and there among them is one proud in the possession of vignette and frontispiece. To look at hundreds of books bound alike is depressing in the extreme. It is pleasant to see a *set* of books in like bindings, but it is not pleasant to see a library under the curse of an act of uniformity. When all the books in a library are bound exactly alike we feel as though we were meeting hundreds of people dressed exactly alike. All individualism has gone out of them. "The little libraries with which so many of us have to be contented owe their bright and cheerful appearance to the cloth covers of the books, in which each book stands out with modest directness, wearing its individuality instead of losing it in a crowd of neighbors dressed exactly alike." (*The Story of Books*, by Gertrude Burford Rawlings.) A gorgeous binding is a work of art, but only a rare literary treasure or a much-loved book should be so decked out.

A book is not written merely to be bound. The inside is of more importance than the outside.

A splendid Vesalius deserves a noble binding, but a manual of surgery does not. Royalty is entitled to its robes, and beauty to its furbelows, but the sober citizen wears modest garb. I am always a bit suspicious of the overhandsome medical book. It reminds me of an overdressed man. It tries to draw my attention away from essentials and to infatuate me with externals, as a gambler does with his diamonds or a confidence man with his conversation. I suspect the gentility of an overdressed and perfumed man, and I suspect the solidity and scholarship of an overdressed book. When all of a man's books are superlatively bound I wonder doubtingly if he ever reads them. A man used to books can tell at a glance if a library is for ostentation or for use. Show me a man's library and I will tell you much of the man, of his habits, his needs, his learning, his moods, and his tendencies. Does he keep his books according to size, to color, or to subject? Which are the books tossed upon the topmost shelf? Is anyone allowed to dust them at will? Are any books uncut, and if so, what are their titles? Are some fresh, clean, and unworn? Which are the dingy, dog-eared, loose-backed, and annotated volumes? Which books does he keep near his right hand, on the desk or upon a revolving bookcase? All of these things serve to speak to us of the man.

There is such a thing as being *too* practical a surgeon. The man who fears, neglects, avoids or hates a library is too practical to be a good surgeon. It is true that one can't learn to operate in a library, but by study there he can *help himself mightily* in learning how to operate, can give himself command of numerous methods, can be informed as to all disasters, complications, and annoyances. By books a man can store his mind with known facts. From them he can obtain myriads of ideas which if left to himself he would never find out. Because of reading he is able to utilize the observations of centuries, to coordinate numerous apparently contradictory statements, to obtain the material for enlarged views, and to cultivate and develop his mind. Truly

reading "maketh the full man." One who would depend entirely
on his own limited experience is surely bereft of reason.

> "Each to himself must be his final rule,
> Supreme dictator, to reject or use,
> Employing what he takes, but as his tool.
> But he who, self-sufficient, dares refuse
> All aid of men, must be a god or fool."

Books are absolutely necessary tools of our calling. The
jest of Sydenham is not true now, even if it once were.

One must not limit his reading to surgery. To do so means
that surgery itself will not be profoundly known or completely
understood.

All the chief branches of medicine must be systematically followed and studied. One of the worst of evil customs is to be a
mere case reader, and the overworked surgeon is always being
tempted by tire to become that. The learning of a case reader
is in spots and between the spots are howling wastes of ignorance. Wide reading and regular study are among the imperative
duties of the profession. One must read carefully in order to
understand. Hasty reading is responsible for much misinformation and misinformation on a subject may be more harmful than
no information.

The greatness and influence of a book are not in proportion
to its size. Sir Joshua Reynolds said that a man who paints with
a very large brush is not of necessity a very great painter. A
man who writes an enormous book is not of necessity a very
great author. A very large book may happen to be a very great
one, but it is not great because of its size. Every sentence may
be valuable and then the size is necessary. Often, however, the
bulk of such a book is mere padding, just as many women are
shaped by padding. Some books are merely written around pictures and are in reality descriptive catalogues. In others pictures
are lugged in not to clarify a description, point a truth or emphasize a statement, but to fill out a book with useless material into
dropsical dimensions. Size, in such a case, is disease, not healthy
growth.

I see on my shelves a one-volume book weighing 4½ pounds and it deals only with appendicitis. I notice a still larger book treating of a branch of surgery. It contains 900 huge pages. It boasts 700 pictures and space is sinfully wasted by using an entire page to show the print of a normal foot and another page to exhibit an electric drill. When one tries to read this book he has greatness thrust upon him, for the treatise weighs exactly 8½ pounds. We may well say of this book what Macaulay said of *Burleigh and His Times,* by Nares: "The work of Doctor Nares has filled us with astonishment similar to that which Captain Lemuel Gulliver felt when he first landed in Brobdingnag, and saw corn as high as the oaks in the New Forest, tumblers as large as buckets, and wrens of the bulk of turkeys. The whole book, and every component part of it is on a gigantic scale, - - -.

"Such a book might, before the deluge, have been considered as light reading by Hilpa and Shalum. But unhappily the life of man is now threescore years and ten; and we cannot but think it unfair of Doctor Nares to demand from us so large a portion of so short an existence."

In contrast to such dropsical volumes I think of the epoch-making lectures of John Hunter on the *Principles of Surgery,* in 400 small pages—Hilton on *Rest and Pain,* in 514 octavo pages—A. Pearce Gould's admirable *Surgical Diagnosis* in 606 very small pages, and Treves's *Manual of Applied Anatomy* in 566 very small pages.

The wail of Ecclesiastes (xii : 2) is—"Of making many books there is no end." Some write because they have something new to say—others because they want to say old things in newer and perhaps in clearer and more attractive ways—others to present particular theories—others to furnish a side light—others to aid them in getting a position—others because they have position and writing is expected of them—some few because they have the real call to authorship.

A surgeon must buy quantities of books. Some of them are invaluable. Some are useful for one or two or a few articles.

Some are needed to refer to rather than to read systematically. Some are irritatingly useless. The less a man knows of books the more useless ones he buys. A man who only wants books to set off a room might as well buy them as did a steward engaged in furnishing a country house. He ordered: "Six feet of theology, the same quantity of metaphysics, and near a yard of old civil law in folio."

Thomas Jefferson wrote: "A library book lasts as long as a house, for hundreds of years. It is not then an article of mere consumption but fairly of capital, and often in the case of professional men setting out in life, it is their only capital." Though the book on the shelf may physically last "as long as a house" the world soon forgets it and its author and buys something else on the same subject. The lives of most books are very brief. The lives of medical books are particularly brief. Medical opinions change constantly and new facts are being added daily to science. Hence medical books soon become obsolete. Carefully made new editions may keep a book alive for years, but very few medical books live after an author dies. When we abuse publishers we must remember that the death of an author will usually destroy a book at once, and this is a risk a publisher must take. I am informed by a prominent publisher that it is an exception when a medical book sells at all four years after publication.

In general literature, too, most books live brief lives. Out of 50,000 books published in England in the seventeenth century, probably less than fifty are ever read today. Only fifty books out of a thousand live seven years and less than ten live twenty years. A very few medical books have lived long, for instance, Gray's *Anatomy*. The first edition of this book was in 1858. It has had numerous editions in this country and England, and is still a text-book in many colleges. Gray wrote the book before he was thirty-one years of age, and he died in 1861 at the age of thirty-four. He made his own dissections for the pictures. The remarks on surgical anatomy made the book intensely practical and aided its popularity. Most of us here present were doubtless brought up on Gray.

To look at Gray's *Anatomy* brings up the old question as to the possibility of killing a good book by a slashing review. Bentley, in the controversy on the *Letters of Phalaris*, said: "No man was ever written down but by himself." The history of Gray's book goes far to prove the truth of Bentley's statement. Few books have ever been more fiercely assailed. The author was particularly denounced for alleged plagiarism from Quain and Sharpey. Here are some extracts from the review which appeared in the *Medical Times and Gazette* of March 5, 1859. The reviewer states that he "sits down to the task with the oppressive feeling of sadness which comes over a man when he has seen wrong done, when he finds the occasion of such wrong has been unnecessarily sought for, and that the ill deed is, after all, ill done."

He says that the book "is not wanted."

"It is low and unscientific in tone."

"It has been compiled, - - -, in a manner inconsistent with the professions of honesty which we find in the preface."

"It is not even up to the mark of the existing vade mecums."

It is "an unphilosophical amalgam of anatomical details and crude surgery."

"Not a word about the homologies of any part or organ appears. Mr. Gray ignores that aspect of anatomy altogether, and rests contented with such unalloyed description of parts that must be crammed for examination, or that may be cut in operation, as would be welcomed by a college of barber surgeons."

"We feel confident every right-minded reader will join with us in repudiating this book of Mr. Gray's, and in lamenting that those for whom it was mainly intended, the young men of the profession, ——, should be exposed to the contagion of such an example of debased compilation and unscrupulous assumption."

Poor Gray did not live to see the second edition of his much-abused production.

Who wrote that review? I do not know. I doubt if anyone does know. The name of the cocksure critic and most inaccurate prophet is in oblivion, and the year 1910, half a century after

Gray's death, saw the publication of the seventeenth English and the eighteenth American edition of the *Anatomy*.

Certain older books should be in every surgeon's library. Among them I would particularly mention the following: The *Essays and Observations* of John Hunter, and the *Principles of Surgery* by the same author. Hunter was probably the greatest surgical philosopher that ever lived. He brought comparative anatomy and pathology to the study of surgical problems. He taught us that every belief must be tested by experiment and that the basis of all knowledge is scientific observation. He was the first to teach the principles of surgery and he has profoundly influenced surgical thought for all time. I repeat one of his sayings which should bid us consider today: "Surgery consists in curing a disease rather than in the removal of it by mechanical means. But so differently do most think upon this subject that a surgeon who performs most operations and gives most pain is commonly thought the best."

No library should be without the admirable *Clinical Lectures* of Sir James Paget. He was the greatest surgical philosopher since Hunter and made to surgery some of the masterly contributions of the nineteenth century. His lectures on surgical pathology were regarded as the best ever given. In his *Clinical Lectures* all sorts of topics are discussed, for instance, risks of operations, cases cured by bone setters, dissection poisons, etc. One of the most famous essays is upon the *Calamities of Surgery*. In this he fearlessly speaks of his own mistakes. Paget was a much-admired public speaker and he wrote in a charming style. He stands always and in every particular for the dignity and honor of the profession. Were I able to enforce it I would have every senior student read Paget's works.

It is a misfortune that the great surgery of Samuel D. Gross has been allowed to die for the want of a new edition. The last edition was in 1882. Gross, in this book, embodied the results of an enormous personal experience, wide reading and profound thought. In his preface he truly says that the book may be regarded "as exhibiting surgery as I myself understand it, and as I, for so many years, conscientiously taught it." When I use this book (and I do so often) I seem to see the handsome face of the grand old teacher before me, and I seem to hear fifty years of American surgery speaking through his lips.

The Practice of Surgery, by Thomas Bryant of Guy's Hospital, is a book of the highest value. I do not think that there has been an edition of it in twenty-five years. It was written from a most extensive personal experience, contains admirable descriptions of injuries and of surgical diseases, and dwells much upon diagnosis and treatment. It is one of the best treatises on surgical practice ever written. Hilton, on *Rest and Pain*, is a surgical classic. Jacobson calls it "one of our few surgical classics." The first edition was brought out in the early sixties. The fourth edition (1887) was edited by Jacobson, the author of the great text-book of *Operative Surgery*. Hilton teaches the importance of reasoning out many problems of disease from anatomical facts. The book is filled with the most interesting and important speculations. I would have every senior student read Hilton.

The *International Encyclopedia of Surgery*, edited by that profound and accurate scholar, the late Professor Ashhurst, is an invaluable book of reference.

The *Memoirs* of Baron Larrey should always be in a surgeon's library. The book is more interesting than a novel, is filled with striking cases, contains a multitude of interesting and valuable observations, and furnishes a wonderful picture of the wars of the Emperor Napoleon. Here we learn of what stern stuff those grim old marshals of the empire were made, and what sort of men those soldiers were who marched as conquerors into most of the capitals of Europe. Larrey was the greatest military surgeon that ever lived and he was in twenty-six campaigns, "from Syria to Portugal and from Moscow to Madrid."

Among other books it is well to have are: Joseph Bell's *Operations of Surgery*, Tidy's *Legal Medicine*, Tuke's *Influence of Mind on Body*, Carpenter's *Mental Physiology*, Maudsley on the *Pathology of the Mind*, Hyrtle's *Anatomy*, Trousseau's *Lectures on Clinical Medicine*, Agnew's *Surgery*, Watson's *Lectures on the*

Marjolin's ulcer is an epithelioma springing from a scar or from the margin of a chronic ulcer.

Roux's amputation at the ankle joint is a modification of Syme's, and his name is also given to a method of cheiloplasty, excision of the hip, excision of the elbow, closure of exstrophy of the bladder, excision of the tongue, and other operations.

The apical mucous glands of the tongue, on either side of the frenum, are called the glands of Nuhn and Blandin. We still at times use Blandin's operation for double harelip and for excision of the upper jaw.

Most modern text-books of anatomy contain the drawings of the veins of the diploe, which were made long ago from Brechet's preparations and the diploic canals are named the "canals of Breschet."

Dupuytren's clamp for artificial anus is still in the catalogues and Dupuytren's splint is occasionally employed in Pott's fracture. Contraction of the palmar fascia is named Dupuytren's contraction. A bilocular hydrocele is called Dupuytren's hydrocele. The Dupuytren suture is a continuous obliquely crossing inversion stitch for the intestine which is frequently used. Dupuytren's disarticulation of the shoulder joint and operations for fistula of the lachrymal duct, contraction of the palmar fascia, artificial anus, resection of the elbow, and lithotomy are named after him. In Dupuytren's amputation in continuity, the surgeon makes double flaps, cutting the skin from without inward and dividing the muscles by transfixion.

Velpeau's bandage is known to every student. It is a classical dressing. Velpeau's hernia is a femoral hernia in front of the vessels. Text-books of today contain Velpeau's method for excising the upper jaw and wrist, for iridotomy, and for neurectomy of the inframaxillary nerve.

We may amputate the hip joint, the shoulder joint, or the tarsometatarsal articulation by Lisfranc's method, and several excisions bear this surgeon's name.

Berard's operation is a method for removing a nasopharyngeal tumor.

18

Cloquet's hernia is a femoral hernia behind the vessels. Cloquet's fascia is the septum crurale. The ganglion of Cloquet is in the incisor foramen and its roots are the nasopalatine nerves. The canal of Cloquet or the hyaloid canal is the canal through the vitreous. Cloquet's test for death is the introduction of bright needles into the muscles. In the live body needles rapidly oxidize, in the dead body they remain bright.

Civiale is quoted in all treatises on stone in the bladder, as he devised lithotrity and perfected the lithotrite.

Jobert was the first surgeon to use Lembert's inversion suture on the intestine of a living man. His method of castration is still described. Boyer's cyst is an enlargement of the subhyoid bursa.

Guérin developed subcutaneous tenotomy, and Guérin's mucous gland is just within the female urinary meatus.

Gerdy is quoted in discussions of hypnotic anesthesia. Ricord is freely quoted by all syphilographers. Hugier's canal is the canal in the temporal bone for the chorda tympani nerve, and Hugier's glands open into the vagina.

Amussat devised torsion for arresting hemorrhage and his forceps are still used for that purpose.

A few years ago Malgaigne's hooks were frequently used for fracture of the patella. Every text-book on fractures quotes Malgaigne repeatedly.

Sappey's pictures of the lymphatics are used in even the most recent anatomies. Sappey's accessory portal system is a development of vessels during the course of hepatic cirrhosis. A fracture of the radius is named after Gosselin. Surgeons of today amputate at the hip and shoulder by Larrey's methods.

Cruveilhier's *Atlas* is often consulted. Cruveilhier's ulcer is a round ulcer of the stomach. Cruveilhier's disease is progressive muscular atrophy. Cruveilhier's fascia is the superficial layer of the perineal fascia. The plexus of Cruveilhier is formed by the great occipital nerve and the first and second cervical nerves.

Guy Lussac discovered the law of the combination of gases, the element boron and cyanogen. He proved that iodine is an element and named it and first made synthetically its hydrogen compounds.

Dumas's studies in organic chemistry are famous.

Orfila discovered that certain poisons when given tend to accumulate in the liver and other viscera besides the alimentary canal, and in sufficient amount to be certainly detected by chemical tests. Orfila is extensively quoted in all works on toxicology.

These were the men suggested by the names of Dupuytren and Velpeau. They put their marks on medical science for all time and in our daily work we still feel their influence. They were true workers in the field of medicine and were swayed by the same spirit that was in the lion heart of Abernethy, filled the lordly soul of Hunter, stimulated the labors of Paré and of Harvey, of Paget, and of Gross—which guided the scalpel of Agnew and lured the eager mind of Senn.

I wish I could speak to you of the patients a surgeon sees in his office, of the problems he meets there, of the strange letters he gets, of the deluge of advertisements the postman brings; of the beggars by letter and in person, of the various schemes for getting a doctor's hard-earned and elusive dollars, of the irritations caused by the telephone, of the journals waiting to be read, of reviews, and a score of other things. But enough, I have traveled far afield. The afternoon wanes. Already I have spoken much too long and must now bid you farewell.

> "Farewell! a word that must be, and hath been—
> A sound which makes us linger:—yet—farewell!
> Ye, who have traced the Pilgrim to the scene
> Which is his last, if in your memories dwell
> A single thought which once was his, if o'er ye swell
> A single recollection, not in vain
> He wore his sandal—shoon and scallop-shell."
> —*Farewell.*

CRAWFORD W. LONG*

Now and then a real leader, an original force, a truly great man comes into the world, and moves us as one inspired. He dares to lift the veil which hangs before the mysteries, the veil which lesser men are too ignorant to observe, too indifferent to regard, or too cowardly or incapable to displace. Such a man seeks truth and scorns wealth—courts labor and forgets ease—fights dragons and slays giants—is the slave to duty, is contemptuous of popularity, and finally wrings

> "the secret of deliverance forth
> Whether it lurk in hells or hide in heavens."

He originates. "Every institution," says Emerson, "was once the act of a single man."

All such men have earned the reverent love and the eternal gratitude of humanity. Love and gratitude are the debts men owe to the memories of the heroes of progress, because of their labors, pains, perils, and sacrifices. What would have become of the world without such men?   "Men

> Perished in winter-winds till one smote fire
> From flint-stones coldly hiding what they held,
> The red spark treasured from the kindling sun.
> They gorged on flesh like wolves, till one sowed corn,
> Which grew a weed, yet makes the life of man:
> They mowed and babbled till some tongue struck speech,
> And patient fingers framed the lettered sound.
> What good gift have my brothers, but it came
> From search and strife and loving sacrifice?"

* In the preparation of this address I have quoted freely from many sources, especially the following: "Crawford W. Long, Discoverer of Anesthesia," by Rosa Pendleton Chiles (*Munsey*, August, 1911); "Long and his Discovery," by Isham H. Goss (*Journal-Record of Medicine*, November, 1908); "Long, the Discoverer of Anesthesia," by Hugh H. Young (*Johns Hopkins Historical Bulletin*, August–September, 1897); "Crawford Williamson Long, the Pioneer of Anesthesia," by Dudley W. Buxton (*Proceedings of the Royal Society of Medicine*, January, 1912). I am greatly indebted to Mrs. Frances Long Taylor, Doctor Long's daughter, for several interesting and important communications. Reprinted from Special Bulletin, University of Pennsylvania.

Crawford W. Long.

The world is often ignorant of its greatest men. Men, to us nameless, made some of the grandest discoveries and perfected some of the most remarkable inventions.

"Who found the seeds of fire and made them shoot,
Fed by his breath, in buds and flowers of flame?
Who forged in roaring flames the ponderous stone,
And shaped the moulded metal to his need?
Who gave the dragging car its rolling wheel,
And tamed the steed that whirls its circling round?
All these have left their work and not their names."

When a man has found a radiant truth, has done some gleaming deed, but has received no tribute of praise or glory, it is a peculiarly grateful thing to see the conscience of the world awaken, and to find men place the name of their long neglected benefactor

"On Fame's eternal beadroll."

Seventy years ago today, on March 30, 1842, and in the little village of Jefferson, Jackson County, Georgia, anesthesia was first intentionally produced to permit of the painless performance of a surgical operation. This discovery was one of the greatest in the history of science and ranks in importance with the discovery by Harvey of the circulation of the blood, by Franklin of phenomena of electricity, by Jenner of vaccination, by Pasteur of bacteriology, and by Lister of antiseptic surgery. The giving of ether as a surgical anesthetic was not a haphazard accident, but was reasoned out from observations.

The man who first gave ether for surgical purposes was Crawford W. Long, a native and resident of the State of Georgia, and a graduate of the University of Pennsylvania in the class of 1839. There seems a peculiar adjustment to the eternal fitness of things in the fact that a son of the University founded by the great practical philosopher, Benjamin Franklin, should have made one of the greatest practical discoveries of all time.

Long's great discovery was not made in a splendidly equipped institution of world-wide fame, nor by a professor whose lecture room was packed with eager students, but by a modest, unassuming country doctor, dwelling in an isolated village. Truly! greater things for mankind have come from the hut than from the palace, from the peaceful country than from the roaring town.

We meet today in commemoration and celebration: in commemoration of the 70th anniversary of the discovery of ether anesthesia, and in celebration of the noble achievement of a great son of this grand old school.

We will strive to:

> Part the mists which almost hide
> A man of former days
> And spin upon the Wheel of Truth
> Some golden threads of praise.

No one disputes that Long gave ether for surgical purposes over four years before Morton did, and at least two years before Horace Wells pulled the tooth of a patient who was under the influence of nitrous oxide gas. There is no claim that Morton knew anything of Long's observations. It is freely admitted by all that Warren, in the operating room of the Massachusetts General Hospital, gave to Morton the opportunity to dramatically impress the world with his views. Morton and Warren made the world hear, Long made the discovery, and would also have made the world hear had he had a great city hospital as a forum from which to speak, and a celebrated surgeon as a spokesman and advocate. Long has been criticized for not publishing his discovery at once. Jenner waited twenty years to publish his and after twenty years had only made twenty-three observations. Suppose someone had published about vaccination after Jenner had worked nineteen years, would Jenner any the less have been the discoverer?

Long made no official claim to the discovery until 1849, when he told his story to the Medical Society of Georgia. He did so then only because his friends thought he would be doing himself injustice to keep silent. His intention had been to collect enough cases to thoroughly test the method. This was slow work in a country district in which surgical operations were few and far between. He used ether seven or eight times in four years. In December, 1846, he read of Morton's success. Soon afterward

Morton, Jackson, and Wells became involved in a bitter controversy and Long shrunk from such things and abhorred the patenting of ether.

In the statement to the Georgia Medical Society, Long presented an affidavit of James M. Venable, then living, stating that ether had been given to him by Long on two occasions in the spring of 1842—an affidavit of Andrew J. Thrumond stating that he saw Long do one of the operations on Venable—affidavits of E. S. Rawls and William H. Thrumond declaring that they witnessed one or both operations, and other conclusive evidence. The original affidavits still exist.

Morton patented ether in 1846 under the name of "letheon." Wells opposed Morton's patent, went insane, and committed suicide in 1848. The government never enforced the patent right and army surgeons used ether freely in the Mexican War, Morton getting no return for it. In 1849 Morton applied to Congress for a grant of $100,000 as compensation for his losses and reward for his alleged discovery. Jackson opposed Morton's claim. Jackson claimed that he had suggested ether to Morton.

The controversy was acrimonious and protracted. In 1852 the French Academy of Sciences granted a prize to Jackson as the discoverer of ether, and a like amount to Morton, as the first to apply it.

In 1854 Doctor Long was persuaded to write a letter to Senator Dawson of Georgia telling the story of the discovery in 1842. Jackson had a conference with Long and finally withdraw his own claim in Long's favor. In the *Boston Medical and Surgical Journal*, April 11, 1861, will be found a letter from Jackson giving Long the credit. No money was ever granted by the government.

Jackson, like Wells, went insane, and died in 1880. Morton died in 1868, getting an apoplexy while enraged at learning of attempts to deprive him of the glory of the discovery. Long, free from such heart-burnings, pursued the calm ways of a country doctor, and made no further attempt to establish his claim. He led a useful and happy life and died in 1878. Morton, probably because men thought that the government had treated him

shabbily, came to be regarded as the real discoverer, and until
1877 there was no one to say nay. In that year, Dr. J. Marion
Sims published an article in the May number of the *Virginia
Medical Monthly* claiming that Long had made the discovery.
There is one serious mistake in the article of Doctor Sims.
He stated that S. C. Wilhite, a student of Long, suggested to his
preceptor the use of ether.

Wilhite was not with Long in 1842, in fact did not go to him
until 1844. Wilhite corrected this error in a letter to Doctor
Long, dated June 27, 1877. Professor Gross, in commenting on
Sims' paper (*System of Surgery*), says: "Although he (Long)
may have been, and probably was, the first to use this drug as a
means of preventing pain, he failed to interest the profession in
it and has thus lost all just claim to the honor of one of the greatest discoveries ever achieved by human genius." Professor Agnew
must have felt as Gross did, for in his book (*Principles and Practice of Surgery*) he gives Morton the credit for the discovery and
does not even mention the name of Crawford Long. The claims
of Long have since found able champions in Sir James Paget,
Dr. George Foy, of Dublin; Dr. Hugh H. Young, of Baltimore;
Dr. Isham H. Goss, of Athens, Georgia; Dr. Luther Grandy, and
Rose Pendleton Chiles. Dr. Francis R. Packard tells the story
very impartially in his admirable *History of Medicine in the
United States*, which was published in 1901.

Frederick W. Hewitt in his work on *Anesthetics* (1901) says:
"There seems to be no reasonable doubt that in 1842 Dr. Crawford W. Long, a country practitioner of Jefferson, Jackson County,
Georgia, United States of America, administered ether vapor with
the distinct object and fortunate result of producing insensibility
to pain during a surgical operation which he performed, and that
he subsequently employed the same means with equal success."
Henry M. Lyman in *Ashhurst's International Encyclopaedia of
Surgery* (1889) says that Long gave ether in 1842, but as he
"resided in a remote and isolated portion of the country, and as
he published no statement of his experience, his discovery remained unknown."

Of late years Long's claims have been more and more regarded until justice at length prevails.

The Medical Society of Georgia has erected a monument to Long in Jefferson, where ether was first used as an anesthetic. The Legislature of Georgia has resolved to place his statue, with that of Alexander H. Stephens, in the statuary hall of the National capitol.

On December 1, 1911, Dr. Dudley W. Buxton, the distinguished English anesthetist, presented to the Section of Anesthetics of the Royal Society of Medicine an article which seems final and conclusive. It is written with that literary grace and painstaking accuracy which characterize all of Doctor Buxton's productions. In this article will be found a résumé of Long's life—the story of the discovery and reproductions of various convincing documents; among them are: A letter from Doctor Long to R. H. Goodman (dated February 1, 1842), ordering the ether for the first operation, and a covering letter from Goodman—affidavits of James M. Venable and others, previously referred to—Long's bill to Venable charging twenty-five cents for the ether used and $2 for the operation—extract from Long's record book of the operation done on Venable and charge for the operation and ether used. It is dated March 30, 1842. Certificate of Mary Vincent and her husband, declaring that Long gave Mrs. Vincent ether in 1843. There are also copies of other important and interesting papers. Buxton's complete and masterly study may be read in the published *Proceedings of the Royal Society of Medicine*, January, 1912. It gains greater emphasis by coming to us across the sea from a gentleman free of any possible prejudice or partiality. It is the unvarnished truth, and the world now regards Long as the real discoverer. Hence I do not stand here courting controversy. I am not obliged to search dusty records in order to clear up controverted points. I do not need to delve deep in obscure mines after the nugget of Truth. Sims, Young, Buxton, and others have found that nugget and the gleaming metal may be seen and can be tested by all men.

Crawford Williamson Long was born in Daniellsville, Madison County, Georgia, November 1, 1815. His family was prominent socially and in public affairs.

Crawford's grandfather was Captain Samuel Long, an Irishman by birth and an adopted son of Pennsylvania, who resided in Carlisle. He married Miss Williamson of Ulster, Ireland; served in the army of Washington and at the Yorktown surrender, was a captain in the command of the Marquis de Lafayette. At the termination of the war with the Mother Country, he became a citizen of Georgia. His son James Long was a planter and was for years Clerk of the Supreme Court. He sat in the State Senate for two terms, and was the intimate and trusted friend of the celebrated statesman, William H. Crawford, a man who was successively United States Senator, President *pro tem* of the Senate, Minister to France, Secretary of the Treasury, and candidate for President of the United States in 1824, against John Quincy Adams, Andrew Jackson and Henry Clay. The subject of this address was named Crawford after the great statesman and Williamson after Captain Long's wife. Doctor Long's mother, Eliza Ware, was a Virginian, and an energetic, warm-hearted, ambitious, sympathetic woman, of refined taste and much literary ability.

As a boy Crawford was educated in the Academy of his native town. He was bright, interesting, studious, and lovable. He was an entirely normal boy and loved dogs, horses, fishing, shooting, and out-door sports. He entered Franklin College (now the Department of Liberal Arts of the University of Georgia) and graduated when only nineteen years of age, taking the second honor. At college he formed a friendship, which was to last a life-time, with Alexander H. Stephens, a man destined to become Vice-President of the Southern Confederacy.

After graduation he studied for a time under a preceptor, and then took a course of medical lectures in Transylvania University. This school was in Lexington, Kentucky. Long rode on horseback from Georgia to Kentucky, crossing rugged mountains and passing through regions not then free from treacherous Indians. In the fall of 1837 he went to Philadelphia and entered as a medical student in the University of Pennsylvania, from which institution he graduated in 1839. Agnew graduated in 1838. The two boys must have known each other and have often ridden out together from the University to Blockley Hospital. While Long was in Philadelphia he resided in a Quaker household at the corner of 19th and Market Streets. When Long went up to college seventy-five years ago the United States was a small country compared with the mighty nation which now reaches into the very portals of the distant sunset. There were twenty-six states and two territories (Florida and Wisconsin). Most of the vast region beyond the Mississippi, out of which twenty imperial commonwealths have been made, was a wilderness haunted by wild Indians and infested by savage beasts. Much of it belonged to Mexico. Texas was a republic and Samuel Houston was its president. The population of the country numbered about 15,000,000 people and approximately one-sixth of them were slaves. Martin Van Buren was President of the United States, and Richard M. Johnson was Vice-President. The navy list still held the names of those old heroes, Rogers, Barron, Stewart, and Hull. Winfield Scott was a brigadier-general in charge of the department of the East.

Roger B. Taney was Chief Justice of the Supreme Court and Joseph Story sat by his side. There was no national debt and the government was preparing to distribute a surplus of $37,000,000 among the states. There were 1600 miles of railroad in operation in the country and 120 miles in Pennsylvania.

In the United States Senate sat Franklin Pierce, Daniel Webster, Silas Wright, James Buchanan, Thomas Clayton, William C. Rives, John C. Calhoun, William R. King, Robert J. Walker, John J. Crittenden, Henry Clay, and Thomas H. Benton.

In the House of Representatives were John Quincy Adams, Caleb Cushing, Millard Filmore, John Sergeant, Henry A. Wise, John Bell, James K. Polk and Thomas Corwin.

To send a one-sheet letter for over 400 miles cost 25 cents— from Philadelphia to New York 10 cents—not over 30 miles 6 cents.

Truly it is a far cry from the United States of the time of Van Buren to the United States of the time of Taft.

The University of Pennsylvania was first in renown among the twenty-eight medical schools of the country, and possessed the ablest faculty in the United States. The buildings were at Ninth and Chestnut Streets, where the Post Office now stands. On the rolls of the University were 400 medical students, over one-seventh of the entire number in the land.

Philip Syng Physick, the pupil of John Hunter and the father of American surgery, died during Long's first course. At the time of his death he was Emeritus Professor of Surgery and Anatomy. He was the first to use catgut as a ligature material—devised the stomach tube and many useful instruments—and advised the treatment of ununited fracture by the seton. A specimen of a fractured humerus successfully treated by Physick is to be seen today in the museum. For months after his death and by his direction his grave was guarded to keep away resurrection men, as he had a great horror of being dissected.

William Gibson, the pupil of Sir Charles Bell, was the Professor of Surgery. He had served under Wellington in Belgium and was wounded at Waterloo. He was the friend and correspondent of Lord Byron. In 1819 he was called from the University of Maryland to succeed Physick in Pennsylvania. He was the first man to tie the common iliac artery (1812). He twice did a successful cesarean section on the same patient, and saved the mother and both children. Nathaniel Chapman, the wit, critic, book lover, social light, jovial companion, and scientist, was Professor of Practice of Physic and Clinical Medicine. He stood without a peer as a practitioner and, in spite of a congenital speech defect, was one of the greatest teachers in America.

Chapman's book on therapeutics was widely celebrated.

George B. Wood, the profound scholar, the keen observer, the original thinker, taught materia medica. With Franklin Bache he edited the United States Dispensatory. For many years he practically determined the views of the whole profession on ethics and practice. His lectures were the pride and glory of the

University and had immense influence in molding the minds of the students. No man who has held a chair in the University brought to it greater reputation than did George B. Wood. His condemnation of the premature reporting of cases and drug actions may well have decided Long a few years later to delay in publishing a report of the actions of ether. Wood spoke of immature views and premature judgments as *ignes fatui*. He insisted that observers must never be content with a single experiment. (See Introductory lecture 1840.)

William E. Horner, he of the feeble frame, melancholy temperament, scholarly faculty, and original bent, was Professor of Anatomy. He is particularly remembered as the founder of St. Joseph's Hospital and the discoverer of the tensor tarsi, which is still called Horner's muscle. Samuel Jackson, who did so much to introduce the principles of Laënnec and Louis to the American profession, was Professor of Institutes of Medicine.

Hugh L. Hodge, who had been forced to abandon a surgical career because of impaired sight, was Professor of Midwifery, having defeated Charles D. Meigs for the chair. Hodge's forceps and pessaries were known all over the world.

Robert Hare was the celebrated Professor of Chemistry. He had been a fellow-student of Silliman, and when only twenty years of age had invented the oxyhydrogen blowpipe. He was called to the University from William and Mary College. He was one of the ablest chemists and electricians then living, was a most impressive lecturer and a highly successful experimenter.

Such were the men of the Faculty of '38 and '39, the men to whom the young Georgia student listened, the men who helped to guide and direct his mind. The session began November 1st, according to the catalog; it ended "about the first day of March ensuing." Commencement was evidently a movable feast, for the catalog states that it is "held generally about April 1st." No text-books were recommended in the catalog, but we know that students used the *Syllabus of Wood's Lectures*, Chapman's *Therapeutics*, Gibson's *Surgery*, Horner's *Anatomy*, and Hare's *Chemistry*.

Blockley stood where it does now, and some of the buildings are very little changed externally. Agnew says that at this period Blockley was "the great clinical school of the country." Every Saturday morning many 'buses gathered at Ninth and Chestnut, and crowds of students rode out to attend clinical lessons within those grim walls. Lectures were given by Samuel Jackson, Robley Dunglison, Joseph Pancoast, and William Gerhard. J. M. DaCosta speaks of Gerhard as "the greatest observer and clinician America has produced."

In those days William Norris, George B. Wood, John Rhea Barton and John K. Mitchell were at the Pennsylvania Hospital.

Samuel D. Gross had not yet gone to Louisville from Cincinnati, and George McClellan was serving his last year as Professor of Surgery in Jefferson. Students of those days were far more turbulent than now, and fierce combats were common between the students of the rival schools.

During Long's student days Dickens's *Pickwick Papers*, *Oliver Twist*, and *Nicholas Nickleby* were published. Thackeray, whose very name was unknown, was a contributor to Frazer's *Magazine*. Oliver Wendell Holmes, who later suggested the term "anesthesia," was trying for practice in Boston. Washington Irving was engaged in active literary work at his home, Sunnyside, in Tarrytown. Nathaniel Hawthorne was in Salem writing *Twice Told Tales*. Motley was writing his first book, *Morton's Hope*. The weird tales of the somber genius, Edgar Allan Poe, were taking hold of the public imagination.

Longfellow was teaching modern languages in Harvard and writing *Hyperion*. James Russell Lowell was a student at Harvard. Andrew Jackson was at the *Hermitage*, in serene retirement after stressful and turbulent years.

The world, now recovered from the great conservative reaction which followed the French Revolution, was full of ferment, investigation, speculation, and novel ideas.

Railroads were reaching out their tentacles on all sides, and the whistle of the locomotive had become the proclamation of civilization.

The steamboat "Great Western" had crossed the ocean from Bristol to New York in thirteen days and eight hours. Itinerant lecturers were showing to amused audiences the curious antics of persons who inhaled nitrous oxide gas, or, as it came to be called, laughing gas. Such exhibitions were called nitrous oxide frolics. Men were on the tiptoe of expectation as to the supposed beneficent powers of hynotism. It was learned with amazement that a hypnotized subject could feel no pain, and that Ward, in London, and Cloquet and Lysel, in France, had performed painless operations upon people sleeping the "magnetic sleep." Everybody felt that we were on the threshold of great events and that the first few hesitating words of truth had, as yet, but scarce been lisped by the baby lips of science.

Medical students must, of course, have heard of these things, discussed them with each other, asked questions of their professors and speculated as to the possibility of painless surgery. Every visit to the surgical clinic must have impressed on their minds the tortures inflicted by operations, and what a beneficent change it would be could a victim sleep under the knife. Neither Gibson, Wood nor Chapman had a word to say in favor of "animal magnetism," or Braidism, as it came to be called. Gibson's book says nothing at all about preventing pain in surgical operations. He certainly followed the usual custom—drugged the patient heavily with opium, and had him forcibly held or firmly strapped during the dread tragedy of the operation.

Nitrous oxide was a well-known drug and was lectured on by teachers of chemistry and therapeutics. Sir Humphrey Davy, in the year 1799, found out that, if inhaled, nitrous oxide would subdue pain, and suggested its use in surgical operations. In 1800 he published his experience and suggestion. Davy's recommendation was never acted on until Horace Wells used the gas as an anesthetic in 1844. Hare taught that when nitrous oxide is inhaled, it produces "a transient, peculiar, various, and generally vivacious ebriety."

Pareira, in his *Materia Medica* (1839), states that he had given nitrous oxide to about 100 persons, that it produces temporary and usually pleasing delirium, which subsides in three or four minutes—that the delirium takes different forms, causing some to dance and some to fight. In some few cases stupor is produced. He recommended it for spasmodic asthma.

Ether had been known for several centuries. Hare, in his *Chemistry*, speaks of the internal administration of ether, but says nothing of the effects of inhalations. Wood does speak of ether inhalations. I find a reference to it in the syllabus of his lectures. He says it may be inhaled, tells what inhalations are advised for, and explains how they are given. It was used in very small doses for spasmodic conditions. Doctor Wood states in his *Therapeutics*, written at a much later date than this, that "ether has been long used by this method (inhalation). The late Dr. P. S. Physick was much in the habit of employing it in pulmonary affections, and invented a small, extemporaneous inhaler for the purpose." Doctor Physick died in 1838.*

Pareira discusses the stomach administration of ether, and says that large doses cause intoxication, and excessive doses, stupefaction. He also speaks of ether drinkers, and refers to a chemist suffering from cancer of the colon, who drank a pint of ether a day to relieve his pain. Pareira speaks of inhalations as follows: "When the vapor of ether, sufficiently diluted with atmospheric air, is inhaled, it causes irritation of the epiglottis, a sensation of fullness in the head and a succession of effects analogous to those caused by the protoxide of nitrogen, ——. If the air be too strongly impregnated with ether, stupefaction ensues. In one case this state continued, with occasional periods of intermission, for more than thirty hours: for many days the pulse was

* Over forty years before Long came up to college Beddoes used inhalations of small quantities of ether to relieve pain. Soon after Beddoes' practice began, Pierson used ether inhalations for consumption, and so did Warren, of Boston. Several years before 1837 Dr. J. D. Mitchell, of Philadelphia, wrote (quoted from *Anesthetics: Ancient and Modern*, by George Foy): "Some years ago a practice obtained among the lads of Philadelphia of inhaling the vapor of sulphuric ether by way of sport. . . . In some instances the experiment excited mere playfulness and sprightly movement, but in several cases delirium and even phrenitis was induced, which ended fatally."

so much lowered that considerable fears were entertained for the safety of the patient. In another case, an apoplectic condition, which continued for nine hours, was produced." The case of lethargy for thirty hours, spoken of by Pareira, was originally referred to in an article published in 1818 in the *English Quarterly Journal of Science and Arts*, and supposed to have been written by Faraday.* Pareira was evidently fearful of the effects of ether by inhalation.† He used it by dropping some of the drug on a lump of sugar and holding the sugar in the mouth, or by dropping ether in hot water and inhaling the vapor mixed with steam. It was recommended for chronic catarrh and dyspnea, whooping cough, spasmodic asthma, and to relieve the effects produced by the accidental inhalation of chlorine.

* * *

We may conclude that when Long left this school he understood the agony caused by surgery and realized what a great thing it would be to be able to operate without causing pain, that he had no belief in the value of "animal magnetism," as a surgical anesthetic—that he knew that nitrous oxide, when inhaled, would produce delirium—that he knew that ether inhalations were given therapeutically and sometimes taken for sport, and that large doses would produce unconsciousness. He had been taught, and probably at that time believed, that only small doses were admissible and that doses large enough to produce unconsciousness would bring deadly peril to the patient. He likewise took with him the counsel of Wood regarding the necessity of being ever cautious in reputing results.

After graduation he went to New York City and "walked the hospitals." In that city he had the opportunity to hear Valentine Mott, J. Kearny Rogers, and Willard Parker. He wished to enter the medical corps of the U. S. Navy, but his father vetoed the

* Foy states that Faraday "acknowledged the authorship of the article" (*Anesthetics: Ancient and Modern*).

† Foy quotes the *Edinburgh Medical and Surgical Journal* as saying that, beyond question, "the inhalation of air much loaded 'with ether' will prove highly dangerous" (*Anesthetics: Ancient and Modern*).

19

plan, so he returned to Georgia in 1841, and began general practice in Jefferson, a village in Jackson County.

The year 1841 was the very year that Esdaile, in India, performed so many operations upon hypnotized subjects, that Braid, of Manchester, began to set forth his views on induced trance, and that Elliotson began to warmly advocate hypnotism as a surgical anesthetic.

Here is the story of Long's discovery, and in his own words*: "In the month of December, 1841, or in January, 1842, the subject of inhalation of nitrous oxide gas was introduced in a company of young men in this village; several persons present desired me to produce some for their use. I informed them that I had no apparatus for preparing or preserving the gas, but that I had a medicine (sulphuric ether) which would produce equally exhilarating effects: that I had inhaled it myself, and considered it as safe as the nitrous oxide gas. One of the company stated that he had inhaled ether while at school, and was then willing to inhale it. The company were all anxious to witness its effects. The ether was introduced. I gave it first to the gentleman who had previously inhaled it, then inhaled it myself, and afterward gave it to all persons present. They were so much pleased with the exhilarating effects of ether, that they afterward inhaled it frequently and induced others to do so, and its inhalation now became fashionable in this country, and, in fact, extended from this place through several counties in this part of Georgia."

We may note that R. H. Goodman, one of the persons who participated in an ether frolic in Jefferson, made an affidavit in 1853, stating this fact and also that he removed to Athens, January 20, 1842, and introduced ether frolics in that community. It is interesting to observe that Long had inhaled ether before the first ether frolic, and that, repudiating the teaching he had received as a student, he regarded it as being as safe as nitrous oxide. To continue Doctor Long's narrative: "On numerous occasions I have inhaled ether for its exhilarating properties, and

---

*Quoted from Buxton's article on Long in the *Proceedings of the Royal Society of Medicine,* January, 1912.

would frequently, at some short time subsequent to its inhalation, discover bruises or painful spots on my person, which I had received while under the influence of ether. I noticed my friends, while etherized, received falls and bangs, which I believed were sufficient to produce pain on a person not in a state of anesthesia, and on questioning them, they uniformly assured me that they did not feel the least pain from these accidents. These facts are mentioned that the reasons may be apparent why I was induced to make an experiment in etherization."

"The first patient to whom I administered ether in a surgical operation was Mr. James M. Venable, who then resided within 2 miles of Jefferson, and at present (1849) lives in Cobb County, Georgia. Mr. Venable consulted me on several occasions in regard to the propriety of removing two small tumors situated on the back of his neck, but would postpone, from time to time, having the operations performed, from dread of pain. At length I mentioned to him the fact of my receiving bruises while under the influence of the vapor of ether, without suffering, and as I knew him to be fond of and accustomed to inhale ether, I suggested to him the probability that the operations might be performed without pain, and proposed operating on him while under its influence. He consented to have one tumor removed, and the operation was performed the same evening. The ether was given to Mr. Venable on a towel, and when fully under its influence, I extirpated the tumor. It was encysted and about $\frac{1}{2}$ inch in diameter. The patient continued to inhale ether during the time of operation, and when informed it was over, seemed incredulous, until the tumor was shown him. He gave no evidence of suffering during the operation, and assured me after it was over that he did not experience the slightest degree of pain from its performance. This operation was performed on March 30, 1842."

When Long finished that operation he must have felt a sense of combined wonder, exultation and responsibility. It was a brave thing to operate under the full influence of a drug when all professional teaching was that it required large amounts of the vapor to produce unconsciousness, and that large amounts were

dangerous. Had the patient died, the doctor would have had a
lifelong self-reproach and would possibly have been sued or prose-
cuted for manslaughter.* It was brave of Venable to take the
chance. Wonder would naturally arise in Long's mind as he
thought of the agonies inflicted by the surgery he had seen in
Philadelphia and New York, as compared with the perfect tranquillity of the patient just operated upon. Exultation would be
inseparable from the accomplishment of what the masters of
surgery regarded as impossible. A sense of grave responsibility
would be in a man who believed he had done a mighty thing, but
felt the necessity of proving it thoroughly in order that he might
not mislead others and do harm.

He saw the beneficent light break into the dark dungeons of
pain. He must have felt as did Sinbad, the Sailor, when, from the
living tomb in which he was immured, he saw the glad rays of the
sun. He and his companions might well have exclaimed with the
ancient Mariner:

"We were the first that ever burst, into that silent sea."

That is the story of the first use of ether inhalation to still the
pains of surgery.

*   *   *

What of the personality, the character, of the man who discovered anesthesia? In August, 1842, he married Mary C. Swain.
It was a peculiarly happy union. His wife was an intellectual
woman and a thoroughly congenial helpmate. She was the
inspiration of his life. She fitted herself to understand and
sympathize with all his wants and needs. They were real lovers
when they married and remained lovers until death parted them.
He remained a resident of Jefferson until 1851, when he removed
to Athens, Georgia. He lived in Athens until his death, in 1878,
and practiced there continuously except during his service in the
Confederate Army.

* Many of Long's friends begged him not to administer ether again, telling
him that if anything happened to a person under ether the doctor responsible would
be mobbed. But Long did give it again.

For nearly thirty years he was in very active practice, was in the habit of riding miles through the country, and endured all the hardships of a busy country practitioner. No man was ever loved more. All his patients were his devoted admirers. His personality impressed itself upon them. He was counselor and friend as well as physician. He always placed the welfare of his fellows before his own. He was more than a great man, he was a good man. He was one of those rare individuals who really practice their religion. The words of his faith were not mere empty formulas, as with so many, but were mandates to fine deeds. He carried with him through life no ignoble rancor. Disappointment there must have been but there was never hatred of his fellows. He had been excluded from honors that were justly his, but he never kept the thought of it as "something bitter to chew on when feeling Byronic." He in no sense became that desolating human calamity, an embodied grievance. A grievance wearies out sympathies and tires out our appreciation. There was nothing morbid in his temperament. He never scoffed at Destiny or denounced Fate. He never claimed to be an unappreciated spirit or a misunderstood soul. He calmly went his useful way, tending the sick, aiding the needy, caring for his own, sure of himself, confident of the future, never boasting, never brooding, kindly and fair to all, generous ever to opponents, courteous even to critics, and making no struggle for stained wreaths or for tarnished rewards. He was a complete man, a rounded character, a true physician, and when we honor him we find no apologies necessary. He never tried to patent and thus coin into dollars a discovery which has brought and will bring comfort unspeakable to countless thousands of the race. He thoroughly loved his profession. He said: "I am as much called to practice medicine as a minister is to preach the gospel!"

He accepted all medical tasks as commands which he was glad to be thought worthy to receive and fit to execute.

He had that splendid combination, strength and tenderness. He inspired trust. Surely he must have done so, else Venable would never have taken ether to unconsciousness. He was wise and self-confident, else he would never have given Venable ether to unconsciousness when all the leaders of medicine taught that such doses were highly dangerous.

He was full of sympathy for suffering and cared for the lowliest as for the richest. He was gentle, forbearing, faithful to every duty and every instinct. He was always dignified and usually reserved, relaxing at times into gaiety in his family circle among those who knew him well. He had a vein of humor, was given to jests when by his own fireside, and now and then sent humorous sketches to the local newspapers. He was simple of heart, and pure in word and act.

He was a close observer; a hard worker; was honest in thought, word, and deed—hated all lies and anything that even savored of deception. His life was lived in the light of day without any stratagems or pretenses. He was straightforward and unsuspicious, hated to hold ill opinions of anyone, and only a native ability to judge character saved him from frequent impositions. His family adored him. He liked to read aloud to his children and brought them up on the works of Scott, Dickens, Shakespeare and other master minds. He was particularly fond of Hamlet. At bedtime he followed the old-time custom of reading the Bible to the assembled family. He was fond of whist and was one of the best of players. He was devoted to farming, was a good business man and an excellent executive.

In slavery days he was, as were most Southern gentlemen, a kind master to his slaves. He believed that slavery was a plan of Providence to civilize the negroes. He thought that to own slaves was a great and terrible personal responsibility, a responsibility which he ranked close after the one owed to his wife and children. In an old journal he writes: "God grant that I may be a tenderer husband and father and a better master." When his slaves had become free he still watched over their welfare, cared for them when sick, relieved their necessities and gave them useful counsel. The blacks loved and trusted him as much as did the whites.

He had a great reverence for womanhood. He would carry a basket for the lowliest woman with the courtly air others might show to a princess. A veritable termagant used to haul wood into town to sell. Again and again when he met her he bought the load and took it to his own house. On one occasion Mrs. Long said to him: "We have plenty of wood, why do you always buy that woman's," and he said,"Because I hate people to see a woman doing man's work." He would go any distance and attend the poorest negress in labor because of his sympathy for those in the pains of childbirth and his reverence for maternity.

At the unveiling of the monument in Jefferson, Dr. Woods Hutchinson said that Long was in many respects in advance of his day—that he treated and cured consumption by food, fresh air, and tonics—that he treated typhoid fever practically as we do now—that he treated that very dangerous disease bilious fever by quinine when few did so—and that he operated many times very successfully for cancer of the breast, always clearing the ribs and removing the axillary glands (*Munsey*, August, 1911).

It is interesting to note that he never charged more than $100 for a "breast operation," even if the patient was very well off.

He was a Whig in politics and strongly opposed to secession. When Georgia resolved to go out of the Union Long said: "This is the saddest day of my life." Naturally he stood with his own people and went with his state. He entered the Confederate army and served through the war. Like all his friends he lost everything by the war, and he suffered along with them the horrors of reconstruction and the infamous tyrannies of carpet-bag rule. Soon after the war Long was offered the position of United States Contract Surgeon to help care for the many sick and wounded soldiers in Georgia. He was not even asked to take the oath of allegiance. The $50 a month, paid him for his work, came as a blessing in those dark days of poverty. After some years he again became prosperous.

Once, when his health was impaired by overwork, his friends and family urged him to take a holiday, but he said, "My sick need me."

In his 63d year he was struck by apoplexy when at a sick woman's bedside. The moment he recovered consciousness he asked how she was. Before he passed into the unconsciousness which was to end in the long sleep and the silent house, he gave directions for the sick woman's care. He was faithful to duty to the last. He died June 16, 1878.

Such was Crawford W. Long. The University of Pennsylvania this day hangs his likeness in the Hall of Fame with her noblest sons. He was an honor to his alma mater, an ornament to his profession, a glory to his country, and a benefactor of the human race.

THE SAMUEL D. GROSS ADDRESS FOR 1914–15*

It is a condition, laid down at the foundation of the Gross chair of surgery, that an annual address shall be delivered commemorative of the personality or achievements of Samuel David Gross, the greatest leader in surgery produced by the western world. This evening, in fulfilment of the obligation of the foundation, I, as Samuel D. Gross Professor of Surgery, address the students of the Jefferson Medical College.

First, some words as to the founder of the chair: of one who passed from life less than six months ago.

It should be known to all of you that the Gross chair, the first endowed chair in Jefferson Medical College, was endowed by Doctor Gross's daughter, Maria Rives Gross, who by marriage with the late Orville Horwitz of Baltimore became Maria Gross Horwitz. She was born in Cincinnati in 1839. Her father, at that time Professor of Pathologic Anatomy in the Medical College of Ohio, was laying broad and deep the foundations of his fame. When about one year of age Maria Gross was taken to Louisville by her parents, her father having become Professor of Surgery in the University of Louisville. In that pleasant southern town she grew into young womanhood, and in it she received many of the elements of her superior education. It was in her eighteenth year that her father was elected Professor of Surgery in Jefferson Medical College. She came to Philadelphia with her parents, and resided with them in that fine old house at the southeast corner of Eleventh and Walnut Streets, a house still standing but sadly altered. Here she dwelt until her marriage in 1861.

She was a beautiful, graceful, and highly educated girl, and had inherited remarkable talents from her father and mother.

* Reprinted from *The Jeffersonian*, March, 1915.

Early in life she passed under the sway of the great masters of poetry, history, and the drama, and the spell held her for all her days. She was a devotee of Shakespeare and a disciple of Milton. The divine gift of music was hers, a gift which had belonged to her mother and also to her grandmother. Her very being vibrated in harmony to music, vocal or instrumental. She had a superb voice, sang operatic airs like a professional artist and rendered the sweet old English ballads with pathos and expression. Her mind was extraordinarily brilliant, comprehensive, and powerful. At times she studied and mastered the most unusual subjects. When still a young girl she wrote for the *North American Medico-Chirurgical Review* (a famous journal of those days) a review of a learned book on cretinism. For this work she received recognition and praise from leaders of the medical profession, and, what was even more unusual, a fee from the journal.

In 1861 she married Orville Horwitz and moved to Baltimore. All of you know and love that name, for my dear old friend and comrade, so long a distinguished professor here, so recently taken from us, was nephew and namesake of the husband of Maria Gross. Orville Horwitz of Baltimore was one of the leaders of the bar, but was far more than a great lawyer. He was a delightful conversationalist, a fluent linguist, an able mathematician, a man widely read and deeply learned in many departments of knowledge.

After the death of her husband in 1887 Mrs. Horwitz resided abroad.

Her letters were masterpieces of epistolary style. Though purely spontaneous, they were without erasures or interlineations, were full of information imparted in the most entertaining way, and were rich in apt quotations, wit, and humor. She was entitled to stand in the front rank of the small group of great letter writers, a group headed by Mademoiselle de Scudéry and Madam de Sévigné. She wrote much poetry and many songs and musical compositions, but published nothing save the beautiful ballad, "If to Wish and to Have Were One." Had she chosen, or been forced by circumstances to devote herself to literature, she would have left a celebrated name. Her gift for languages was unusual. She spoke Latin, French, German, and Italian. Her knowledge of English and French literature was not only exact but profound. Her conversation, which shone with wit and sparkled with quick repartee, recalled those greater days when conversation was a fine art and an education.

Her house in Baltimore was a salon frequented by all that was most learned and cultured in that attractive and cultivated city. In Rome, her thronged reception room was neutral ground where ambassadors, statesmen, artists, and political rivals met in the friendliest spirit.

To her final days she retained the captivating grace and dominating charm which impressed all beholders. Two years ago, while in Geneva, she was injured by a fall. For the balance of her life she used a cane and was the victim of harassing pain. She died in Dinard, France, August 25, 1914.

She was surely one of the most learned, charming, and brilliant of women. But beyond even her learning, her brilliancy, and her charm, were her kind heart and generous nature. She helped the unfortunate, she relieved the needy, she lifted the fallen. She was devoted to her friends, adored her family, and fairly worshipped her father. It is because of that filial love that the Gross endowment exists and that I address you this evening as the Gross Professor. Such was Maria Gross Horwitz, to whom this College owes so much. It is with a peculiarly tender feeling of gratitude, admiration, and affection that I pay this tardy tribute to her name.

But one of her generation is left, her brother, Mr. A. Haller Gross, who honors us with his presence. He, too, has the notable ability which distinguished the entire family, for he is scholar, linguist, orator, litterateur, musician, and one of the most distinguished song-writers in the country. As you look upon him you will see a striking likeness to his brother, my revered old master, the late Prof. Samuel W. Gross.

Mrs. Orville Horwitz left four dauthers, all of whom are living. They are Mrs. T. G. Key of Baltimore; Mrs. William C.

Bullitt of Philadelphia; the Countess Andreozzi-Bernini of Rome, and Mrs. Brooke of Valescure, France.

I shall now speak of Samuel D. Gross, America's foremost surgeon. I will give no consecutive study of his life and character. I attempted that on a former occasion, and Dr. Wm. L. Rodman, a short time ago, set forth his life in Louisville. He was the leader of surgical opinion and of concerted medical action: the law-giver of his profession in the United States. He was the best example of professional propriety as well as of professional excellence. He was the friend of the worthy man, the implacable foe of the shady practitioner, the gallery actor, the impostor, and the liar. He was the chief member of the brilliant American constellation which contained Agnew, Joseph Pancoast, Mussey, Willard Parker, Valentine Mott, Van Buren, James R. Wood, Marion Sims, Moses Gunn, Bigelow, Sayre, Cheever, Yandell, John Ashhurst, Jr., Battey, Warren, Parks, and some others. The words of such a man are of interest and importance. His unstudied sentences straight from the heart swing aside the curtains which often hide character, and show us a real man. This evening I purpose setting forth and discussing a few of his sayings and some of his views and commenting upon them.

When I first came to see him and hear him he bore with dignity the noble crown of Age and wore the splendid robes of Fame. To those of us who looked upon him he seemed what he was, the beau-ideal of a great surgeon. His face showed force, intellect, kindliness, and confidence. His eyes had now the fire of command and now the light of tenderness. Every one of us felt that fifty years of American surgery were speaking through his lips. He now and then told a story or related an experience to emphasize a point. He was accustomed to say that you could "nail a lesson on a student's mind" as tight as you pleased and it might get loose, but an apt story "clenched the nail the other side of the board and held the fact in place."

His stories always fitted, and were never vulgar. He was accustomed to denounce the telling of vulgar stories to students. He used to say, "There is one thing worse than a foul-mouthed

Samuel D. Gross.

youth and that is a foul-mouthed old man." "Experience," he said, "is a name not only for successes but for many ghastly errors and dreadful mistakes." He spoke of a certain teacher who in his lectures only used part of his experience, forgetting the ghastly errors and dreadful mistakes. Alfred de Musset makes the mistake of defining all experience as "the name men give to their follies, or their sorrows." He forgot successes. Each of us has in his memory experiences which he cherishes. Each of us has some experiences he is ashamed to look upon face to face. Yet at times we ought to face even the worst ones, that we may learn their lineaments and avoid embracing any other members of the family. Such experiences hurt, but as De Finod said: "Experience is a keen knife that hurts, while it extracts the cataract that blinds."

Gross was born in 1805. He died in 1884, aged seventy-nine years. What a wonderful life span! In the year 1805 Napoleon Bonapart won his mightiest victory, the victory on which the sun of Austerlitz shed its golden rays. Nelson achieved the great naval triumph of Trafalgar. George III, stupid and arrogant, who had lost the American Colonies some twenty years before, still reigned over England. Richard Brinsley Sheridan was rioting with the Prince Regent, Beau Brummell and other distinguished Corinthians. William Pitt, the statesman, received his death stroke by the news of the battle of Austerlitz. England was building with wonderful speed the greatest monument which exists to Napoleon, the English national debt (Doyle). Southey was doing literary work at Greta Hall. Byron was a student at Cambridge. Wordsworth, the "bard of the lakes," was in Grassmere. Coleridge was secretary to the Governor of Malta (Apollo tending the sheep of Admetus!). Sir Walter Scott completed *The Lay of the Last Minstrel*. John Abernethy was assistant surgeon to and lecturer on surgery in St. Bartholomew's Hospital. Astley Cooper, not as yet Sir Astley, was surgeon to Guy's Hospital. Antonia Scarpa was Professor of Anatomy in Padua, and was writing his great work on *Hernia*. Thomas Jefferson was President, and George Clinton was Vice-President of the United States; James

Madison was Secretary of State, and Albert Gallatin was Secretary of the Treasury. The population of the United States was less than 7,000,000. Louisiana had been purchased from France in 1803, but Florida was still owned by Spain. Then, as now, our commerce was crippled and our trade impeded by the warring Continental nations. Fenimore Cooper was a student at Yale. Washington Irving was traveling abroad. Ralph Waldo Emerson was two years of age. Daniel Webster had just begun to practice law. Noah Webster was in New Haven completing his great *Dictionary*. Henry Clay was for the first time a candidate for United States Senator. Winfield Scott was a student at William and Mary College. John C. Calhoun was studying law in Litchfield, Connecticut. Philip Syng Physick of Philadelphia was the leading American surgeon. Benjamin Rush of Philadelphia, the leading teacher and practitioner of medicine in the country, was director of the United States Mint.

Fitch and Rumsey had both moved boats by steam. Fulton was experimenting with steam power, but two years had yet to pass before the "Clermont" was to make the historic trip to Albany. Roads were inconceivably bad, and stages were uncomfortable and slow. Few traveled unless obliged by imperative necessity.

In the early days of the 19th century the district school was a cheerless place, was presided over by a human threshing machine, whose only method of imparting knowledge was to beat it in with a stick. The school kept only during the winter months. The text-books were few and unsatisfactory; there were no maps, globes, explanations, or demonstrations, and there was a preponderance of Watts's hymns and of the most ominous chapters of the Scriptures.

Gross began to go to school in 1812, and he says, "no boy ever detested it" more than he did. It was held in a log cabin about a mile from his home. The road was bad and in stormy weather abominable, and a rainy day meant sitting in school with wet feet. The room was well warmed. There were about thirty pupils between the ages of seven and twenty years. Boys and girls were together. The exercises opened with a hymn and prayer. Every boy who had been for a time at the spelling book was obliged to rise each morning and read a verse from the Bible. After that the ogre in charge licked most of them impartially. The favorite punishments were three in number. Two of them carried mental humiliation and a sense of degradation, one of them also physical pain. One was to make a boy assume a pair of large leather "spectacles," another was to put on him a fool's red cap, another was to beat him with a rod of hazelwood. If a boy spoke aloud, whispered, or laughed, he was instantly punished.

The children recited in common, producing, Gross says, "a jarring, buzzing noise, which fell harshly upon the ear and was in every way objectionable, as tending to cause confusion and to assist in concealing ignorance." Such was the district school. Few Americans got more schooling than could be obtained in a place of this sort. Few went from the school to the academy, as did Gross. Fewer still went to college. It was a brutal system, from which all natures emerged more or less scarred and twisted and none got from it more than slender benefit. There has been no improvement during the last hundred years more notable than that which has taken place in schools and schoolmasters.

The old Puritan spirit dominated the schools. The teachers proposed to make the pupils loving followers of the meek and lowly Prophet who preached in Galilee, if they had to beat them to a pulp to accomplish it.

Gross was fond of sport and play, particularly of pitching quoits, playing ball, rabbit snaring, shooting with the bow gun and shotgun, fishing, fighting bees and wasps, locating and protecting birds' nests in the orchard, and (oh! rigid hypocrite who snuffles lugubrious warnings, I bid you close your ears) pitching pennies. He says he seldom attended church, and he pitched pennies, yet, oh! austere preacher, he was clean and pure and brave and honorable all his days, and it was said at his death that his deeds were crowned by "the milk-white flower of a stainless life." He says, "Pitching for 'keeps' was always very exciting, and never failed to be attended with advantage." He continues thus:

"Even now, at the distance of half a century, I can most vividly recall many of the very spots which served as the arenas of this agreeable pastime. One hundred and fifty to two hundred pennies were not infrequently clustered around the 'meg' at a time, and formed too great a bulk to be removed in one handful. To pick up the 'heads' was most exciting sport, not unlike that which a lucky sportsman experiences in bagging his game." So far was Gross from the views of the narrow bigot who would arrest a boy for pitching pennies in an alley or a lad for snaring rabbits on a farm, that he declared these exercises and amusements had greatly benefited his health and even helped in after life in the practice of his profession. He says, "They served to impart precision to the eye and hand, compelling them to move in concert with each other, so necessary in handling a knife in performing operations. Pitching quoits is particularly useful in this respect, and should be diligently cultivated by young men destined for a profession in which manual dexterity and great accuracy of eye are essential elements."

Gentlemen! a man like that would have been capable of approving of billiards had he thought the game beneficial, and he would have done it irrespective of the most acrid prejudices of the most narrow and bigoted people. At the present day most amusements are being stopped by law and Lord Haughton's view is becoming more and more our own; that is, that everything really agreeable and desirable is either "unhealthy, expensive, or immoral."

Gross's childhood until he was twelve years of age was filled with superstitious fear. He firmly believed, as did all his boy companions, in "ghosts, witches, hobgoblins, devils, evil spirits, and, in short, everything that was weird or supernatural." He finally, by native strength of intellect and force of will, fought down and shook off these terrible impressions. These beliefs were not derived from parental superstitions, for his parents knew better. He lays the sole blame upon a system of education which even in this modern world finds a myriad of advocates. He says his superstitious beliefs resulted from "an education designed to make me good by inducing me to believe that all my acts were watched, and that these acts would be rewarded or punished according as they were good or bad."

"Children are emphatically the creatures of circumstances. The prejudices in which they are reared are sure to influence them, if not during their whole lives, at any rate for a long time, or until they are counteracted by other surroundings or by riper reasoning powers." All of which goes to show that the training of the young is a task too important for ignorance and too delicate for bigotry.

At the age of seventeen he began the study of medicine in a physician's office, a physician who gave him no aid and simply turned him loose on a small library of obsolete books. He then made a great discovery which was the turning-point of his life. He says the discovery was the knowledge of his own ignorance. He found he did not have enough education in Latin and Greek to understand technicalities and to study medicine as he felt it ought to be studied, and as he intended to study it. He had the rare courage to face the situation, succeeded in obtaining his release, and during the next two years he studied in the Wilkesbarre Academy, a school in New York City, and the famous school at Lawrenceville, New Jersey. At the age of nineteen he again began the study of medicine, this time in the office of Doctor Swift, of Easton. After a year's study his health broke down and he developed what we would now call neurasthenia.

"I became very weak, my appetite gave way, and my nervous system was thoroughly wrecked. Sleep forsook my pillow and I was harassed by horrid dreams. I kept a light burning all night in my room lest I should die in the dark." On one occasion he dreamed that his grave was being dug and he awoke completely shaken. "Any unexpected news greatly alarmed me. The ringing of a town bell for a funeral was most fearful to me. As to studying, that was impossible." He treated himself by riding to Niagara Falls on horseback, a distance of 350 miles, going about 25 miles a day. Miles of the way were through forest and wilderness. Rochester was a little hamlet of recent origin. In Buffalo

20

he saw some of Red Jacket's Indians, Red Jacket the celebrated and eloquent chief of the Wolf tribe of the Senecas, the Indian Rienzi, who followed Brant as the chief man of the Six Nations, who fought for England during the Revolution and for the United States in the War of 1812, and who was the implacable foe of the whites and missionaries. These Indians were not as yet depraved by alcohol, poisoned by tuberculosis, ruined by deprivation from their natural nomadic life and by association with Indian agents, representatives of Eastern societies, and congressional committees. Gross found Red Jacket's braves magnificent specimens of manhood, "tall, handsome, and straight as arrows." A few miles from the Falls he saw the remnant of the Tuscaroras; civilization was "getting in its work" upon them. They were not comparable to Red Jacket's warriors, but were dirty, squalid, and ugly. After an absence of six weeks he returned home completely cured. This experience influenced his opinions all his life. He believed that such cases did not require drugs, but rest and open air. He used to quote, "All work and no play makes Jack a dull boy," and say, "There is a time for idleness as well as work." He believed that if you don't let a little grass now and then grow under your feet, a lot of it may long grow over your head. He says in his *Autobiography:* "I had simply been overworked and overdrugged," and, "I regard exercise on horseback as the most salutary exercise an invalid can take." He quotes approvingly a story of Thomas Sydenham, the English Hippocrates:

"A patient whom nobody had been able to cure came for advice. Sydenham told the sufferer that Doctor Roberts of Inverness, Scotland, was the man to cure his dyspepsia and nervousness; it was true that the distance from London was considerable, but he could accomplish it on horseback. The patient rode throughout the necessary days, feeling better daily, but on reaching Inverness found that no Doctor Roberts lived there. In a towering rage he rode back to London and demanded an explanation. "How is your health?" said Sydenham. "Excellent," said the patient, "but you told me an untruth and I want an explanation." Sydenham replied, "I knew that there was no such physician as Doctor Roberts of Inverness, but I also knew that, buoyed up with hope, the journey at this genial season of the year would cure you of your maladies."

Most of the alleged triumphs of the imbecilities of Christian Science (which, by the way, isn't Christian and isn't science) are due to the rousing of hope and the abandonment of overdrugging. If Christian Scientists believed their own theories not one of them should scratch when he itches, cough, hiccough, get seasick, apply a corn plaster, wear eye-glasses, or warm clothing, get a tooth pulled or filled, have wax taken out of the ear, the nails paired, or the scalp washed. It has always been a regret to me that this movement was not sufficiently active in Gross's day to have caused him to express some vigorous opinions about it. They would have been worth listening to.

In 1826 Doctor Gross entered the Jefferson Medical College as a student, and also became an office student of the founder of the school, the celebrated George McClellan. From this time until his death he belonged to the medical profession. In it were his work and happiness, his ambitions, and his pride. He worked earnestly and conscientiously, and took his degree in March, 1828. He loved work. All his life he wore the iron crown of duty. As Yandell put it, his life was "an unbroken process of laborious years." He did not believe in a man knocking off work for good and going in for life-long idleness simply because he could live without working. He used to say that he would rather "wear out than rust out." To illustrate his views he would tell the story of Doctor Pope of St. Louis. For twenty-five years Charles H. Pope was the leading surgeon of St. Louis. He was a brilliant operator, an admirable lecturer, had an immense practice, was rich, and highly respected. In his various duties he was happy. Gross says, "This man, still young, was happy in the possession of a very remunerative practice, and of numerous and warmly attached friends; happy as a teacher in a highly respectable school, in great degree the creation of his own talents and exertion, and happy in the enjoyment of every worldly good."

He was persuaded to give up work and to go to Paris to pass his remaining days in idleness. In 1868 Gross met him in Paris: "I soon saw that he was out of his natural element. He had occasional fits of despondency, felt himself out of place, and longed to be back in the harness in a city where he had achieved so many triumphs." About three years later he paid a visit to St. Louis, where he was warmly welcomed by his old friends. He returned to Paris, grew more and more moody and despondent, and finally committed suicide. Gross says, "I have always thought . . . that Pope would never have committed this rash act if he had remained at his post in St. Louis."

I am convinced this is true philosophy. To give up the loved occupation of a lifetime, to be busy for years and then to suddenly stop, to be accustomed to awake wondering how you are to finish the daily tasks and instead wonder how the weary hours are to be gotten through, produces fatty degeneration of the mind. Just as the heart of an athlete degenerates if he abandons exercise, so the mind degenerates in prolonged idleness. Again, to pass from a position of proud usefulness and importance to become a nobody in a foreign land or a strange city, humiliates, mortifies, and drives the iron into the soul. The labor a man has long loved is necessary to him. If deprived of it he longs for it as a drunkard does for his dram. The only men who can successfully give up medicine are those who are able to keep constantly occupied with other interests. Some love travel and become busy idlers.

Some immerse themselves in literature.

Some ride the Rosinante of a hobby.

Some few, like my venerated chief, Doctor Keen, become active in a multitude of things. Think of him. He writes valuable books, delivers important addresses, is President of the American Philosophical Society, and plays a leading part in the social, literary, scientific, charitable, and religious life of the city. Doctor Keen's life shows that one can be happy and useful after retirement. But few of us can hope to emulate him in ability, energy, or enthusiasm.

Doctor Levis and many others tried and failed.

But it does not do to stay too long. As age comes on, sooner or later, the surgeon's eyes dim, his hands tremble, and his judgment fails. There is no fixed period for this. Some last years longer than others. Gross did a successful lithotomy in this hospital when he was seventy-eight, although nearly two years before he had retired from teaching. When Doctor Keen stopped he was at his very best. Both he and Gross were fit to continue indefinitely. Each one had a horror of showing any sign of failure. Each wished to be remembered as he was at his highest level, and each is.

Many men stay too long and become dangers to patients and clogs to a school. A man may do it from the highest motives and believe that he is necessary to a school. Gross used to say, "No man is necessary to any school." This is undoubtedly true. The minute a man gets a notion that he is necessary he becomes about as useful as a sundial in a rainstorm, an ulster on the Guinea coast, last year's calendar, or a canceled postage stamp. The man who thinks he is necessary is usually the man who knows it all. Any man who knows it all knows a multitude of things which are not true and is a veritable geyser of misinformation. It's hard to know how to get rid of such a man in medicine. Were he a preacher he would be given a colleague. Were he a lawyer just fit to be put on the shelf he would be put on the bench instead.

Gross had in him no faintest trace of the snob or tufthunter. He was no admirer of mere wealth. He had a hearty contempt for the man who would buy his way. In making a medical appointment he was not swerved by family, religious, or political influences. When a doctor tried to use those things he would say, "That seems like a good man to beat." The man who seized or made opportunity, who wrought with tireless brain and body, who came from small beginning to distinction and power, he had great respect for. He respected the self-made man. In speaking of a certain man he said, "He is a self-made man, and all the better for that." Of course, he meant the best type of self-made man; not the type of the arrogant, perfidious, and blatant Bounderby who considered it creditable to have been dirty and who claimed to have been neglected when he had been cared for with kindness and attention; not the type of the ranting demagogue who abuses all who are better off than himself. Such men claim to be self-made and evidently they are, for the job was ill done, and by an amateur at that. It is rather noble of such a man to claim he is self-made and to thus assume the entire responsibility.

Gross did not scorn society. He approved of cultivated society, and moved in the most cultivated circles of this city. He particularly enjoyed the society of cultured ladies. In society he was charming and his presence was solicited by the best the city had. Some of the genuine, rigid, old-time Philadelphians interested and amused him immensely. One of them was Henry C. Carey, the eminent political economist, the antagonist of Ricardo's theory of rent, the opponent of the Malthusian theory of population, the advocate of a system of protection which would lead to ultimate free trade. Mr. Carey was persuaded that most things in this modern world were bound straight to the dogs. He denounced the women of the present day as frivolous and insipid, and said: "The men are no better. There is no literary talent among them; they are tradesmen and shopkeepers. The Wister Party consisted of members of the American Philosophical Society and comprised men of distinction in the different professions. The Saturday Club, which succeeded that party, is made up of all sorts of men. The Binneys, the Ingersolls, the Duponceaus, the Whartons, the Merediths, the Peterses, the Chapmans have disappeared, and there are none to fill their places. There is no one to take my place at my Sunday evening reunions. We have no historians, no poets, no novelists, no writers, in short, of any great merit in any branch of literature. Philadelphia has gone to the devil." There you hear the real, old-time, genuine, true-blue Philadelphian, with several generations of Philadelphia blood in his veins. It is apt to act on us that way. I don't know why, but it does so. I feel that way myself. It is the same way with elderly officers of the army and navy. In every age, and almost to a man, they declare that "the service is going to the devil." Yet at the very time Carey spoke, Philadelphia boasted Henry C. Lea, the author of the famous *History of the Inquisition in Spain;* George H. Boker, the poet and dramatist; Doctor Furness, the eminent Shakespearean scholar; Joseph Leidy, the investigator and discoverer; Charles J. Stillé, the historian—that man of many powers and of irresistible charm; S. Weir Mitchell, and Gross himself.

No man ever lived who hated humbugs, quacks, and liars more heartily than Gross. He says he has known many medical boasters: "They generally take better with the common herd of mankind than does the modest and retiring physician. People like to be humbugged. . . . Lying never dies; it is a principle of nature, and I have known many cases in which it was hereditary." Barnum said people liked to be fooled, and we observe that Gross was of the same opinion, though Barnum capitalized the idea and Gross did not. He then goes on to say that we may lie by acts as well as by words and cites the historical incident of Cardinal Hildebrand, who crawled around as though stricken with the infirmities of age and with the hand of death upon him. The electoral college was convinced he had only a year or two to live. After his election he at once became erect, alert, decisive. He said he had stooped while looking for the keys of St. Peter. Now that he had found them he had no further need for bending. Mark Twain brilliantly maintained this view about lying, and members of the Senior Class may remember that I have lined up on this question with Gross and Samuel L. Clemens.

Gross mentions that while in Long Branch he saw "three cottages belonging to Mrs. Winslow, the inventor and proprietor of a nostrum known as Winslow's Soothing Syrup." "Charlatans fare well in this country," he says: "Swaim made more than a million dollars by the sale of his Panacea; Jayne, Schenck, Ayer, Brandreth, Townsend, and many other vendors of patent medicines have accumulated large fortunes. Lydia E. Pinkham left nearly half a million from the sale of her Vegetable Compound and Liver Pills. Her likeness still graces many of the principal newspapers of the day. It is said that she spent annually more than $200,000 in advertising."

Gross's view as to the value of advertising is borne out by facts. Beyond doubt the newspaper makes the noted quack possible. Without advertising the vogue of a quack would be temporary and local. As an editor looks over his own great daily and sees it bristling with advertisements of quack methods and quack medicines does he ever feel any qualms of conscience as to the number of persons those advertisements will maim or kill; does he ever have a hint of doubt as to the universal civilizing influence of that great engine, the press? I suppose not. He is hardened. If he were not he would not be in charge. A paper is not a philanthropic venture; it is run to make money, and quacks pay high rates. When papers advertise quacks in religion we need not wonder that they advertise quacks in medicine.

Doctor Gross was indignant on August 10, 1881. He sets down the following: "One does not like to speak ill of one's brethren; but there are politicians and tricksters in the medical as there are in every other profession—men who, from interested or dishonorable motives, do not hesitate to slander or undermine the standing of their superiors. What makes the matter worse is that the injury is usually performed in so sly and underhand a manner as to render it difficult, if not impossible, to counteract its effects." He was moved to these truthful but bitter reflections about some members of the medical profession by the conduct of two practitioners in another city who opposed the wish of a family that Gross should be called in consultation. One of them said, "We don't know Doctor Gross." They said, "Doctor Gross is too old, and no longer practices." They tried to alarm the patient by leading him to fear that if Gross came he would perform venesection. Let me say to you gentlemen on the benches, never refuse a consultation. In a serious case ask for it before the family can ask you to secure one. Always accede when they do ask for it. It shares the responsibility. It is often of great service to the patient. It is invariably a comfort to the family. Don't shrink from it through fear of being shown up. Don't repudiate it through ridiculous vanity. Simply insist that the man you meet must be a regular and a respectable practitioner. No one has a right to ask you to meet a quack. If they do ask you, refuse indignantly. To meet such a man will be of no service to the patient, will harm you with the members of your own school, and will be cited with gratification by the man you met. Hear Doctor Gross on the adoption of new code of ethics in New York State: "The object . . . was to authorize the members of the regular profession to meet in consultation all legally constituted practitioners, of whatever school, sect, or character, thus throwing wide open the doors to all kinds of degrading associations, and thereby humiliating us in the eyes not only of one another, but of the public, and at the same time making us the laughing-stock of eclectics and others who have drawn an impregnable wall around Hippocratic medicine by their peculiar dogmas and practices. How any respectable and honorable members of the profession could persuade themselves to meet these men in this manner is an enigma which it would be difficult to solve. Selfishness was evidently at the bottom of the movement—a desire to enlarge their practice and to increase their emoluments; this, and nothing else."

Gross had no sympathy with a man who decided a question of morals by determining which course was richest in dollars. He did not even believe in charging great fees for legitimate services. He charged what he called fair fees. Only once in his life did he charge a fee of $2500 for an operation. He was no tradesman, handling surgical goods over a counter and haggling about the price. He despised and denounced all who were. He honored his profession too much to drag it through devious courses and foul ways to enrich himself. He says: "The acquisition of money has never been my aim or desire. I have lived solely for my profession." For the gallery actor, the surgeon who proclaims himself repeatedly on the big drum, who is always in the newspapers, and is always being interviewed about milk, water, whisky, tobacco, physiology, the relations of the sexes, the disease possessed by some prominent man, or what not, he possessed an unspeakable contempt. Of such a man he would at times remark, "His press agent is active today."

And how he hated a regular doctor smirched with quackery! A prominent man in another city succeeded in persuading the United States Government to buy a certain alleged remedy for cancer. Gross used to say: "He sold his professional reputation and his honor as a gentleman for $10,000 in gold." Gross would have been burnt at the stake before he would have done such a thing for any money. He regarded death as a natural law and not a penalty. He did not wish to linger out his days as the lean and slippered pantaloon. He hoped to be busy up to the last, and when the time had come, to die suddenly. He says: "The litany contains a prayer against sudden death, considering it as a great evil; but this has reference solely to a man's religious preparation. It assumes that a slow death affords a person a better chance to get ready for the kingdom of heaven. A sensible man should always be ready. . . . I have seen so much of chronic death as it may be called, that I pray God to preserve me and mine from its appalling infliction. What can be more horrible, more truly agonizing, than death from consumption or cancer? When my hour comes I hope the Destroyer will do me a friendly act by extinguishing life in the twinkling of an eye, and thus save me from the pangs of gradual dissolution." To these words of Doctor Gross I speak a solemn and profoundly meant "Amen."

One day, in showing a brain in which there was a huge blood clot that must have caused death almost immediately, he looked at it musingly, and said, "The death of a gentleman."

The surgeon, the real surgeon, is something far above and beyond the mere operator. The man who can only operate and nothing more is simply a skilled handicraftsman. As Sir Frederick Treves says: "The actual manipulative part of surgery requires no very great skill, and many an artisan shows infinitely more adeptness in his daily work. A wood engraver would probably

soon find as little difficulty in baring the carotid artery as a stone
carver would find in performing osteotomy." I am convinced
that knifesmanship is the easiest branch of the profession, the
most readily acquired, the most admired, and the most profitable financially. Young men often seek it out as a career. A
man may operate with admirable dexterity and yet do very bad
surgery, operating perhaps when no operation should be done, or
removing, it may be most skilfully, what ought not to be removed. Real greatness in an operation is never grasped or
exhibited by the mere knifesman. Again, hear Sir Frederick
Treves: "A well-matured and well-balanced judgment guides the
hand of him who shows most skill; he may do well who is bold,
but he will do better who has precise knowledge. The surest
sense of confidence rests with the operator who knows accurately
what he intends to do, and how to do it. The least success follows
the hand of the man who retains throughout an operation a
speculative spirit, who depends largely upon his imagination for
conditions, and upon the fortune of events for results. A shaki-
ness of the hand may be some bar to the success of an operation,
but he of a shaky mind is hopeless. In the handling of a sharp
instrument in connection with the human body a confusion of
the intellect is worse than chorea."

Hear Gross on the same subject: "Persons have often come
to me saying they had understood that I was very fond of
using the knife. Such stories are frequently propagated from
selfish considerations by designing confrères, and the weak and
credulous are only too prone to credit them. As for myself,
nothing could be more untrue or more unjust. I have never
hesitated to employ the knife when I thought it was imperatively demanded to relieve or cure my patient; but that
I have ever operated merely for the sake of display or the
gratification of a selfish end is as base as it is false. I have
always had too much respect for human life, for my profession, and for my own dignity to be guilty of such an outrage.
No man ever had a greater or more unmitigated contempt for
the knifesman, or mere mechanical surgeon and operator, than

I, and I have never hesitated, in season and out of season, to denounce him in the most unmeasured terms."

Gentlemen, I have often said that when a man tells me he never worries about cases, I conclude I would not select him to operate on me or mine. A man who does not worry has no proper sense of responsibility. Worry is a device of nature to give us a sense of responsibility, to make us careful, and to lead us to be conscientious. The surgeon should have a proper anxiety, first of all for the patient and next for his own professional reputation. Surgery is surely the most responsible of callings. Gross speaks of the "terrible anxiety" and "the utter wretchedness" which so often attend a surgeon. He continues thus: "What other profession or pursuit is there that involves so much mental anguish, so much awful responsibility, so much wear and tear of mind and body? The physician and obstetrician certainly have their trials, and many sad and even bitter ones, but compared with those of the surgeon, they are comparatively insignificant. The surgeon, like them, not only frequently of necessity loses his patient, but his patient, if in case of accident he should survive, is often, in consequence of his mutilated condition, literally a living monument of the surgeon's disgrace." Gross points out that for such conditions the surgeon is very often most unjustly blamed, and continues: "The physician, on the contrary, either hides his bad skill in the grave, or, if his patient survives, no matter how crippled he may be, no blame is ascribed to the treatment. The hepatized lung does not, like the ankylosed joint or deformed limb, obtrude itself at every step upon the eye of the observer."

Ponder well these words of Gross before you decide to follow surgery for good or ill, ponder these words, and be sure, in the words of Joseph Pancoast, long Gross's beloved colleague, that you have will and force "to make your shoulders broad enough" to bear the dread responsibilities of surgery. Believe me, it is only the small men who disregard them and scoff at them. Men like Sir James Paget and D. Hayes Agnew, Joseph Pancoast and Samuel D. Gross speak for those who really feel proper responsibility and hence are really fit to do surgery.

Gross was scrupulously exact as to time. He was always just on time for a lecture, operation, or consultation. He used to say it was a cruelty to an expectant patient to keep him waiting a single minute beyond the time agreed upon. It made him very angry when an assistant or colleague was late. When a belated assistant would come sidling into the clinic room, hoping to escape observation, the Professor, on catching sight of the late one, would break off what he was saying, look at him with terrifying reprehension, note the time by his watch, and then continue his remarks without adding words to this reproof of the luckless offender, except perhaps to quote, "Punctuality is the politeness of kings." He was always on time, and he was the king of this institution. I said "always." I should have said "but once." One day, to the consternation of the assistants, and the amazement of everybody, he did not enter as the hand of the watch touched the hour mark. Several minutes of waiting ensued and then he entered. As he came in every assistant and every student took out his watch, noted the time, and then glared at the Professor. He smiled and said, "Well, young gentlemen, it is true that I am for once late, but let me say, if any one of you had had such a charming young lady in your office as I just had in mine he would not have been here at all."

I have endeavored, gentlemen, to give you some glimpses of what sort of man he was who earned the D. C. L. of Oxford, the LL. D. of Cambridge, the LL. D. of Edinburgh, and the spontaneously given royal title of the Emperor of American Surgery, to show you something of his personality, his opinions, his philosophy, his views about men and things. If I have succeeded in even hinting to you a tithe of the splendor of his intellect, the force of his character, the profundity of his scholarship, the genius of his surgery, the influence of his books and lectures, the geniality of his nature, and the kindliness of his heart, you will have no doubt that the highest niche in America's temple of surgery belongs of right to Samuel David Gross, the 4th, Professor of Surgery in the Jefferson Medical College.

WILLIAM WILLIAMS KEEN: A SKETCH*

DOCTOR Keen's resignation from the Professorship of Surgery, and his assumption of the position of Emeritus Professor of Surgery, remove from activity the most notable figure in the Jefferson Medical College; and it is singularly appropriate that *The Jeffersonian* should devote this number to some consideration of our great surgeon's personality, achievements, and position in the surgical world.

William Williams Keen was born in Philadelphia, January 19, 1837. He is of Swedish descent; and those of you that go to the churchyard of the Old Swedes Church, in the district of Wecacoe, Philadelphia, will see headstones bearing the name of Keen which were placed in position over two hundred years ago. The house of his birth has been, of late years, destroyed. It was on the site now occupied by the Old Ladies' Home, on the north side of Chestnut Street above Thirty-sixth.

Doctor Keen was graduated at Brown University in 1859, and took his degree in medicine at the Jefferson Medical College in 1862. During his student days he was an office-student of Dr. John H. Brinton, whose colleague he afterward became in the Chair of Surgery, at Jefferson. Immediately after Doctor Keen's graduation, he became an Assistant Surgeon in the United States Army, serving until the termination of the Civil War. In one of the military hospitals in Philadelphia he was closely associated with two gentlemen that became noted in after life. The first of these was Dr. S. Weir Mitchell, also a graduate of the Jefferson Medical College, who really founded the modern science of neurology, who has become most distinguished in both literature and science, and who occupies an altogether unique position in the profession today—a position so distinguished and remarkable that when he shall pass away there will be no one to fill his

* Reprinted from *The Jeffersonian*, April, 1907.

William Williams Keen.

place. The other associate of Doctor Keen was Dr. George R. Morehouse, also a graduate of the Jefferson Medical College; a man of high scientific attainments, who was very successful as a general practitioner and received the LL. D. of Princeton University because of his scientific studies. Mitchell, Morehouse, and Keen studied particularly the effect of injuries of the nerves; and they published a book on this subject, which has become a medical classic, having been translated into most languages and being quoted in every treatise on disease of the nervous system. It is seldom in the history of medicine that we can find the record of three young men thrown together accidentally by the exactions of military service, who have labored together with such harmony and have produced such admirable and enduring scientific work.

At the close of the war Doctor Keen went to Europe and studied in Paris, Berlin, and Vienna. He heard Velpeau, in his old age; he listened to Civiale, Nélaton, Trousseau, and other eminent Parisians; he followed Billroth and Cohnheim in Vienna; and in Berlin he was particularly impressed with the greatness of Bernard v. Langenbeck, the illustrious leader of German surgery. It was then that he acquired that admiration for and confidence in great, broad-minded, philosophical, deep-thinking Germany, which he has retained throughout his life. I have heard him state that the two greatest operative surgeons he ever saw were Bernard v. Langenbeck, of Berlin, and Joseph Pancoast, of Philadelphia.

All students of Jefferson have heard him relate, when he wished to emphasize the necessity for caution in making a diagnosis, how he had seen v. Langenbeck remove the female mammary gland for what he believed to be carcinoma, and then open it to the gland after its removal only to find an abscess. Von Langenbeck was not nonplussed, but turned to the class and said: "I have done that but twice before in my life." Doctor Keen also used to relate the tradition about v. Langenbeck, which has likewise been told of other surgeons—notably of Syme and of Fergusson, that a man attending v. Langenbeck's clinic to witness an amputation paused for a moment to take a pinch of snuff; and when his sneeze was over, the arm was off at the shoulder joint, and he had missed the spectacle.

When Doctor Keen returned to Philadelphia he began to practise surgery; and I have heard him state that in the first private case upon which he operated, he undertook to do the operation in his office, and the patient died from the effects of the chloroform. This event would have shaken the nerve of the strongest, and would have deterred all but the strongest from following a surgical career. Immediately after his return, he began to lecture on pathologic anatomy at the Jefferson Medical College, laying in his mind that solid foundation which was to be of such splendid use to him in his subsequent life. Toward the end of 1866 he became a Teacher of Anatomy and Operative Surgery in the Philadelphia School of Anatomy on Chant Street, a school that had had connected with it so many able and brilliant men— notably Joseph Pancoast, James McClintock, and D. Hayes Agnew. This position he continued to fill with conspicuous success until 1875. It was at this time that he began to use the living model in order to teach surface anatomy and surgical landmarks; and Professor Cunningham, of Edinburgh, one of the most distinguished of living anatomists, has recently stated that he obtained the idea of this sort of teaching from Doctor Keen. His lectures on anatomy were masterpieces, clear, definite, and comprehensive; teaching the part in relation with the whole; and showing in each region the surgical and medical relationships which are of the utmost importance.

During this period he laid, broad and deep, that anatomical knowledge which made him the great operator that he has become; for a man can no more do good surgery without anatomical knowledge than a pilot can safely guide his boat without knowing the channel. A different belief has become somewhat popular in recent years, and some have gone so far as to say that the surgeon simply cuts and ties; but it always has been true that one must be a good anatomist to be a good surgeon, and it will be just as true a thousand years from now as it is today.

In 1876 Doctor Keen became Professor of Anatomy in the

Pennsylvania College of the Fine Arts, a position that he retained until 1890. From 1884 to 1889 he was Professor of Surgery in the Woman's Medical College; and from 1889 to 1907 he was Professor of Surgery in the Jefferson Medical College. It was the latter institution that was his real forum. His reputation, considerable when he came to us, broadened and expanded with every year; and from our arena he came to speak with a voice so authoritative that it sounded throughout this hemisphere and echoed beyond the sea.

In his later life honors have trodden upon each other's heels. He is an A. M. and an LL.D. of Brown University; and LL.D. of the Northwestern University, the University of Toronto, the University of Edinburgh, and Yale University; a Trustee and Fellow of Brown University; a Trustee of Shaw University, of the Crozier Theological Seminary, and of the Pennsylvania Dental College; a member of the Philadelphia Academy of Natural Sciences, and of the American Philosophical Society. He is an ex-President of the Philadelphia County Medical Society, of the College of Physicians of Philadelphia, of the American Medical Association, and of the American Surgical Association. He was the Honorary President of the First Egyptian Medical Congress, in 1902; he is an Honorary Fellow of the Royal College of Surgeons of England; is Foreign Corresponding Member of various learned societies of Europe, and is Consulting Surgeon to several Philadelphia hospitals. He is also an Honorary Member of the Clinical Society of London, a member of the Royal College of Surgeons of Edinburgh, and an Associate Fellow of the American Academy of Arts and Sciences.

His contributions to literature have been numerous and important. He wrote with Doctors Mitchell and Morehouse the work upon *Gunshot Injuries of Nerves;* and is the author of a sketch of the *Early History of Practical Anatomy and of a History of the Philadelphia School of Anatomy.* He delivered the Toner Lectures in 1876, his subject being the *Surgical Complications of Fevers.* These lectures first served to direct attention to the numerous and important surgical complications and sequences of

21

typhoid fever. His study of the complications of typhoid fever has been placed in a permanent form in a book that has had a large circulation. Doctor Keen was joint editor with Dr. J. William White, of the *American Text-book of Surgery*, which has had an enormous sale. He was one of the writers in Dennis's *American System of Surgery* and in Dercum's *Diseases of the Nervous System*. He wrote the *Sections on the Surgery of the Brain and the Spine* in Buck's *Reference Handbook of the Medical Sciences*, and also a History of the First Baptist Church of Philadelphia. In 1905 he published a book containing his addresses and other papers. He is at present editing Keen's *System of Surgery*. He was the editor of Heath's *Manual of Anatomy*, in 1870; of Flower's *Diagrams of the Nerves*, in 1872; and of the *American Health Primers, Nos. 1 to 12*, in 1879 and 1880. One of his most notable literary achievements was the editing of *Gray's Anatomy* in 1887. Besides these productions he has published a multitude of important scientific papers.

When the younger Gross died and Doctor Keen was elected to succeed him, we of the Surgical Out-patient Department were profoundly anxious as to the retention of our positions. We felt that it was not at all unlikely that he might want men connected with him personally to be his assistants. He was, however, entirely too broad-gauged to do this thing. Not a man of us in the department knew him personally; we simply knew of him as a teacher in the Woman's Medical College, as a Surgeon to St. Mary's Hospital, as the editor of *Gray's Anatomy*, and as one doing wonderful work in the surgery of the brain.

One morning he stepped into the Out-patient Department, although "stepped in" is scarcely the term, because, with his superabundant energy, it would be more correct to say that he bounded in. He introduced himself, said a few genial words, and assured us, as a matter of course, that we should all be retained. The first clinic that he held in the institution secured the complete admiration of the class. He did an operation of the most formidable nature, and demonstrated it step by step as he went along; and during the clinic hour an emergency case of strangulated hernia was brought in, upon which he operated before us. Everyone present at that clinic knew beyond doubt that one of the masters of surgery now held the Chair.

At this period I was an assistant in the Surgical Out-patient Department of the Hospital and also in the Anatomical Department of the College. In the College I was not only the under dog, but was very much the under dog, and was going through, with the official Pangloss of that day, a series of difficulties that threatened my collegiate existence. It is needless to dig up this old story. It is not an altogether pleasant one, and it bred many prolonged enmities. Doctor Keen knew nothing whatever about me, and he had heard merely the other side of the controversy. Nevertheless, instigated by a sense of justice, he sent for me and told me that he was quite sure that I must have a side to the story as well as the others. He asked me to tell him frankly and freely my position in the matter. I did so, and he said I was right and that he would sustain me. He did sustain me. He, so to speak, took me by the hair of the head and lifted me out of the waters when I was near the cataract. It was his strong arm that set me on terra firma; and everything that, since that time, I may have gained in professional life I owe entirely to his early aid at a critical period; to his enduring friendship and to his constant support.

As a surgical teacher I think that Doctor Keen has had few equals and no superiors. He always knew his subject most thoroughly, and was always perfectly prepared in everything that related to its literature and its history. He used good, clear English; his sentences were well arranged, his delivery was clear cut, expressive and vigorous, and he employed emphasis to the greatest possible advantage. He clearly differentiated the essential and fundamental from the nonessential and extraneous. His lectures were masterpieces in the presentation of individual topics, and many of them would have borne publication without the alteration of a word.

As an operator he was and is wonderful. He is absolutely fearless, and his judgment seems at its very best when the surgical situation appears at its very worst. I have helped him in operations in which there have been presented the very greatest difficulties and dangers; but, to drop into the vernacular, in all these years I have never seen him turn a hair. Emergencies seem to act upon him as they are said to have acted upon General Picton, of the British Army, one of the heroes of Waterloo, of whom it is said that he was always in the best humor in moments of danger; and that he was always in a heavenly temper when the ground was entirely mined with explosives and the situation almost hopeless. His temperament has in it a considerable vein of what might be called innocent gaiety, which occasionally bubbles over during the midst of a perilous operation. This mental condition is not the result of levity, for it actually serves to strengthen him and his assistants against some threatening catastrophe. Over and over again, in an operation, I have seen him calmly and thoughtfully originate a valuable new step as he went along. These new steps have in many instances become part of the literature of surgery. One of his greatest strengths was the habit of reviewing an operation after its completion, interrogating, questioning, striving to find out if he had erred, and if he could do better next time, and gladly listening to any one of his assistants who might offer a suggestion or point out a mistake.

In the presentation of a topic at a society meeting I have never heard his superior. If half an hour is the time allotted to him, he just covers the subject in that time; if fifteen minutes is allotted, he also just covers the subject. He is never superfluous in language, and he always presents each topic with a completeness that is to me amazing. He also has this same strength as a speaker at important dinners, and all who attended the meeting of the British Medical Association at Montreal will remember with delight the charming address he gave and the great enthusiasm it evoked among all present.

There never lived a man more ready to give credit for a hint or a suggestion. There never lived a man more anxious that his colleagues and assistants should do good work and obtain reputation by it. Some small men appropriate the work done by their assistants, he helped his assistants to name and position. He put cases at their disposal, gave them access to his library, aided them with advice and suggestions, and then gave them every bit of credit for the work. When I began to do surgery he would let me do an operation at the end of the clinic, would assist me himself and afterward give me good advice as to how I must improve myself. Then he let me do operations without his assistance, although he remained in the room. Later still he would go away and leave me alone, and I will never forget how glad I was to see him return the first time he did it. Finally, he let me hold clinics for him now and then. Never was a man given a better chance by his chief.

On account of my close relations with Doctor Keen for so many years and of my gratitude to him for countless acts of kindness, it becomes an extremely difficult matter for me to set him before the public from the personal standpoint. On one side is the danger that, out of the fulness of my heart, I may say too much; and on the other, the peril that, owing to my fear of saying too much, I may evince an absolute leanness of expression. It is best that I close by expressing the conviction that, in his retirement from the school, the greatest man in American surgery has laid down his scalpel. We, of the Jefferson Medical College, an institution which he loves so much and for which he has done so much, have lost a model, a leader, an inspiration, a glory, and we shall not soon look upon his like again.

THE FOUNDATION AND THE FOUNDER OF JEFFERSON
MEDICAL COLLEGE*

ON the lot numbered 518 and 520 Locust Street stood the original Jefferson Medical College, and until a very few years ago the building remained there. It has since been destroyed by fire. It was originally a cotton factory and then became the Winter Tivoli Theater. The Locust Street of those days was called Prune.

Directly across the street from the College was the Walnut Street Prison for criminals and debtors, and an interesting rule of that establishment was that the yard must be "kept free from cows, hogs, dogs, and fowls."

On the east of the College was the burial ground of the Free Quakers, those members of the Society of Friends who had gone out to fight under Washington in the Revolution and had been expelled from the Meeting for their patriotism. On the western side was Washington Square, then used as the Potter's Field. Directly back of the College was a popular ale-house, and within a block or so were several churches. In other words, there were crime and misery in front, death on either side, and consolation in the rear.

The first course of lectures opened in November, 1825, and the last lecture heard in this building was in March, 1828; and in August of 1828 the College moved to Tenth Street below Sansom into an altered church.

The first matriculate of the College was Henry D. Smith, and the first class consisted of 107 members. The illustrious Samuel D. Gross entered there as a student in the second class. He graduated in the spring of 1828. In that old building McClellan was the Professor of Surgery; Nathan R. Smith taught Anatomy; John Eberle taught Practice of Medicine; W. C. P. Barton taught

* Reprinted from the *Jefferson Medical College Alumni Bulletin*, January, 1930.

Materia Medica; Washington L. Atlee was a student; and George McClellan, the Professor of Surgery, invented teaching by public clinics, that is, the bringing of cases before the students in the collegiate lecture room. It is strange to think today how this plan was opposed by conservatives, but it was adopted as the most prominent factor of the curriculum by the famous faculty of '41; the faculty which contained John K. Mitchell, Joseph Pancoast, Robley Dunglinson, Benjamin Franklin Bache, Charles D. Meigs, Thomas D. Mütter, and Robert M. Houston.

The new building, set up at Tenth Street below Sansom, was twice enlarged and was succeeded by the present structure at the northwest corner of Tenth and Walnut Streets. The ground once occupied by the College is covered by the present hospital. The College made no attempt to have a hospital until 1844. Most of the operations performed were trivial, and when a serious one was done, the patient was taken home in a carriage and was cared for at home by the Professor of Surgery or his assistants.

In 1825 it was practically obligatory that a teacher wear a swallow-tail coat at the lectures and that he drive a chaise on his rounds. A hungry student went out into Fifth Street and bought hot corn or pepperpot from the colored women who sold these articles in the street. If he felt religious he could go to St. Peter's, St. Mary's, or St. Joseph's Church. If he had convivial instincts he satisfied them in the Goose and Gridiron or the Robinson Crusoe. Feeling a leaning toward the drama, he went to the Olympic Theater at Ninth and Walnut Streets or the Chestnut Street Theater on Chestnut Street above Sixth. If a reading streak struck him he went to the Philadelphia Library on Fifth Street above Walnut. If he longed for combat he went to Ninth and Chestnut Streets, where he was sure to meet some worthy foeman in a student of the University, the building of which institution stood in that region.

The Almshouse, which afterward became Blockley, was then on the lot between Spruce and Pine Streets and Tenth and Eleventh. The Law Courts were at Sixth and Chestnut Streets. The Mayor's office was at Fifth and Chestnut Streets. The United

States Bank, about which a national political contest raged, was in the building that is now the Custom House. There were no uniformed policemen, but the streets were indifferently patrolled by watchmen who were also lamp-lighters. When a group of students went out on a festivity it was a favorite amusement to beat up the watch.

At this time revolutionary ideas were still immensely influential, and many men were living who had crossed the Delaware with Washington, and had been acquainted personally with Benjamin Franklin, had wintered at Valley Forge and had seen the surrender at Yorktown. The year we opened, John Quincy Adams became President of the United States and Henry Clay, Secretary of State, and it was the year Lafayette ended his final tour of America. It was the year Oliver Wendell Holmes went up to Harvard, in which Washington Irving set out for Spain, in which Fitz Greene Halleck made his European journey, in which Nathaniel Hawthorne graduated from Bowdoin College, in which Webster threw overboard his free-trade views, in which Poe prepared for the University of Virginia, and in which Andrew Jackson became embedded in the heart of the Democratic Party at St. Andrew the First of present-day tradition.

The founder of the Jefferson Medical College was Dr. George McClellan, born in Woodstock, Conn., in 1796. He was of distinguished ancestry, and the blood of gallant Highlanders and of Revolutionary patriots ran hot in his veins.

In 1745 the bloody Duke of Cumberland defeated the adherents of the House of Stuart in the Battle of Culloden. Many of the rebels were caught and died by the gallows; many were thrown to moulder in jail; some were fugitives in Highland fastnesses and became marauders. Some went abroad to take their chances in the new world. McClellan of Kirkcudbright, from the region of the Firth of Solway, was one of the followers of Prince Charlie. He escaped to America and settled in Worcester, Mass. A son, named Samuel, fought in the French and Indian War, moved to Woodstock, Conn., went out with the militia when the Revolutionary War began and became a brigadier-general

George McClellan.

under Washington. Samuel's son, James, was a merchant, wool-raiser and prospector and much respected. James married Miss Eldridge, whose father had fought for the Revolution, and from this union was born George McClellan.

George received his preliminary education in the Woodstock Academy. As a boy he was short, and though well-made, his companions called him "Little Mac." He could not possibly have dreamed at this time that a son of his, also called "Little Mac," was to come to the command of mighty armies, was to inspire the devotion of tens of thousands of heroic soldiers, was to stand upon the flaming brow of Malvern Hill and ride between the lines at Antietam. Even as a boy our Founder was possessed of a most positive character. All his life he was amazingly ener-getic, absolutely intrepid, rapid in his movements, quick in com-prehension, positive in his conclusions, emphatic in every expression of opinion and enthusiastic for whatever cause he embraced. His memory was remarkably retentive. His eye was quick as a flash and his hand as steady as a rock. At the age of sixteen he entered the sophomore class of Yale and was graduated from that insti-tution in 1815, when nineteen years of age. The celebrated Doctor Silliman was attracted by his remarkable ability. George was a natural mathematician. All sciences came easily to him. His inclinations were always toward the study of medicine, and he began to study in the office of Doctor Hubbard and later entered as a student in the University of Pennsylvania and an office student of Dorsey. He read extensively, worked extremely hard and proved unusually bright in anatomy and surgery, and during his student days was a resident student in the Philadelphia Almshouse, a post corresponding to the intern of today. Darrach in his memoir of McClellan says he was the mental stimulus of all his colleagues, and they were particularly impressed by his mar-velous coordination of eye and hand, and the association of a rapid mind and tongue. He was at it and at it hard in everything connected with the duties of an intern. He read medicine omniv-orously and used to tell his colleagues about his reading and expound it to them. He used to delight in postmortems and in

trying operations on the dead body. He used to try out everything new that he heard of. One day he jumped up from his chair
and cried out, "Mott of New York is said to have taken up the
innominate artery for aneurysm and I believe it." He ran out
after a while and came back and told us he had just done it on a
dead body.

Such was George McClellan who graduated from the University of Pennsylvania in the spring of 1819 and stepped out in the
arena to fight his battle with the world.

Soon after his graduation McClellan obtained an extensive
practice. He devoted all his reading and attention to surgery
and during his first year performed many surgical operations.

In 1820 he married Eliza, the daughter of John H. Brinton.
In the same year he began to teach. He rented a house on Walnut Street above Sixth, at the corner of Swanwick, and in this
house, on the Walnut Street side, were his office and lecture room.
The great Curtis publication building now covers the site.

He had private classes in anatomy and surgery which were
largely attended. His lectures captivated the students, and
within a couple of years he had the most successful of the private
schools of Philadelphia. He was regarded as one of the best of
teachers in anatomy and surgery and was looked upon by keen
observers as the coming man in Philadelphia surgery. His classes
soon became so large that he moved his lecture hall to George
Street, which is now Sansom.

In 1823 he removed the lower jaw for sarcoma, the operation
requiring but four minutes. The same year he put forth his
views in advocacy of tearing out tumors so as to lessen hemorrhage, and strongly opposed preliminary ligation.

It was in 1823 that he first began to think about founding a
new school. There was no chance for him in the University of
Pennsylvania. Physick was Professor of Anatomy and had the
place nailed down for Horner as his successor. Gibson, the Professor of Surgery, was only thirty-three or thirty-four years old,
and the chances were that he would remain Professor of Surgery
for many years to come.

Many felt that a new college was needed. The University was lethargic, arrogant, arbitrary, and subject to influence of a social nature in making appointments. Many brilliant men, without the necessary influence, had no future in the great institution at Ninth and Chestnut Streets, and such men were in favor of a new school. Other men, who were not teachers, wished for a new school because they desired Philadelphia to remain great and to advance as a medical center. It was the old argument between competition and privilege. The University had 550 students and was crowded to inconvenience. The discussion of the matter was extremely acrimonious. Most people believed that a new school must fail, as the most it could do would be to draw students from the old school. As the row deepened and broadened denunciation became violent. In fact, the University adherents looked upon the establishment of a new school as a churchman looks upon heresy. McClellan was driven into a position of practical isolation in the Philadelphia profession. The fierce contest and the personal abuse affected McClellan's character, opinions, and methods of thought for the rest of his life.

The first movement for a new school had been headed by W. C. P. Barton, Professor of Botany in the University of Pennsylvania, but a charter was refused. The students of the University in meeting protested against granting a charter. The meeting of protest was presided over by Dr. John K. Mitchell, who was destined to become the celebrated Professor of the Practice of Medicine in the College he did not wish founded. The resolution of protest was defeated. In 1824 Doctor McClellan, Doctor Eberle (then a teacher in McClellan's private school), Dr. Joseph Klapp, and Mr. Jacob Green (the son of R. Ashbel Green, former President of Princeton College) made a proposition to the authorities of Jefferson College at Canonsburg. In this letter the gentlemen mentioned stated that they had come together to form a medical faculty and wished to become connected with the Jefferson College at Canonsburg. The trustees of Jefferson College of Canonsburg agreed. The University of Pennsylvania made a protest to the Legislature against the medical department of

Jefferson College being allowed to open in Philadelphia. The same school went to law in order to keep the new school from issuing diplomas, and as late as the spring of 1826 it wasn't settled that we could issue diplomas.

Dr. Washington L. Atlee used to tell that, in the spring of 1826, he and several other students were being quizzed in John L. Atlee's office in Lancaster. There was a peremptory knock at the door, and a young man jumped into the room. The young man Dr. John L. Atlee introduced as Doctor McClellan of Philadelphia. He said that he had ridden the 60 miles from Philadelphia since early morning, that he must be in Harrisburg that night, and that his horse could not go another mile. He borrowed a horse and buggy from Doctor Atlee, started immediately and reached Harrisburg, 96 miles from Philadelphia, in less than twenty-four hours after his start from Philadelphia. The next morning he obtained the legislative charter giving the new institution full university powers. He arrived in Lancaster the next evening, changed horses and set out for Philadelphia. He had gone but a few miles when the wagon upset. With the help of a farmer he raised the vehicle, resumed the drive, and the next day the charter of the Jefferson Medical College was in the City of Philadelphia.

In the organization Doctor Klapp was appointed Professor of Anatomy, but he resigned before the doors of the College were opened. The active Faculty included the following: George McClellan, Professor of Surgery; Nathan R. Smith, Professor of Anatomy; John Eberle, Professor of Medicine; Benjamin Rush Rhees, Professor of Materia Medica and Institutes of Medicine; Jacob Green, Professor of Chemistry; Francis C. Beattie, Professor of Midwifery. The Rev. R. Ashbel Green, former President of Princeton College, became President of the Board of Trustees. McClellan was twenty-nine years old, Beattie was thirty-one, Smith was twenty-eight, Eberle was thirty-eight, Green was thirty-five, and Rhees was thirty-three. Not an old man on the list and not a man of national reputation. Energetic, enthusiastic young men, hard workers, confident of the future, honorable in their personal and professional relations, and ready for a fair fight, no matter how hard it might be. They ran against the dominant medical authority of Philadelphia and each man of them put his career at hazard, for every man of them was under a ban; but these brave young men won the fight, and their legacy to us is our present great institution, an institution which arose from the private school of George McClellan. It was born of genius, and the very character of its founder entered into it and is present in it still and helps to give it its abundance of life and strength.

THE LAST SURGICAL CLINIC IN THE OLD AMPHITHEATER OF THE JEFFERSON MEDICAL COLLEGE HOSPITAL, HELD BEFORE THE SENIOR AND JUNIOR CLASSES, MAY 10, 1922, BY PROFESSOR JOHN CHALMERS DaCOSTA*

In this, the last surgical clinic which will ever be held in this room, I purpose deviating from the ordinary clinical routine and instead of showing cases will tell you something of the history of this room, a room which Dr. Nicholas Senn referred to as historical in the annals of American surgery.

For nearly half a century right in this room man has wrought for his fellowman, and wherever man has wrought for man that spot is holy ground. I intend briefly and necessarily in a superficial manner to touch upon some of the fine surgical traditions, some of the splendid recollections which are contained in the memories of this arena. These traditions and memories are lodged within our hearts as swallows' nests are built in house eaves. As I speak it seems to me as though the spirits of departed great ones arise and hover about us. I seem to look again upon loved and well-known faces and to hear the voices of many who have been gathered to the bosom of Infinity. I am as one who stands

"In Thebes the hundred gated in the thoroughfare,
Breathing as if consecrated a diviner air;
And amid discordant noises of the jostling throng,
Hearing far celestial voices of Olympian song."

The first clinic was held in this room by the elder Gross, the final surgical exercises are being conducted by one who now humbly tries to fill the Samuel D. Gross Chair of Surgery.

When this room was first put to use there was no science of bacteriology and no attempt at surgical cleanliness, although

* Reprinted from the *Jefferson Medical College Alumni Bulletin*, February, 1925.

334

Pasteur had made some of his revolutionary discoveries and Lister some years before had put out his first papers on antiseptic surgery. The first surgeons in Philadelphia to use antisepsis were Dr. W. W. Keen and Dr. J. Ewing Mears in St. Mary's Hospital. The first person to use it in this room was the younger Gross. There was no laboratory of experimental pharmacology and no laboratory of experimental physiology in the United States. There was no journal devoted purely to a special branch, for instance, no *Journal of Experimental Medicine*. Local anesthesia had not been discovered except a poor apology for it as obtained by cold. The patients had to bear the pain or take a general anesthetic. Such a painful operation as opening a felon was done without giving ether. There was a certain recognized method used to cut a felon cleanly, deeply, and widely. The patient stood back of the surgeon. The surgeon drew the patient's arm between his arm and side and entered the knife at the base of the diseased digit. With an explosion of expletives the patient dragged his hand away and thus cut himself to the length desired.

Spinal anesthesia was undreamed of, although I am not entirely persuaded that we would not be almost as well off today without it. The first brain tumor had not yet been operated upon. The first brain abscess had not yet been localized and operated upon. Appendicitis was unknown in spite of the discovery made by Mellier of Paris back in the 20's of the 19th century. This brilliant young Frenchman believed that inflammation in the right iliac fossa came from the appendix. He showed a gangrenous appendix and a perforated appendix. Furthermore he thought the disease might some day be operated upon. Dupuytren maintained that inflammation in the right iliac fossa came from the cecum and the profession elected for sixty years to follow Dupuytren who was wrong and to reject Mellier who was right. The thousands of unnecessary deaths which resulted cannot even be guessed at. It was not until 1886 when Reginald Fitz of Boston wrote his epoch-making paper that the profession came to hold the appendix responsible for inflammatory conditions of the right iliac fossa.

The chest was never opened except to drain an empyema and this was regarded as a very dangerous operation. When the celebrated Dupuytren lay dying from empyema he refused to be operated upon on the ground that he had never seen such an operation succeed.

During the early years of this arena aspiration of empyema had great popularity and was doing much harm. It was frequently used as an excuse to avoid operation and because of the absence of asepsis commonly led to mixed infection, particularly to putrid empyema. At the present day it is valued as a temporary expedient and as a diagnostic aid, but is not relied upon as a method of curative treatment.

At that time we had not the faintest conception of the bronchoscope or the esophagoscope or of the marvelous skill that was to be developed in the use of these instruments, skill such as is displayed by my distinguished colleague, Dr. Chevalier Jackson, and which suggests magic or at least legerdemain. He extracts foreign bodies from the air passages as easily as one might lift a jack knife from the trousers pocket.

The suprapubic cut was almost never made for stone in the bladder. The stone was removed by lateral lithotomy or was crushed and washed out by Bigelow's operation, which latter procedure is, of course, still used in proper cases. The first operation in this city for stone in the kidney was performed by the younger Gross and in this arena.

Goiter was never touched surgically, unless it was cystic, when it was perhaps tapped or injected with a coagulating or irritating fluid. Tapping did not cure the case and injection was a dangerous method.

I have given a bare sketch of the state of surgery when this arena was opened. Now let us see something of the distinguished men who have labored here.

The elder Gross was beyond all comparison the Emperor of American Surgery and the most distinguished surgeon of his day. Such a position of distinction had never been held before and in all probability will never be held by anyone again. He was one of the founders of the American Medical Association and he was the founder of the Philadelphia Pathological Society, the Philadelphia Academy of Surgery and that very distinguished body, the American Surgical Association. He always insisted on the close association of pathology, surgery, and medicine. He did not believe that a man could be a good surgeon unless he was a good pathologist and a good physician. In fact, he prided himself on his skill as a practitioner of medicine. He was a teacher of the first order. He taught with perfect clarity and with an emphasis that caused his hearers to imprint his words upon their memories. He was the very embodiment of dignity. Tall, erect, handsome, white haired and speaking with the highest authority. His experience was immense and his knowledge of literature was profound. He had written a pioneer book on surgical pathology, another on the bones and joints, another on the urinary organs and another on foreign bodies in the air passages. As Doctor Keen pointed out some years ago, he wrote the first system of surgery ever written in America, a system of surgery which was regarded as the most authoritative text-book of its day. He wrote many professional articles, read many papers, wrote upon medical history and biography and upon military surgery. In fact, he was the greatest of surgical philosophers. Whenever I heard him lecture I felt that fifty years of American surgery were speaking through his lips.

He was a man of many honors, LL. D. of Cambridge; D. C. L. of Oxford; LL. D. of Edinburgh. Finally, on his death bed, when he was too far gone to realize it, he had conferred upon him that reluctantly and rarely given distinction for a Jefferson man in those days, the LL. D. of the University of Pennsylvania.

Let us look for a moment at a clinic in the elder Gross's day.

At that time there was a doorway on the northern end of the clinic, opening into a corridor, and which has since been closed up. By this doorway was the sink. The floor of the arena was wooP. Above the northern doorway was a bust of Joseph Pancoast. Above the southern doorway was a bust of George McClellan, the founder of the school. In the center of the arena stood

22

a wooden operating table, the table which is to be seen today in the Gross lecture room of the College. As a preliminary to the clinic a number of little tables would be brought in to hold the cases of instruments. The knives had ivory handles and were beautiful tools. Assistants set out different sizes of silk, various shapes and sizes of needles, marine sponges in basins, wax for strengthening ligatures, and perhaps a furnace for the actual cautery, such a furnace as is used by the tin roofer. Suppose the case was lithotomy. The patient was brought in under ether (Doctor Hearn administering the anesthetic), and he was pulled down to the end of the table, put into the lithotomy position and held in it by a frame and straps. On the floor, at the foot of the bed, was a wooden box of sawdust placed to catch as much of the blood as possible. Doctor Gross wore a long blue coat, a costume worn in many previous combats. Dr. James M. Barton was the chief assistant. The bladder was filled with water. A stone sound was passed into the bladder and was held by the chief assistant. Doctor Gross bent down on one knee, picked up the knife, passed it into the urethra until it struck the sound, carried it on into the bladder. As he withdrew the knife he inserted a finger, thus blocking the wound and the stone dropped right on the end of the finger. He then carried a forceps into the wound and extracted the stone. The whole operation was performed with a speed and dexterity simply marvelous, from twenty to thirty seconds being usually sufficient for the procedure. Of course, before the operation was begun, the case was lectured on, the contemplated procedure being carefully explained. Doctor Gross talked during the operation, demonstrating every step of it. Gathered around in the arena one could usually see Doctor Keen, Dr. Oscar Allis, Dr. Richard J. Levis, Doctor Brinton, the younger Gross, Dr. Frank Maury, Dr. Joseph Pancoast, Dr. Thomas A. Andrews, and others. Any distinguished surgeon visiting Philadelphia at that time was certain to be there. In fact, it was seldom that Doctor Gross did not have some eminent man to introduce to the class. It was the foremost surgical clinic in America.

In this arena the celebrated Joseph Pancoast operated. He

was one of the greatest operating surgeons that ever lived, ranking
certainly on a level with Syme of Edinburgh and Von Langenbeck
of Berlin. He was so widely celebrated that when a daughter of a
Lord Chancellor of England was terribly deformed as a result of
a severe burn, Sir William Fergusson, the great London surgeon,
referred the case to Joseph Pancoast of Philadelphia as the master
plastic surgeon of the world. He was the author of a celebrated
book on operative surgery. For years he was Professor of Anatomy
in the College and a teacher of clinical surgery in the Hospital.
This combination was common in former days. The anatomist
then taught pure human anatomy and every surgeon was required
to be a real anatomist. I fear that we with our great progress have
lost much in the average operator's knowledge of anatomy. Pancoast was one of the most wonderful operators that ever lived.
Years ago I stated he had a hand as light as a floating perfume and
an eye as quick as a flashing sunbeam. At the time of which
I speak there was a man on Eighth Street who made and sold
surgical instruments and it was the oldest store of its kind in the
United States. The name is still there, namely, Gemrig. Mr.
Gemrig told me that when in his old days Dr. Joseph Pancoast
came in and picked out needles with a pair of forceps from the
tray, the coordination between his eye and hand was so perfect
that he would take his forceps, pick out the needle he wanted with
lightning-like rapidity and with unfailing certainty and put it
aside. Remember that was when he was an old man. He had
some odd and striking expressions. Professor Keen will remember
more about them than I can; for I only saw him as a school boy
when I used to come to clinics long before I had begun the study
of medicine. One of his favorite expressions was "the antiphlo-
gistic touch of the therapeutic knife," for he believed profoundly
in the immense value of local bloodletting in the treatment of
certain inflammations.

In those days it was the custom of both the rival colleges for
the first two weeks of the session to hold in the early fall surgical
show clinics, so that all individuals coming to Philadelphia to
study medicine could look these clinics over as a help to their

decision as to which institution they were to embrace as their Alma Mater. They were advertisements to students about to invest. Pancoast used to try to have a case requiring removal of the upper jaw. He performed this operation with the patient almost erect and only partially anesthetized. He would incise the face with a speed that was simply marvelous and tear out the bones caught by huge forceps with a celerity almost inconceivable. The scene was not only bloody but actually ferocious. The patient partially conscious was spitting out blood, bones and teeth over the surgeon and his assistants. In fact it was a real spectacle. It was a usual thing to see a student fall over here and another faint over there and others to get violently sick at the stomach. Those so affected were, of course, novices. Some of them decided at that moment that they did not want to study medicine at all. I saw a man, a few years ago, upon whom Pancoast had done this operation forty years before.

Next in my memory comes the younger Gross, Samuel W. Gross, who, in my opinion, was one of the very ablest men that ever stood in this arena. In many ways he was a queer, an unusual, a strange man, and one very difficult to know well. He was not only learned in surgery and in literature of surgery, but also in pathology, in fact, he personally sectioned and examined all the tumors he removed. He was a teacher of the very first order, even a greater one, I believe, than his illustrious father. He was a formidable person and we, his assistants, had a proper dread of him. A few weeks after I had been appointed a clinical assistant he said to me: "Where is that Juniper-Oil Catgut I gave you?" I said: "You did not give me any, Sir." He glared at me like an enraged Bengal tiger and said again, "Where is that Juniper-Oil Catgut I gave you?" I said to myself: "Here goes the job" and responded: "Why in the name of all that is inflammable you put this on me I'll be blessed if I know. I will be something or other if you gave me any —— catgut." He raised his head, looked at me through the center of his eye-glasses and with a hint of a smile on his face said, "That's right, young man, if you have anything to say, say it and say it so as everybody can understand." From that moment he stood my friend. During one clinic there was an amusing episode. The patient was a man suffering from a sinus, the result of a lodged bullet. The man said he had been wounded at the Battle of Gettysburg. Gross looked at me and said, "Something is getting wrong with my memory, I don't remember whether Gettysburg was fought in 1863 or 1864." I said, "It was in 1863," and he said, "How do you know it was?" I made answer, "That was the year I was born." He responded, "Well, the year you were born no doubt was important, but it doesn't affect the date of the battle of Gettysburg." I said, "I can prove it to you, Sir, so as to convince you." He said, "Go ahead." So I quoted

> "That was in July of '63,
> The very day that General Lee,
> Flower of Southern chivalry,
> Baffled and beaten backward reeled,
> From a stubborn Meade and a barren field."

Gross turned to the class and said: "This bullet was lodged in July of 1863."

He was the first American surgeon to insist on a radical operation for cancer of the breast. He shares with Halsted the glory of establishing radical surgery for breast cancer. His removal of the breast was so extensive that he called it the dinner plate operation, and he left a large unclosed wound. I believe that up to the time of this radical operation no woman had ever been cured of a cancer of the breast. As is well known our results now for the operation, if done early, are splendid. One evening he presented to a society a paper which attracted wide attention. My recollection is that he reported 100 cases of operation for cancer of the breast. That evening he gave an exhibition of several of his leading characteristics; viz.: clearness, brevity, and emphasis in statement. A young man who perhaps might have performed two or three operations in his life got up and objected to Doctor Gross's method on the ground that the large wound left open would reproduce cancer. At the close of the debate Gross arose and said:

"When oak trees produce polar bears and when fireplugs produce whales, then will granulations (which are connective tissue) produce cancer (which is epithelial tissue), and not until then." Doctor Keen can recall how characteristic was this answer.

His last lecture in this arena was on a spring day. At the end of the clinic, after he had changed his clothes, he threw a light overcoat over his arm and started out. I said "Doctor Gross, it is pretty windy, you had better put on your overcoat." He answered, "You young people are made of sugar in these days. I wasn't brought up that way. I am going down to Third Street now and buy a bond for my wife out of that $1000 I got this morning." In a few days he was dead of pneumonia.

It is a curious coincidence that there was a like ending to Dr. William L. Rodman. Doctor Rodman, originally of Kentucky, but for many years of Philadelphia, was the first resident physician of the Jefferson Medical College Hospital, and was a devoted friend of the younger Gross. One day he came into my house and as he departed, I said to him: "You had better put on your coat, you remember how pneumonia got Doctor Sam," and he said: "I only live a short distance from here and I won't need it." In a few days he was dead of pneumonia. I will be afraid to predict again.

Dr. Samuel W. Gross had written a celebrated book on *Diseases of the Mammary Gland* and another one on *Impotence*, and had been largely responsible for causing the profession to realize that it was just as proper to tie large veins as to tie large arteries. He was a master of principles.

Now I seem to see my dear old friend, Dr. John H. Brinton; an old practitioner of wide experience and a very interesting personality. He had been one of the chief field surgeons of the Army of the Potomac and a close friend of General Grant. He loved military surgery above anything else and was one of the founders of the Army Medical Museum. He was a splendid anatomist and most skilled in ligations and amputations. He had written a very remarkable article on the attitudes of persons killed on the battlefield, advocated amputation through the knee joint, and was

the American editor of *Erichsen's Surgery*. He had been Doctor
Keen's preceptor.

Doctor Brinton had seen so many people make so many
mistakes and had heard so many false prophecies that as he advanced in years he became very chary of giving a positive prognosis. I heard him one day give one of the most remarkable opinions on record. A man asked me how his son (who had been
operated upon) was doing. I explained to the best of my ability,
but the father wasn't satisfied, he wanted to see the Professor.
I realized that he wouldn't get anything very specific, but I took
him to the Professor. Doctor Brinton put forth what I maintain
is the most undeniably broad opinion ever given except that
announced by Jack Bunsby of the "Cautious Clara." He said, "If
he gets well he will get about again, if he doesn't get well he will
not get about again, and if his condition doesn't change he will
remain about as he is." The remarkable thing is that the father
appeared perfectly satisfied because he had it from the Professor.
After the conversation had terminated I said to Doctor Brinton:
"Whereby, why not? If so, what odds?" He said, "Yes, Dombey
and Son," smiled and walked out.

Many others come before me whose names I can do little more
than mention:

That handsome, courteous, generous, warm-hearted gentlemen,
William H. Pancoast. One of the most brilliant, promising and
unfortunate of all of them, Frank Maury. Richard J. Levis, the
master operator, the surgeon of marvelous mechanical ability.
His studies of fractures influenced the whole profession. A few
years ago I attended a meeting of a society in which a paper was
read on the reduction of Colles' fracture by a new method. The
reader stated that the plan was to bend the lower fragment back,
drag upon it forcibly and force it down into place by acute flexion.
I called his attention to the fact that long years before Doctor
Levis taught the following: hyperextension, longitudinal traction,
and forced flexion. The alleged new plan was the old plan of
Levis. He didn't wear the surgeon's white gown as we do now and
he wore long cuffs when operating. As a dodger of blood he was

wonderful. He would make a long cut, step back out of range and say to his assistant, Dr. John B. Roberts, "John, put a string on that."

Then I seem to see Dr. Oscar H. Allis, a man full of original ideas, a profound thinker, in fact, a genius. His work upon dislocations of the hip joint and lateral curvature of the spine is classical. He was a most original and painstaking operator. He was opposed and profoundly opposed to the use of bad language in the operating room. Only once in his life did he explode in this arena and it always pained him to hear the incident referred to, and the elder Hearn used to enjoy reminding him of it. He was operating on an ununited fracture of the tibia and had spent an hour and a half in beveling the bones, putting the fragments together and inserting screws. It was one of the neatest of surgical jobs. Doctor Allis leaned back and looked at it approvingly. An assistant picked up the extremity by the heel and splintered the bone. Doctor Allis said: "Damn it and may God forgive me for saying it." Whenever Doctor Hearn would remind him of it, Doctor Allis would say, "Now, Hearn, please stop and don't recall that affair."

Dr. James M. Barton I have already spoken of. He was for some time chief assistant and later was surgeon to the Hospital and finally Clinical Professor of Surgery. He was a pioneer in abdominal surgery and did an enormous amount of valuable work. I believe that he is the only man of the great group gathered about the elder Gross who is now living. He resides in Atlantic City.

Dr. Charles B. DeNancrede, long a surgeon to this Hospital, was afterward the distinguished professor of surgery in Ann Arbor University. He was a profoundly learned surgeon as well as a great clinician and his operations were remarkable for speed, certainty, and dexterity. He was learned in the principles of surgery and his book on that subject was long popular.

Doctor Andrews, the demonstrator of anatomy, used to assist Professor Joseph Pancoast in the clinic. He was an extremely able man and a very popular teacher. He used to like to tell about the famous Siamese twins, for he had made the postmortem on that remarkable pair. One of the twins had been a Northerner in feeling and the other a sympathizer with the South during the desperate days of the Civil War and they used to quarrel fiercely. Each of them was married and the custom was to spend alternate weeks at each other's house; and the wives fought as fiercely as the husbands. It is said that one of the twins hated liquor and the other liked it. When the one who liked liquor got drunk his brother had to get drunk with him. Doctor Andrews was an excellent teacher of anatomy.

And then comes that man who was the best loved of all the men around Jefferson, Dr. W. Joseph Hearn. During long years he was the anesthetist for the elder Gross and was then Chief of the Clinic, Surgeon to the Hospital, and finally, Clinical Professor of Surgery. He died as the result of a lamentable runaway accident. He was one of the best practical surgeons who ever lived and he was physician as well as surgeon. If any physician connected with this Hospital had to be operated upon or if one of his family had to be operated upon, Doctor Hearn had to do the operation or was at least called in to the case. He was a wonderful diagnostician, in fact, he seemed to be a natural-born diagnostician, if there is such a thing. His experience was enormous. He was one of the best, most generous and most lovable of men. I pause to think of him in love and affection, and I seem to see him in this arena where he spent such a large part of his busy life.

"Green be the grass above you friend of my former days.
None knew you but to love you or named you but to praise."

I have not mentioned one of the greatest men who ever stood in this arena, our Emeritus Professor, Doctor Keen. I have not mentioned him because I have restricted myself to those who are no longer connected here or who have passed into the Great Beyond.

Doctor Keen is, of course, the greatest product of the school of the elder Gross. In his presence I cannot say all I would wish to say about him, but I can say and will say that everything I obtained in professional life came directly through his kindly aid.

When he came to this school, my friend, the younger Gross, was dead and I was very much the under dog in a raging combat. He reached out his strong right hand, seized me, so to speak, by the hair of the head and dragged me to safety. When I started to crawl along, step by step, he would sometimes advise me and always wisely; sometimes urge me, sometimes stimulate emulation in me, and sometimes drag me along by the scruff of the neck. That is the reason I am today the Professor of Surgery. Doctor Keen has put his stamp on the surgery of the world. His record is lustrous with achievement. His system of surgery is beyond any question the greatest system existing and it is universally recognized as such by all the leading journals, domestic as well as foreign. I could say a great deal more of him, but will not in his presence.

Among others who lectured or operated in this arena were Lawson Tate of Birmingham, one of the most celebrated of abdominal surgeons. He was always engaged in some active controversy, but was a great man and a pioneer especially in pelvic and gallbladder surgery. Mr. Bryant of London, Senior Surgeon of Guy's Hospital, lectured here on aneurysm. He was a handsome, ruddy faced, white whiskered gentleman and the author of a splendid text-book of surgery. As he walked about the Out-patient Department he said: "A lot of those people should be in doctors' offices paying fees." He then told me that shortly before he left home he was passing his clinic room and was struck by a person he saw sitting among the out-patients. Coming into the hospital he had noticed the carriage of a wealthy but miserly English peer and that peer was the patient he recognized in the out-patient room. "Knowing that he was very sensitive to criticism," said Bryant, "I went back into the consulting room and had him brought to me and told him I had recognized him and that the charge for consultation was so much for the Hospital (a very considerable fee), which he paid and departed."

Another who honored us was Sir William Macewen of Glasgow, one of the founders of cerebral surgery, a very great man. Another was Professor Chiene of Edinburgh. He lectured to us, but wouldn't operate. He said to Doctor Keen: "You may talk all you please, but I won't touch a knife, I am on a holiday." Then there was Annandale of Edinburgh, the man his old students referred to as "Tommy" Annandale. He had written an extremely useful book for house surgeons. He operated for a tumor breaking into the pharynx from the basilar portion of the occipital bone. In order to reach it he split the hard palate by use of the saw, separated the two parts of the palate by opening a pair of powerful forceps and through the gap removed the tumor.

Another visitor was Mr. Ballance of St. Thomas's Hospital, London. He had, with Mr. Edmunds, written a very valuable work on the ligation of arteries and he afterward wrote a book on the surgery of the brain. Another was Mr. Durham, the Senior Surgeon of St. Bartholomew's Hospital, London, a man of interesting and delightful personality. He had observed the condition of the brain in a case in which there was a great loss of substance in the skull. He had inserted a watch crystal and observed the brain while the man was sleeping and waking. He found that when the sleeping man was obviously dreaming, the previously shrunken brain swelled up. He gave a delightful lecture.

Sir William MacCormac of St. Thomas's Hospital, London, was a very notable surgeon. He used to come to Philadelphia every year or so and stayed with one of the Gross's. During the Franco-Prussian War he had been, with our own Marion Sims, in charge of the Anglo-American Ambulance Service. The last time the elder Gross was in this arena he introduced Sir William to the class. Just outside the door Gross said, "Sir William, my friend, I am going to introduce you to those I love next to my own family, the members of the great class of the Jefferson Medical College." On MacCormac's last visit Doctor Keen gave him a dinner. It was a reeking hot July night and as we emerged from the house on Chestnut Street, MacCormac said to Doctor Hare: "Please tell me, for God's sake, where I can get a glass of beer." On one occasion, when here, he did a suprapubic operation for stone in the bladder.

J. Marion Sims paid a visit to us every fall. With the exception of the elder Gross, Dr. S. Weir Mitchell, and Doctor Keen he was the most distinguished graduate of this school. He was the founder of gynecology. One of the most attractive of books was the one he wrote which is called *The Story of My Life*. It is a strange story of the depths of poverty and a poor country practice in Alabama and of devising, after infinite effort, the operations for rectovaginal and vesicovaginal fistula. He tells of the great difficulty he had in obtaining professional recognition, of mounting to fame in Europe and finally how he became surgeon to the Emperor of the French, Napoleon III. His book on uterine surgery was extensively used and he did the first deliberate operation ever done on the gallbladder. He was a general surgeon who specialized and had not been a specialist from the start, hence his philosophical mind and breadth of view. On one occasion, as a student, I sat on the front row to witness a clinic by the younger Gross. The elder Gross came in with Sims and they seated themselves directly in front of me. The younger Gross said to his father, "Professor Gross, will you do us the honor to hold this clinic?"—and the elder Gross said, "Thank you, Sir, I would prefer not, I would rather sit here and learn something." Wishing to hear what pearls of wisdom would drop from the lips of two such eminent men as Gross and Sims, I committed the impropriety of leaning over and listening. Gross nudged Sims and said, "You and I are going to have a fine time at lunch today," and Sims said, "Why, Sam?" and the elder Gross said: "All the women are away from home and we are going to have corned beef and cabbage and beer."

Victor Horsley, afterward Sir Victor Horsley, visited us. He was one of the founders of the surgery of the brain and for years stood in the very front rank in that branch. He lost his life from sunstroke while patriotically serving his country during the World's War in the British Campaign in Mesopotamia.

Hans Kehr operated here for gallstones. When he operated on the abdomen he took no chance of missing anything. He made a huge incision and one didn't look in through a window but through a doorway.

Sir W. Watson Cheyne, who had been the assistant of Lord Joseph Lister, operated here for movable kidney. He said to Doctor Keen: "What have you got for me?" and Doctor Keen said: "A movable kidney." He said, "Well, I will sew it in place, but they always come loose."

Faure of Paris did a most extensive operation for peritoneal adhesions. As he spoke in French, Doctor Keen translated sentence by sentence. Tillman of Germany operated here and made an artificial anus. He was a big, robust German. As he spoke in German, Doctor Keen translated sentence for sentence. Esmarch, then of Kiel, had by marriage become a member of the imperial family. He had introduced the elastic bandage and the elastic band for the prevention of loss of blood during operations on the extremities. Dr. Joseph Pancoast had devised the principle and had used a wet gauze bandage for the same purpose, but the elastic bandage was a great improvement. Before he came to see us he had been to another institution where there was an extremely ornate marble clinic room. He said he was not used to operating in palaces and felt happier with us because "I am now where the real work is done."

Mikulicz of Breslau, one of the foremost surgeons in the world, an LL. D. of this school, a man who had added chapters to the surgery of the stomach, lectured here, and Gottstein, his assistant, was also here. Gottstein was a pioneer in the use of the esophago-scope. I will tell you a story Doctor Keen never heard before. Doctor Keen was to take Gottstein around and show him various historical structures. It was a reeking hot summer day. Doctor Keen said to me, "John, I have to go out of town, you take this list which I have made out and show the Doctor the various places which I have indicated." Among them was Old Christ Church, the Old Swedes' Church, Independence Hall, etc. I thought our German guest looked pretty hot and miserable. We paused at the corner of Broad and Chestnut Streets, and mopped our faces. I looked at him and said: "I will be perfectly frank with you, but please don't tell Doctor Keen. Half a block from here is an excellent Rathskeller which dispenses Munich beer. Would you rather visit the sights of the city or drink Munich beer and take a rest." He said, "I would so love to go to the Rathskeller." Further deponent sayeth not.

On one occasion we had Doctor Keen's old friend who had been his chief during the Civil War, Prof. Robert Weir of New York. He operated for stone in the ureter and when he reached the ureter the stone had passed. This very case made my colleague, Doctor Gibbon, and me cautious about operating for stone in the ureter.

Prof. John A. Wyeth of New York came over here to see Doctor Keen use the Wyeth pins for the prevention of hemorrhage in amputation of the hip joint. He was a very eminent man and a charming gentleman.

Prof. Nicholas Senn of Chicago operated here for ununited fracture of the patella. He was a great surgical genius. He and Halsted of Baltimore were the two men who did the most to make intestinal surgery and he was a pioneer in the surgery of the pancreas. He had been born in Switzerland, had left there as a boy and had worked his way up through the greatest poverty to a position in the very front rank of the profession. He dedicated his great work on tumors to the elder Gross and did so out of gratitude. He told me that one of his early articles was much criticized by his medical neighbors and he felt profoundly dejected. Just then he received a letter from the elder Gross congratulating him on the work and urging him to go on to greater things. This letter encouraged him so much that he persevered until he reached the goal of success. He always insisted on the enormous importance of the principles of surgery.

William S. Forbes, formerly the Professor of Anatomy in this Institution, held clinics here for many years. He was very fond of doing Bigelow's operation for stone in the bladder and had invented a very powerful lithotrite. He devised the operation for liberating the ring finger of musicians by dividing the accessory tendons and was the father of the present anatomical law of the State of Pennsylvania. This law exterminated the hideous old custom of grave robbery and secured to medical colleges sufficient anatomical material. Professor Forbes was a courteous and dignified gentleman of the old school.

William L. Rodman lectured here. He came from Louisville, graduated from this school, and was the first resident physician in this Hospital. He was for a long time the distinguished Professor of Surgery in the Medico-Chirurgical College. He was particularly expert in the surgery of the breast and the surgery of the stomach. We all loved him.

Hunter McGuire lectured here. When the Civil War broke out he was a junior teacher in this institution and returned to the South to serve, as he felt was his duty, the cause of his native state; and when he went he was accompanied by scores of our students. He became the celebrated surgeon of Stonewall Jackson's corps and attended that great soldier on his death bed. He was one of the very great surgeons of the country.

Dr. Joseph Price held a clinic. He was one of the greatest of abdominal surgeons and used the fewest instruments I ever saw as the armamentarium of an operator. His trained and slender fingers were those of a prestidigitateur. He was very outspoken, hence had bitter enemies and warm friends. He was usually referred to as "Uncle Joe." He was a strange, forceful, whimsical, eccentric, lovable, and very able man.

Baron Takaki, the surgeon general of the Japanese Navy during the Russo-Japanese War, lectured here on the medical organization of the Japanese Navy.

Among other distinguished men who have held clinics in this arena, I may mention Sir Morrell Mackenzie of London, George deSchweinitz (once a Professor of Ophthalmology here), Roswell Park of Buffalo, Ellerslie Wallace, our Professor of Obstetrics, J. Solis-Cohen (who on one occasion performed laryngectomy), William Thompson (celebrated for his operations for cataract), the Yandells of Louisville, Louis R. Sayre and Conner of Cincinnati, who had been one of the attending surgeons on President Garfield and who made the opening address at the inaugural ceremonies of the present College.

I do not mention the medical men, although much could be

said about them, particularly of J. M. DaCosta and Roberts Bartholow. I could go on indefinitely, but I will not because the time is nearly up. I have simply skimmed the surface and have given a few hints from the memory of one who has passed his surgical life in this arena, for I became connected with this Hospital as a surgical assistant to the younger Gross on the first of May, 1887. This arena has been as the well of the Patriarch in which all the tribes of Science's Israel own an equal right and to which they owe an equal homage.

FACTS CONCERNING THE OLD OPERATING TABLE

An old wooden table! It is not artistic or dainty but rather solid and capable. It was made for grim practical uses and not for show. It is not like a Chippendale chair, a Sheraton sideboard, or a Hepplewhite table adorning a white colonial drawing room or a parlor containing a hodge-podge of furniture of various makes and ages. It is not meant to be a part of any society affair which would draw a crowd of the most uninteresting people in the world, herded by social ambition, fear or mental vacuity to that last possibility of imbecility, an afternoon tea.

It is an old and scarred veteran, retired after years of active service to end its days of vivid experience in the familiar surroundings of a bull pit surrounded during certain hours by medical students.

This table, we assistants were told by Prof. S. W. Gross, was made in the early fifties of the last century, and has since then been repaired and freshened up once or twice. It stood originally in the arena of the upper lecture room of the old Tenth Street College, the room that was used for anatomy lectures, obstetrical lectures, and surgical clinics. At that time we had no hospital. We did not have a hospital until 1877. When an operation of moderate severity was performed an assistant returned the patient to his home in a cab and the surgeon and assistants looked after him afterward. For the care of more severe cases a room was rented on the third floor of the S. W. corner of Tenth and Sansom Streets, a room which was accessible from the operating room and which was pleasantly placed over a cigar store and an oyster saloon. When a severe operation had been performed the patient was taken into the small ward, which contained a few beds. He was cared for by the surgeon and the assistants and was nursed by relays of students during the days and nights. The professor of surgery always furnished the students a mid-

354   PAPERS AND SPEECHES

night lunch of oysters, cigars, and beer. When the Sansom Street
Hospital was opened in 1877, the Jefferson College was the second
medical college in America to have its own hospital. This table
was moved into the arena of the hospital. It stood there for many
years; in fact, it was very gradually displaced. Some surgeons
clung to it, though others had taken to more modern appliances.
It disappeared and could not be found. I conducted a search
for it and discovered it down in the basement being used to hold
oil cans and various sorts of waste. "Apollo tending the sheep
of Admetus!" I rescued it, had it brought up to this room and
told the class about it. The Class of 1916 had the table cleaned
up and repaired and put a plate upon it; and the Class of 1917
had placed upon it the additional tablet. So it has finally attained an honored and distinguished old age.

At times to look at that old table acts upon me as a magic
potation and "stirs the Hades of my heart." It brings before
me faces and figures which have long since been gathered to
infinity and puts in my ears voices which have long been stilled
in the arenas of this College.

When this table was young Franklin Pierce was President of
the United States. Washington Irving and Prescott were still
active in literature. Hawthorne was a clerk in the custom house
at Salem, Oliver Wendell Holmes was Professor of Anatomy at
Harvard, and Longfellow was Professor of Modern Languages in
the same institution. Emerson was regarded as a mystic and
most people looked upon his verse as unintelligible and Lowell
was saying of him that he built a wonderful temple but "left
never a window to get in a God." Motley was thirty-eight years
of age and was studying in Europe obtaining material for his great
work on *The Rise of the Dutch Republic*. Valentine Mott of
New York was the leading surgeon of the United States. Samuel
D. Gross, then a greatly distinguished surgeon, was Professor of
Surgery in Louisville. Marion Sims had not yet left Montgomery,
Alabama. Daniel Webster died about the time this table was
made. Abraham Lincoln was an Illinois politician with little
more than local repute. Jefferson Davis was the Secretary of

The old operating table.

War in the Cabinet of President Pierce. The forces of slavery and antislavery were breaking into desperate fury. The Kansas-Nebraska question embittered parties to the degree of bloodshed and the Ostend Manifesto was put forth by slavery advocates to try to force the acquisition of Cuba by the United States.

Ether was still to a certain extent a novelty and there were some surgeons in Philadelphia who had declined so far to use it. Efficient local anesthesia and antisepsis were totally unknown. Cerebral localization had not been dreamed of and it was believed that the brain, like the liver, functionated as a whole. Intracranial surgery, except for extradural suppurations and traumatisms, did not exist. There was no surgery of the chest except for empyema and the operation for that condition was regarded as so fatal that many practitioners declined to recommend it.

There was no operative surgery of the abdomen except for wounds, intestinal obstruction, and strangulated hernia. Nobody had ever heard of appendicitis. Nobody had ever thought of operating for gallstones or kidney stones. The wiring of ununited fractures and bone plating were not practiced. The theory of bone grafting had not been worked out even in embryo.

The great operation of surgery was for stone in the bladder, and it was nearly always performed by the lateral method. The suprapubic operation was reserved for those few cases in which there was an enormous stone. Surgery consisted only of the treatment of wounds and suppurating areas; the performance of amputations and resections; operations for caries, necrosis, tumors, aneurysm, stone in the bladder, strangulated hernia, empyema, tracheotomy, trephining of the skull for depressed fracture or extradural abscess, and a few other procedures. Radical cure for hernia was never attempted.

I think of the men who have operated upon that table or who have stood by it and delivered lectures. I seem to see before me the strong, handsome face of the elder Gross as he kneels upon one knee at the foot of that table operating for stone in the bladder—that marvelous operating surgeon Joseph Pancoast, full of energy, the embodiment of decision, a man of whom I have spoken before as having had an eye as quick as a flashing sunbeam and a hand as light as a floating perfume.

The stern, rather grim face of the younger Gross as he operated for cancer of the breast and developed his views as to a radically curative operation for cancer; views which became largely the foundations of our modern methods. John H. Brinton, who amputated with more precision and ligated with more anatomical accuracy than any other surgeon of his time in Philadelphia. That splendid operating surgeon Levis, a man with marvelous mechanical ingenuity in correcting difficult displacements in fractures and in maintaining the bones in proper position. The supreme diagnostic ability of that prince of kindly and manly gentlemen, Dr. W. Joseph Hearn, and that greatest of modern American surgeons, W. W. Keen.

Did Mütter ever operate upon this table? I do not know. It must have been about the time that the table came here that Mütter was seized with the chronic and progressive sickness (rheumatoid arthritis) which forced him to resign his chair. Whether before his period of inaction he used this table or not I am unable to say. Among other figures that come before me, some of whom operated, some of whom lectured, are Theophilus Parvin, J. Ewing Mears, Frank Maury, Nicholas Senn, J. M. DaCosta, Roberts Bartholow, William S. Forbes, Oscar H. Allis, J. M. Barton, Robert F. Weir, Charles B. deNancrede, Thomas Bryant of London, Lawson Tait of Birmingham, Arthur Durham of London, Thomas Annandale of Edinburgh, Professor von Esmarch of Kiel, Professor Faure of Paris, Sir William MacCormac of London, Sir Morrell Mackenzie of London (the noted laryngologist), John Wyeth of New York, W. H. Pancoast, and many others.

I have seen the hand of Roberts Bartholow and the hand of J. M. DaCosta laid on this table during the delivery of lectures. By this table Marion Sims stood and addressed the class. Bryant of London spoke upon aneurysm, Durham of London upon artificial anus, Sir William Macewen of Glasgow spoke about abscess of the brain and Lorenz of Vienna operated upon several cases

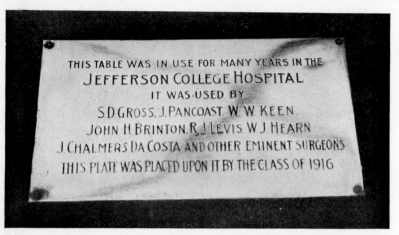

Plate placed upon the old operating table by the Class of 1916.

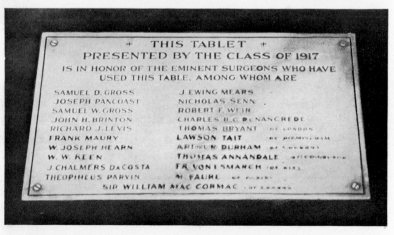

Plate placed upon the old operating table by the Class of 1917.

for congenital dislocation of the hip.   Sir Morrell Mackenzie, the London laryngologist, lectured and paid in that lecture a great tribute to Prof. J. Solis-Cohen, and Wyeth of New York made one of his very early demonstrations in the use of his pins for the prevention of hemorrhage in amputation of the hip joint.

On this table Hans Kehr operated for gallstones employing the huge incision he advocated; Weir of New York operated for stone in the ureter; Sir Watson Cheyne for movable kidney; Nicholas Senn for fracture of the patella; Professor von Esmarch for a fibrosarcoma of the neck; Annandale of Edinburgh for a sarcoma of the base of the skull, splitting the entire bony palate and separating the two sides to gain access to the seat of disease; Faure of Paris for extensive adhesions of the abdominal cavity; Sir William MacCormac of London for removal of a stone from the bladder by the suprapubic operation; Dawbarn of New York for recurrent dislocation of the shoulder.   The writer of this article had the honor of operating many times on this table.

It is evident that this table has had the closest association with some of the greatest men who ever adorned the surgery of the last three quarters of a century and it should be held, cherished, and cared for as a precious relic as long as the school shall stand.

W. W. Keen, the loved and celebrated Emeritus Professor of Surgery in this school, who operated upon this table, is still, I am glad to say, alive and well, and a number of the gentlemen whose names I have mentioned were present as his guests.   He could probably give you more of the active history of this table and certainly could go further back in giving it than I have been able to do.

CERTAIN TENDENCIES IN MEDICINE*

MOST of us in the modern world live our lives under the inexorable domination of *Routine*. We are forced into the rut of *Habit* which is a labor-saving device, and the demands upon our time and energy, our minds and bodies, are so great and exhausting, that we must possess labor-saving devices. Our energies are apt to be concentrated purely on material details and many of our aims are of necessity vulgar and even unworthy. Individualism withers from timid acquiescence in conditions, and originality is blighted into paltry eccentricity or malignant antisocialism. We plunge along the dusty highway with the hurrying crowd, often gloomy, disheartened, thirsty and weary. The joy of life is not in us. The sunlight does not pass back of the retina. At times we glance longingly at some sunlit slope flecked with brilliant flowers —at a distant mountain torrent which downward veering springs toward the distant sea, and leaves a "rainbow hanging o'er the ruin of its fall"—or at the dark and restful wood shadows which our long dead childish fancies were wont to people with fairies and goblins, gnomes and dryads, nymphs and satyrs, dwarfs and giants, sylphs and dreamy hidden goddesses with eyes full of sleep and lips rich with laughter. But we go with our fellows on their quest and we adopt the habits, the manners, the modes of thought, the ideas, the ideals, the hopes of our companions. We become entirely conventional. The contagion of example infects us. The psychical influence which arises from a multitude enters into our souls. By this influence a crowd sways its individual members, sways them into panic terror, into brute ferocity, into beastlike compliance, into cold-hearted indifference, into bounding sympathy, into unreasoning hate or unreasoning enthusiasm, into pulsing gallantry that knows no fear or abject fear which

* Read before the Medical Society, District of Columbia.

358

permits no gallantry, into meanness or generosity, envy or approval, tears or laughter, as the case may be. The psychology of crowds is a wonderful study.

The very lazy man may never go upon the crowded highway at all, because his nature is too low and not because it is too high. The rich man seldom has to. The working man *must* take his chance there, but beggars and thieves need not. Every man, as was said long ago, is either a working man, a beggar man, or a thief. Those who receive without return are beggar men. Those who take without consent are thieves.

If one journeying on the highway tries to stop, he is shoved and jostled, and must bare his arm for combat. If he falls he is usually trampled down. One must be strong and brave indeed to fight this living stream of tendency. He has not time to think, he is too busy doing nothing.

> "Many things and mighty are furthered in the West,
> The Ancient peace has vanished before today's unrest,
> For how among man's striving, his gold, his lust, his drink
> Shall he find time for dreaming or any space to think."

He can scarcely ever get alone, even in his study, for his daytime thoughts pursue him still with whispers of the conventional, the popular, and the superficial. Now and then a great man does stop, does fight, does walk out from the crowd, and does think real thoughts beneath the silent stars. Sir Thomas Browne did, and gave us the *Religio Medici*—William Harvey did, and gave us knowledge of the circulation of the blood—John Hunter did, and pointed the way to modern surgery—Edward Jenner did, and gave us protection from smallpox—Louis Pasteur did, and became the Columbus of the great Continent of Bacteriology—Lord Lister did, and because of it the surgeon is now clad in purity, "as the bride in Comus was arrayed in chastity"—William T. G. Morton did, and as a result we have the divine gift of anesthesia—Oliver Wendell Holmes did, and the world is the richer by the knowledge of the contagiousness of puerperal fever and by such books as the *Autocrat* and *Elsie Venner*—Weir Mitchell did, and we have

Hugh Wynne and the rest cure—Osler did, and in the minds of all of us are thoughts from his teeming brain.

All of these men cast off the shackles of conventional thought and stopped to think for themselves. Poetic fancy led them and the poetic instinct leads to all that is really great and original. The details may go to others for solution, the idea comes from the dreamer of dreams. The great steamboat which tears across the Atlantic in five days is a slow evolution and has been completed by the labors of hundreds of minds, but the idea of steam and what it would do was first a dream, a flash, a breath, an inspiration in the brain of a single man. There is a poetry of science as truly as of the emotions, and it leads to the Fairy Land of which Tennyson dreamed.

The men I mention peered into Immensity and among the shadows of Eternity saw the great figures of the Possible. They dwelt in an ampler heaven "than that in which the Nations sun themselves"—they snatched great treasures from the storehouse which is forever closed and barred to the lesser men of mere details.

Of course it is given to but few to think as those men did, but we can all, if we will, do some thinking. We can all observe, study, analyse, compare, seek to know if we are on the right road, or if, in blind haste, the real way has been passed unseen; if the goal sought is obtainable; if some of the bluster and hurry, and infinite detail might not with safety be abandoned. If we do this we will soon conclude that it is more necessary to reason than to rush—that calm analysis is better than unrestrained haste— that luminous logic is as necessary as are countless experiments— that the oldest custom may happen to be wrong and the newest fashion may at times be right—that change is not of necessity synonymous with improvement—that alteration is not always progress, for a movement may be retrogression instead of a step in advance, and some people, like the glowworm, carry a head-light on the wrong end.

Then many absurdities will become apparent—many truths will be identified—the casual will be separated from the causal, the accidental and transitory from the essential and fundamental. Then we will learn to welcome truth whether it appears as a slow evolution from laborious and multiplied observations or as a good fairy in the guise of a discovery. Then we will be able to read the guide posts on the road of tendency and to see the milestones on the way to progress. So even I venture to *try* to think a *little;* I, who have often been contaminated by the blight of low ideals; I, who have been stained by worldly contacts and have felt what John Brown called "the pestilential lust of novelty."

So let us ask "whither are we going?" We are as those on a ship. Are the navigators competent—are the charts correct— is the harbor we seek reachable—is the aim worthy? If we reach a port will we have to stay in malarious levels because the steps to the heights are of sand, or will be we able to ascend the sun- lit summits where the storm cloud broods? Will we have to return to whence we came and with other officers and fresh charts set out again upon our journey?

I speak of certain commercial tendencies among doctors and to what they lead, bearing in mind that even apparently trivial things may lead to revolutionary changes, for a thousand forests may lie hidden in a single acorn.

Time will permit me this evening to discuss but two tendencies. One relates to practicing physicians; the other to laboratory workers. The first I call:

THE REMEDY OF CORTEZ IN THE MEDICAL PROFESSION

When Cortez went into Mexico, he said to the Indians: "I and my men have a disease of the heart and gold helpeth it." Men seek today as ardently for the remedy of Cortez as ever did any bloody buccaneers who cut throats and scuttled galleons on the Spanish main.

The business world seems to be in a lamentable state. Legis- lation on which the prosperity of the nation may depend is often formulated by men so small mentally that could we read their thoughts we would be indulging in light reading, men who go knocking about after ideas like a blind dog in a butcher shop. In many states and cities, and perhaps higher up, the naked arm of public theft is plunged into the coffers of the treasury. Nearly everybody wants to live without work. This is the answer to "Why is a broker?" All sorts of people seek all kinds of perquisites, and a perquisite is only a gilded tip, and bears the same relation to a bribe that an incognito does to an alias, intoxication to drunkenness, hot gallantry to licentiousness, and rapidity to dissipation. This is an age of euphemism and a spade is called "an agricultural implement."

Individual fortunes grow while men waste and perish. In spite of beneficent inventions and labor-saving devices, labor is at the lowest level and workmen are but slaves of the Lamp. Slaves have no conscience in their work, and even if conscience were catching like smallpox, they would seldom catch that expensive luxury from their employers. "If the abbot plays cards what can be expected of the monks?" The iron fetter of the trade union has reduced the best to the level of the poorest workman; has wiped out individual ability, ambition, thrift, and intelligence; has left the mere man-machine that does, is able to do, and is allowed to do only a very limited work, requiring only a certain narrow dexterity or common muscular force. Such work is easily learned and the machine that does it needs little intelligence and always stops work the second the whistle blows. Colossal combinations of capital wipe out all competition and destroy small producers and traders. The ablest lawyers devote their best abilities to driving a coach and six through stupidly drawn acts of Congress, and advising people how they may violate with impunity the plain intent of the law. Such men sell their talents and are mental prostitutes. Combinations in restraint of trade which three hundred years ago Sir Edward Coke decided were against the common law of England, flourish like green bay trees in this land of the free, where the common law is *supposed* to run.

The golden rule is as dead as witchcraft, as alchemy, as astrology, as the humoral pathology, as the doctrine of signatures, as the iatrochemical school. It is entirely forgotten except on

Sunday, when it is occasionally verbally resurrected and exhibited from pulpits as an antique curiosity long retired from active service. Six days in the week spiders may weave their webs upon it if they will, for men put aside the very memory of it with their Sunday trousers. Great advertisements, brazen impudence, impossible schemes—gambling ventures—swindling companies—crooked corporations—subtle promoters—adulterated foods, drugs, dry goods, and tobacco—and imperfect work—are common features of the day. When any attempt is made to check these things, we hear a shriek that vested interests are sacred though men perish. When occasionally some isolated individual, no worse than a horde of others, is caught and punished, we hear the horde denounce the law. This is quite natural, for

> "No thief e'er felt the halter draw
> With good opinion of the law."

The rule of the world today is rapidly becoming the rule of the highwayman as set forth in Wadsworth's *Rob Roy:*

> "The good old rule
> Sufficeth them, the simple plan,
> That they shall take who have the power,
> And they shall keep who can."

The medical profession *ought to be* and *is* in a vastly better condition than the business world. It still has *many* high ideals. It can't go very wrong if its members adhere to the Principles of Medical Ethics of the American Medical Association, which we used to call before 1903, the Code. This Code has been the subject of frequent and vicious abuse by nonmedical people who know nothing at all of what they criticize. It is popularly supposed to be a sort of iron-clad arrangement by means of which physicians are enabled to coerce and rob the general public. As a matter of fact its intentions are exactly the reverse. It is meant to prevent anyone from wronging the public. It is intended to cause all physicians to appreciate the high nature of their duties, to realize their responsibilities, and to treat their patients with fairness and humanity. Furthermore, it is meant to cause physicians to conduct their personal and professional relations as professional and personal relations ought everywhere to be conducted by gentlemen. When a man bears the Principles in mind he is sure to remember that he is a part of the best, the most charitable, the most ancient of professions; that he follows a calling older than Christianity, and more ancient than the civil law.

Every good physician knows that he has entered this calling not as goods pass through the Custom House in a free trade country (that is—*free of duty*), but that he is to wear through all his days the iron crown of *duty*.

He has not entered it for wealth. If he has he will almost certainly be disappointed. The popular ideas as to the magnitude of medical compensation are ludicrous exaggerations. A man who seeks for money as a pirate seeks a richly laden ship, or who regards the dollar mark as the very perfection of drawing, or who listens for "the jingling of the guinea" usually adopts, and had always better adopt, some other calling. If an individual possessing sufficient talent and industry to make himself a distinguished physician or surgeon were to expend the same amount of energy and exercise the same amount of ability in any one of a hundred other callings, he would almost surely reap many times the pecuniary harvest that he could in the medical profession.

If a man enters medicine as a field of graft, sooner or later "the sheriff Fate will put a hand on his shoulder and arrest him as a moral bankrupt." It is true, of course, that we do not study from pure philanthropy. Let us brush the dust of hypocrisy from our knees and admit that learning is a commodity. We appreciate the opportunities afforded us to do good. We try to regard duty and desire as synonymous. The sympathetic imagination stirs us as we strive among "God's poor toiling suffering millions," but as a matter of fact medicine is a career by which most of us must earn our living and it is well to always remember that some of the purest nuggets of science have been delved from the profound mines of Truth by hands that wrought for their daily bread.

We do not claim to have a holy mission as do the clergy. A physician will accept a salaried chair and cheerfully admit that he was called to it by the Board, not by the Lord. But we all understand that we have such elevated duties, noble responsibilities, and sacred trusts, that our conduct must be guided by other rules than the purely selfish ones of business. Rewards more valuable than money may be ours and punishments worse than poverty may be meted out to us.

Because of its retained ideals the medical world is in a vastly better state than the business world, but it seems to me that the widespread deterioration of the business conscience has an unfortunate reflex upon medicine and that certain deplorable tendencies have begun to appear here and there among us, tendencies which require vigorous condemnation, and which cannot be suppressed a moment too soon.

The symptoms of these tendencies we may well fear are the prodromata of grave disease.

One of these symptoms is the *medical tradesman*, and the medical tradesman is a potential quack. The very fact that medicine is not an exact science stimulates the naturally crooked to be quacks. Failure to do our duty also favors quackery. We must remain *professional men* and must not become *medical tradesmen*.

A trade is a mechanical or a mercantile employment, a handicraft, carried on purely and solely for personal profit and without a thought of the public good. Trades serve the public good, but this is not the end sought for. A profession is a vocation in which a professed knowledge of science or learning is applied to benefit others. A profession is broad, a trade is narrow. A profession is liberal, a trade is bigoted. By the practice of a profession as by the exercise of a trade, a person obtains a livelihood; but in the profession there are other aims than monetary reward and other duties than a full day's work. The tradesman works purely for the pecuniary return. The professional man should work also for progress, humanity, and elevation of thought and character. A profession has greater responsibilities, greater dignities, greater rewards (not of money) and heavier retributions than has a trade. Many a man in a profession had just enough ambition and aspiration to take him *into it*, but has not enough to keep him up to the high level of his duty, and such a man is only a *spoiled tradesman*. He is like a mixture of good water and good wine, a mixture that means the ruin of all that is best in both of these excellent liquids.

A professional tradesman may be an honest man, a virtuous man, a good husband, a kind parent, but the *highest* is not in him and the *highest* cannot come out.

The tricks that are expected in a trade are disgraceful in a profession. The medical tradesman is a being extremely low in the scale of animal creation and such men are responsible for most of the evils under which the profession labors. From this class come the prescribing and operating quack, the divider of fees, the recipient of commissions, the exploiter of formulas and dogmas, the advertiser, the stealer of patients, the deceiver of the sick, the swindler, the dealer in innuendo and calumny, the jealous villifier of his professional brethren.

Such men make frequent and vociferous claims for public notice of their great professional ability. Francis Bacon said: "Medicine is a profession which hath been more professed than labored." As a general rule, the more a man professes the less he knows, just as the house with the loudest dinner-gong is likely to have the poorest food and the least of it, and the clock which strikes out the greatest din may keep the worst time. Such persons seem to think that the prizes of life, like the walls of Jericho, will fall from noise.

It is only the medical tradesman who calls out his wares upon the highways. The real physician is more modest and understands that the more medicine a man knows the less he believes. As Montaigne said: "Nothing is so firmly believed as what we least know." The boasts, the pretensions, the quarrels of medical men help the medical tradesman, allow him to pose as the possessor of great truths of healing or as a martyr to bigotry and hate.

Doctor Johnson defined a quack as a boastful pretender; an artful, trickling practitioner of physic. Most quacks hold no diplomas, but some *genuine quacks* are medical graduates. What makes the quack is the boastful pretending, and the artful tricking, whether or not the pretender and trickster holds a diploma from a regular college.

These are the sort of individuals that Hooker said: "Sturdy, patient getting more than patient, curing." There is no doubt whatever that the world dearly loves a quack. The late P. T. Barnum said "people like to be fooled." The mysterious appeals to most natures. Francis Bacon said: "The weakness and credulity of men is such that they prefer a mountebank or a witch to a learned physician." Humbug is still a god to the credulous and ignorant, cunning is his instrument, and the daily press too often his good friend. Hence the systematized delusions of dogmatic schools, the dangerous obsessions, and gibbering imbecilities of Faith Cure and Christian Science.

Medicine is not the only calling cursed with quacks. They are found in all occupations as loud-mouthed pretenders seeking to gain confidence by unworthy methods and claiming to have specifics which will amend disorders of morals, manners, finance, and politics.

The business world is full of quacks. They exploit gold fields devoid of gold, silver mines virgin to the touch of silver, asphalt which runs like molasses on an August day, trust companies that cannot be trusted, and insurance schemes that do not insure. There is the quack in statesmanship who would reform every abuse by the application of a favorite or profitable formula; the quack in law who stimulates litigation and conducts legal procedures with a total disregard of all interests but those of his own pocket-book; the quack in religion who claims to possess personal influence with the Creator, who speaks as a self-constituted oracle of the Almighty, and who would wild-cat his particular adherents to Heaven in the private parlor car of a special lightning express. So medicine does not stand out alone in possessing "undesirable citizens."

A test as to whether or not a practitioner of medicine has or has not the spirit of the quack is the direction *to* which he looks for reputation. The decent man seeks reputation among the members of his own profession; the other sort of person attempts to gain notoriety with the general public. As Sir James Paget said, such notoriety may be obtained by the most ignorant "through self-assertion, self-advertising, or mere impudence."

There are various ways of advertising. The mere ignorant shameless quack advertises directly in the newspapers, asking people to consult him "when all others fail," etc. The regular practitioner, who is a medical tradesman, advertises by means of interviews and copious newspaper references to his sayings and doings. He is the man sought for by reporters when they want news as to paresis among actors, scrofula in royal families, the illness of a railroad magnate, the influence of meat in causing cancer, the value of Fletcherism, and why Senator Somebody was operated upon. All reporters know to whom they had best go for such information. This sort of thing I fear is gaining ground. In my own city there are several who repeatedly sin in this way. It is a reflex from the world at large which has a veritable passion to be named in the paper. Some men are in the paper every day and at length who never did anything greater in life than give a dinner, attend a box party, ride on a tally-ho, or lead a cotillion. Yet the paper makes them known far and wide, and in consequence they glow and expand from a proud sense of great personal importance.

A bad thing about newspaper medicine is that it gives the people many wrong ideas. We feel it now in surgery. Some people insist on obtaining spinal anesthesia instead of ether because of newspaper articles commending the method. They know nothing of the objections and dangers, and if a surgeon denies the request they regard him as ignorant or behind the times. When the Brown-Séquard Elixir was introduced, the Jefferson Hospital was thronged with aged men soliciting injections that they might at once get married. It speaks much for the popularity and influence of newspapers, but little for the judgment and intelligence of doctors who give them such information.

Some medical tradesmen commit the crowning infamy of

modern practice, that is, obtaining a division of the fee with the man who comes to operate or who comes to consult. If a specialist divides a fee he does just what a shyster lawyer does when he pays a commission to an ambulance chaser for bringing him the name of a person injured in a street accident. The method of commissions is allowable in the business world, but because they do it does not justify us in doing it. Such a procedure is robbery of the patient. The family attendant does not *dare* to tell the patient of it. A *joint bill* is entirely proper, but a joint bill is not what these worthies want. The patient is compelled to pay the surgeon more than the surgeon's fee and the surplus goes to the attending physician as a bribe. Thus the surgeon bribes the family physician to bring him cases, and the family attendant, if he is bribable, is led to select the man who pays the largest bribes, and not the man who is, according to his judgment, the best man to handle that particular case, but who will not pay a bribe.

Such a procedure is trafficking in human life. Bringing this business method into medicine is humiliating and disgraceful. It puts us on a level with the most crooked lawyers. It is a foul taint upon the profession and should be entirely wiped out. Recently, the House of Delegates of the American Medical Association, on motion of Doctor Bevan of Chicago, resolved to expel from the association any member on whom such conduct should be proved. This is the answer of the profession at large to the attempt of some few rascals to introduce certain business methods into medicine. We scorn such methods and we spurn them.

The second tendency we are to discuss is the perversion of the laboratory, and I call it:

The Laboratory Light That May Fail

Medical lore is not fixed, unchanging, immutable. It is always undergoing change. It is ever in process of construction and disintegration. It is always growing, but is never complete. The supposed established fact of yesterday may be cast aside as worthless today. The vague hypothesis of last week may be the accepted

24

certainty of this week. The error of one year may be the truth of
the next. Our supposed scientific knowledge is plastic and the
potters who mould it are largely laboratory workers. The laboratory has taken possession of some of the finest minds in medicine.
In the laboratory great problems are in process of investigation,
and we trust of solution. In laboratories great discoveries have
been made and will be made. Clinical medicine and surgery look
to the laboratory for light to show them pathways to diagnosis,
prognosis, and treatment, look to it perhaps too entirely and too
often and a bit too trustingly.

When we realize the vast and gaining influence of laboratories
and the huge sums of money required for their support (sums
wheedled out of the often reluctant millionaire) it becomes evident that only highly qualified men should control them. The
instrument is too powerful to be entrusted to the money seeker,
the lover of notoriety, the untruthful, or the weakling. The man
in charge should never be there because he has money or because
he wants money; because he is somebody's brother, or son, or
nephew; because he belongs to a particular church or political
party; or because he has "pull."

If he is saturated with the commercial views of the age they
will stain the agar in his test-tubes and blur the glasses of his
microscopes, taint his chemical reagents, and incorrectly set
his balances. The torch of science will not burn in a foul abode
and the only lights that show will be marsh meteors bred by
miasm.

Immature views—self-interested opinions—sordid aims—over-
stated cases—unreasoned influences—bungling experiments—
dubious assertions—faulty observations—untruthful or careless
reports, might lead us all wrong, bring grave disaster to humanity,
infinite disgrace to medical science and serious discredit upon
the profession. The head of a laboratory should be a man who
is a king because of learning and truthfulness.

A laboratory of anatomy, of pathologic anatomy, of histology,
or of embryology may be admirably conducted by a well-trained,
hard-working, honest, well-read, clear headed, strong-brained,

quick-eyed, logical, and *practical* man. In these branches there is little room for idle speculation. As Herter points out, the men who successfully investigate the problems of "structure and arrangement" crave "the positive, the definite, the attainable" and either shun "the speculative aspects of science" or move "uncomfortably in the midst of ill-defined and challengeable facts."

But a different kind of laboratory requires a different sort of man. I agree with Herter that the man who would study function should be of a speculative turn. The investigator of structure must be essentially practical. The investigator of function must be essentially speculative.

The small group of men who investigate function should always contain the greatest original minds in science. Such men dream of possibilities, speculate upon probabilities, build chateaux in Spain, and castles in the air, suggest hypotheses and found comprehensive theories. Their fancies take possession of them and they are always devising experiments to prove or disprove their fancies, their guesses, and their beliefs. They fail repeatedly, but are not discouraged and return from each failure stronger and more earnest than before, as Antaeus was rendered stronger by being cast upon the earth. They are in close personal contact with the deepest mysteries of nature and are ever peering into infinite space which the hand of Omnipotence has strewed thick with star dust.

Sir Michael Foster says that the creative power of the man of science is best shown by "the putting forth of the hypothesis."

We mean the *good* hypothesis, not the *stupid* one. Sir Michael Foster says (*Life of Claude Bernard*): "An hypothesis may be good or may be bad, may be fruitful or may be barren. This may depend on the very nature of the hypothesis, which may, even at the outset, in its very origin be worthless and wrong." The good hypothesis means creative power.

It is the creative power of the true man of science that makes him kin to Shakespeare and Phidias, to Mozart and Michael Angelo. He has in his veins the blood of genius, and

"Never blood of Burbon grew
So magnificent a blue."

Those who would pursue this vein of thought would do well to take the *Journal of the American Medical Association* for February 5, 1910, and read that most scholarly, impressive, and brilliant address on *Imagination and Idealism in the Medical Sciences*, by Prof. Christian A. Herter of Columbia University, New York.

One of the most important and most perplexing of problems is how to discover, develop, and secure proper men for the highest sort of laboratory work. There never can be a great number of them, but it is hard to get even the few we need and mistakes in selection are common.

The average medical school gives to *all* of its students a superficial training in various laboratory *manipulations*, seeks to awaken interest in research as a career, and tries to lure bright men upon that tortuous pathway. As a matter of fact colleges are very anxious to develop research men, far more anxious, some of us think, than they are to make good doctors, and the making of good doctors is supposed to be *the* function of a medical school. If all schools devote themselves entirely to graduating research men, who, pray, is to treat the injured and diseased; who will there be to stand by the bedside and mitigate suffering and prolong life? The anxiety of the college to develop research work is due to the fact that a notable research reflects credit upon the teacher and the institution and calls *public* attention to both. It is a great and flattering advertisement.

This anxiety of the colleges for fame draws or drives many unfit men into laboratory careers. It takes many men fit only to hew wood and draw water, and sets them by the steps of the throne, steps they are destined never to ascend. In other words, it sends many men into a career in which they are foredoomed to failure because of the type of humanity to which they belong. This yearly increment of the unfit consists of a type of man who can carry out what he is told to do, who knows how to use a retort or a microscope, chemical reagents or a sphygmograph; but a man who never had an original idea, a splendid fancy or a glorious dream; who never had "Tears from the depth of some divine despair"; who never felt a great thought rise in the brain and flush upon the cheek; who never built a palace for his soul to dwell in; and who could no more found a hypothesis than a ward politician could found a theory of the pure, and the true, and the beautiful.

The system of the colleges keeps some eminently fit men from reaching the throne which should be theirs. It exacts from them many things they have not and do not need, and rejects them because they have not certain entirely unnecessary things. Read what Herter says about Ehrlich (*Ibid.*); as a student Ehrlich studied what interested him and neglected what did not. Once Koch was being shown through the laboratory in Breslau. The professor who acted as cicerone pointed out a young student working with dyes, and said: "There is our little Ehrlich, he is a first-rate stainer of tissues, but he will never pass his examinations." As a matter of fact he did pass them, but by what the book of Job calls the skin of his teeth. Had he failed what would we have known today of tangent chemistry toxoids, toxophores and hepatophores, and the modern doctrine of immunity.

The college teaches a man how to work with the instruments of the laboratory, and it may teach him how to accumulate facts, it does not teach him how to speculate, observe, and reason. It teaches him many unnecessary things, and it can't teach him to make discoveries, because it can't create in him the faculty of imagination. It can't teach him

> "To body forth the forms of things unknown,
> And give to airy nothing,
> A local habitation and a name."

The college course which fits men to be medical practitioners does not fit them to be research workers, and vice versa. Most colleges try to do both, and, of course, fail in doing either well. As before stated, the man fit for higher laboratory work must have born in him certain aptitudes, capacities, and powers. He must have received the divine touch. He must be, by mighty ordination, kinsman to the orator, the poet, the artist, the sculptor, the adventurer who bleeds the veins of the mountains, the explorer who tracks the dusky cannon, the musician who draws down harmony from the skies. He must be the unconventional one who is out of place on the crowded dusty highway; one who "Amidst discordant noises of the jostling throng" hears "the far celestial voices of Olympian song."

More of these gifted men come from the farm than from the city, more from the loins of the people than from the shades of ancestoral trees, more from the alley than from the boulevard, more from the hovel than the mansion. If our bosses keep on getting their way such men will soon not be allowed to study medicine at all, and only the rich man's son will be permitted to become a doctor.

Would there were divining rods to point out such men to us, but alas! there are none. We must always be on the lookout for speculative genius, but even with our best efforts, our judgment will often go astray. When we do find such a man, we have done a great thing for humanity. We should guard him, cherish him, and endow him. We should teach him how to use the tools of the laboratory (that is teach him how to experiment), but we should also teach him how to observe, to record, to reason, and to expound. We should strive to guard him from destructive influences: evil passions, bad habits, laziness, vice, and *fashionable* society. It is my belief that the ballroom, the dance, the dinner party, and the afternoon tea have sterilized almost as many fine intellects as have the gambling den, the dram shop, the brothel, and politics.

We should cherish him that he may be gladdened and stimulated by praise for good work done and for that very idealism and imagination he has grown accustomed to be condemned for possessing.

We should endow him in order to free his thoughts from the harassment of financial care, a harassment that forced Hunter out at intervals to make "those cursed guineas." The harassments of poverty are dogs of hungry ruin at the throat. Poverty often hangs upon the best efforts as the Old Man of the Sea hung about the neck of Sinbad the Sailor.

We should teach him how to use the tools of the laboratory in order that he will put his deductions to the right test of careful and accurate experiment.

It takes an imaginative man to form a series of experiments. Hear Sir Michael Foster in his *Life of Claude Bernard:* "On the other hand, failure or success may depend on the framing of the experiment by which the hypothesis is tested. Here, too, the imagination comes into play. The man who constructs a hypothesis without supplying an adequate programme for its trial by experiment is a burden to science and the world; and he who puts forward hypotheses which by their very nature cannot be tried, is worse, for he is a purveyor of rubbish."

We should teach him how to observe in order that he may know how to see things and be certain what he sees. We should teach him how to record accurately, promptly, and systematically his observed facts, theories, hypotheses, guesses, contemplated trials, and experiments in order that nothing may be lost and everything may be definite and clear.

We should teach him how to reason in order that he may have at hand and in good order the only faculty man has which enables him to seek for truth and identify genuine from base scientific coin.

We should teach him to expound in order that all men may read, attend, and understand.

Such is my conception of the highest sort of laboratory worker.

One reason why the colleges fail so often in picking out the right man is because nearly all teachers set inordinate store upon what they call the *practical* mind, and they do this because they are imbued with the Baconian theory of the way to make discoveries.

Lord Bacon maintained that science is to be advanced by making multitudes of observations, classifying them, laboriously sorting out truth from error, and then by induction finding the common influence which underlies all the truths. As a matter of fact no great discovery was ever made in this manner. The discoverer does not make his discovery by induction from numerous observations. Several observations, it may be a single observation, a chance fact, a custom, a belief, a tradition, cause the speculative mind to found a theory which would apply and he puts the theory to the test of careful experiment. If experiments disprove the theory, it is cast aside as worthless. If they prove it, a discovery is made. Sir Michael Foster says: "To the observer brooding over the phenomena presenting themselves to him there comes the thought that if a certain state of things were supposed to exist, or if a certain sequence of events were supposed to take place, the occurrence of the phenomena must necessarily follow, and he forthwith sets about to seek for evidence whether the things so supposed do really exist or not. Observation starts a hypothesis, and experiment tests whether the hypothesis is true or no. Such is research reduced to its simplest terms."

It was thus that William Harvey made his great discovery. It dawned on him after thought and observation that the heart was a pump and he proved it by vivisection. He discovered the circulation. He knew that veins and arteries must join, but he never saw the capillaries. They were demonstrated by Malpighi four years after Harvey's death. Harvey was a man of intense and imaginative mind, and in no sense a man of statistics. To use his own words: "It was believed by the vulgar that he was crack-brained, and all the physicians were against him" (*William Harvey*, by D'Arcy Power).

It was thus John Hunter worked out problems of function. He insisted that the final proof could be made only by experiment. When he wrote to Jenner, "Don't think, try; be patient, be accurate" he meant, don't try to evolve *facts* from the inner consciousness and put all supposed facts and theories alike to careful test. Look at the picture by Reynolds which is owned by the Royal College of Surgeons. We are all familiar with Sharp's splendid engraving of it. That picture shows Hunter plunged in thought, entirely oblivious of his surroundings, and looking into the infinity of the unknown.

It was thus Bernard made some of his greatest discoveries, notably the glycogenic function of the liver. Bernard was essentially a man of imagination and in his youth wrote plays and poems. Sir Michael Foster says that he "always worked under the guidance of some leading ideas." Bernard said, "He who does not know what he is looking for, will not lay hold of what he has found when he gets it." Bernard's view finds notable exemplification in the discovery of the x-rays. Crookes invented the Crookes tube before the x-rays were dreamed of, and Roentgen found the x-rays coming from the very tube devised by Crookes.

It was thus Helmholtz invented the ophthalmoscope. He was led to the invention by asking himself the question "how an optical image is formed by the light returning from the eye" (*Life of Helmholtz*, by McKendrick).

It was thus Pasteur became the founder of bacteriology and Lister the founder of antiseptic surgery.

Jenner dreamed and talked of cowpox for years, but he submitted the claims of vaccination on the basis of only twenty-three experiments.

Thus Newton discovered gravitation. Thus Kirchoff discovered spectrum analysis. Thus Leverrier pointed out the necessary position of the planet Neptune. Thus Franklin habitually proceeded. Thus the great investigators of aviation act today. Thus Marconi was led to beckon the mystic signal out of the mists of the North Atlantic across 1800 miles of lonely sea.

Such instances could be multiplied a hundred-fold. Most people suppose the Baconian method to be true because it looks as though it ought to be true. It appeals to men of this intensely practical modern world. It is a method all can understand and is not wrapped in clouds of many hues and of fantastic shapes. It agrees with the present day view that each worker should do a very limited and special sort of work. The world at large has confidence in the method and medical investigators feel the reflex, or rather the inhibition, from the world at large.

I wish time permitted me to speak of some other existing tendencies which threaten medical science; for instance, the tendency to regulate everything and destroy all freedom of action, the regulations frequently being made by those who know nothing whatever of the matter at issue. This is shown in the conduct of various State Boards of Examiners. Members of these boards are seldom teachers and yet we must all teach in accordance with their views and orders.

I would like to consider attempts to suppress competition in practice as shown by the refusal of various states to register legal practitioners from other states.

I would like to discuss the conduct of the medical boss, which is gathering strength and power, which would keep a man from studying medicine at a period of life when his mind is plastic and formative, when it is "wax to receive and marble to retain" —which would condemn him to take a college degree before he can take a medical degree and which, if it gets its way, will keep the son of a poor man from studying medicine in the United States. By such a system we would never have had Joseph Leidy or D. Hayes Agnew, J. Marion Sims, or Samuel David Gross.

There are many other things I would like to consider with you, but they all warn us of one thing. The warning is that we must *retain our ideals.* If we give them up we will inevitably be dragged down to the leprous level of the loathsome and blighting commercial world. One who would take away our ideals is as one who would take the heat from flame—who would steal the perfume from the rose—who would stain the glorious colors of the sunset— who would strip the splendor from the radiant brow of morning.

ADDRESS AT THE OPENING OF THE NURSES' COLLEGE OF THE ALLENTOWN HOSPITAL, DECEMBER 23, 1915

WE meet today to inaugurate with fitting formality and due ceremonial the Nurses' Home of the Allentown Hospital, an addition made possible by the generous bequest of that noble citizen of Allentown, the late Judge Edward Harvey.

I arise to speak, flattered by the invitation, but oppressed by a sense of unworthiness to meet the high duties of the occasion. Yesterday while reading the paper I perused an advertisement which read: "Well-cut corsets uphold one's self-confidence." I wish I were wearing that corset now. I remember that Jonah journeyed three days into Ninevah before he began to preach and I have started to do so when my visit to this city is not yet three hours in duration. Truly "Fools rush in where angels fear to tread." I recognize too keenly for comfort that the way of oratory, though it may be the road of Pride, is also the path of Peril.

But in one respect at least this audience is peculiarly fortunate, for here as an active participant in the exercises is a celebrated statesman whom we all love, respect, and admire. By his presence he gives renewed assurance of that highly useful interest in medical matters and in medical men which he evinced in a most practical manner while first magistrate of the Republic.

Pennsylvania feels herself honored today in having within her borders the distinguished ex-President of the United States.

I miss one face here. The absence brings sadness to my thoughts. I miss the bright and kindly glances, the hospitable greeting, the cordial handclasp that would have been mine were my old friend, Dr. Charles Stephen Martin, still in the land of the living. Peace to his soul!

"Friends depart and memory takes them
To her caverns pure and deep."

This hospital is one of the best equipped in the State of Penn-sylvania. It is only sixteen years old, yet it now contains 181 beds. Last year 1586 surgical, 638 medical, and 188 obstetrical cases were treated, and 1565 surgical operations were performed. It contains all those things essential to a modern hospital, charity wards, pay wards, private rooms, a laboratory, a diet kitchen, a sterilizing room, and an x-ray machine, fine out-patient depart-ments, a children's ward, a maternity ward, an operating room, an able and active staff, sixty nurses, and now a splendid nurses' home. Truly a complete institution and one in every way an honor to its managers and to this city.

A hospital may be defined as an institution for the best pos-sible treatment of the sick and injured. Were we speaking of a European hospital we would say of the sick and injured poor, for there practically all hospitals are for the poor alone. For instance, in Paris the great hospitals are parts of almshouses. Until comparatively recently the same was practically true of the United States. The change began about forty years ago.

The original function of a hospital was to treat the poor. That is still its highest duty, but in the United States the care of the poor is not its sole field of usefulness.

In the United States the hospital is for rich and poor alike, for the millionaire and the pauper, and admittance to a hospital no longer of necessity implies poverty. The poor man comes in without charge, and no one but the poor man should be permitted to. One who is better off enters the pay ward. One who is well-to-do takes a private room. Board from the private rooms is a most important element in furnishing money to run the hospital. Hence every private room rented serves to pay the cost of keep-ing several poor persons in the ward without charge. To pay board in a hospital is a charity, vicarious, perhaps unrecognized, but nevertheless a charity to others.

A poor man is admitted to the ward without objection, ob-stacle, or degradation. He is unfortunate, but not a pauper. He can't help being sick and poor and to be a free patient in a hos-pital is no possible reflection on his manhood or dignity. One

who can afford to pay ought not to be admitted free. If he is
admitted he is at once deprived of manhood and dignity. His
equivocation and pretenses to get into the dependent class pauper-
ize him. He robs the hospital which cares for him. He steals a
bed and board from some really poor man entitled to them. He
cheats a decent medical man out of a fee to which he is entitled
for attending him. Carelessness in this respect on the part of
hospital officials means a costly and lamentable perversion of
charity from the worthy to the undeserving. Such carelessness
sews tares that may overwhelm the field.

That well-to-do people when seriously ill now prefer a hospital is due to the insistent teaching of the medical profession.
Day in and day out medical men have insisted that a really critical
case is better cared for in than out of a hospital. The public
has become convinced.

When I became one of Professor Keen's assistants the change
was just fairly beginning and as yet many people were operated
upon in their homes. And what a fearful trouble it was. From
a day or two before the operation until a day or two afterward
I was as busy as a bird-dog or a gas meter. A room had to be
stripped of furniture and carpet. The walls and ceilings were
scrubbed. A table was improvised from a kitchen table or an
ironing board on trestles. Great packages of dressings and bags
of instruments were carried to the house. The day of the operation the instruments were sterilized in kettles of boiling water
over the kitchen fire. It took at least two hours to lay out everything in the operating room. The smell of ether permeated the
house, and this smell, with hurrying footsteps, and other sounds
drove the realization of the dread drama of the operation into
the minds of the anxious and perhaps terrified family. If the
operation had been severe I stayed in the house one night, two
nights or more, to do, if necessary, what a resident physician
now does in a hospital. What work it was! What an expenditure
of time it called for! What a strain it inflicted on a family! And
every now and then the surgeon would be put to his trumps to
manage an unexpected complication which could have been more

rapidly and safely dealt with in a hospital. An absent instrument might be suddenly required. There is no instrument room in a private house. The surgeon had to do without it. A drug not then at hand might be badly needed. There is no drug store in residences (although the closet of a nervous man or a hysterical woman might suggest a pharmacy). The absence of a needed drug or instrument always meant trouble and sometimes spelled disaster. A surgeon who has never performed a major operation in a private house can't begin to appreciate what a luxury it is and what a comforting sense of safety it brings to operate in a hospital. Is it any wonder that after such strain and labor we got a little sore when our bills were not paid? In these days I am used to having them unpaid. Many patients never even think of paying, and yet I remain reasonably tranquil under the infliction. I have discovered that more people prefer to pay social obligations than doctors' bills, but in running up bills they take no note of the speed limit and that they like to dwell in the Land of Promise. I have come to doubt that man is made of dust, because dust settles. I am not sure that the good die young, but I am quite sure that only the young die good.

At the present time the public has faith in hospitals. Persons no longer hesitate to go to one. A surgical patient expects to go. A medical patient usually acquiesces when advised to go. After one experience an obstetrical case regards a maternity hospital as a boon. Growing trust in has bred a growing demand for more hospitals. The many hospitals which during recent years have arisen in the smaller cities, in the towns, and in the country districts indicate the increased public knowledge and appreciation of such institutions. A few years ago only cities of considerable size had hospitals. Small towns practically never had them. One might travel for many miles, even in New England and the Middle States, without seeing a single hospital. At present, in the East, and in many regions of the South and West, nearly every prosperous town has an excellent hospital which is a focus of medical and surgical effort for a large region of country.

According to Dr. Charles P. Emerson (*Hospital Management,*

edited by Charlotte A. Aikens) there are in the United States 2600 hospitals for acute medical and surgical cases. In this number we have not counted hospitals purely for eye, ear, nose, skin, and throat cases—for diseases of women—for mental diseases—for epilepsy—for orthopedic cases—for tuberculosis—for cancer—for contagious diseases—for children—for convalescents, nor have we counted sanatoria. During the past ten years the number of general hospitals in the country has almost doubled. The general hospitals contain 155,000 beds. In estimating the number of beds per 100,000 of population Emerson shows that California, Montana, and Nevada stand at the head of the list (above 500 beds). Next come Colorado, Arizona, Idaho, and the District of Columbia (between 401 and 500 beds). Then comes the State of Washington (301 to 400). Then come Connecticut, Delaware, Illinois, Maryland, Massachusetts, Minnesota, New Jersey, New Mexico, New York, North Dakota, Oregon, Pennsylvania, Utah, and Wyoming (201 to 300). Only 8.4 per cent of the institutions in the country have as many beds as the Allentown Hospital (101 to 200), yet in population Allentown, with 60,297, is the 102d city in the country, standing between Portland, Maine, with 62,161, and Charleston, South Carolina, with 60,121.

It is the ninth city in Pennsylvania, standing between Johnstown and Altoona. In this state there are ten general hospitals and 160 hospitals receiving state aid. Allentown stands high on the list in size, perfection of construction, efficiency of management, and public confidence.

The most striking sign of the trust in hospitals is the confidence of the poor. A comparatively few years ago they did not have any confidence, and it is small wonder they did not when we think of what some institutions were. Read Charles Dickens in *The Uncommercial Traveler* on the sick in a hospital:

"A bed in these miserable rooms, here on bedsteads, there (for a change, as I understood it) on the floor, the women in every stage of sickness and disease. None but those who have attentively observed such scenes can conceive the extraordinary variety of expression still latent under the general monotony and uniformity of color, altitude, and condition. The form a little coiled up and turned away, as though it had turned its back on this world forever; the uninterested face, at once lead-colored and yellow, looking passively upward from the pillow; the haggard mouth a little dropped; the hand outside the coverlet, so dull and indifferent, so light and yet so heavy—these were on every pallet; but when I stopped beside a bed and said ever so slight a word to the figure lying there, the ghost of the old character came into the face, and made the foul ward as various as the fair world. No one appeared to care to live, but no one complained; all who could speak said that as much was done for them as could be done there—that the attendance was kind and patient—that their suffering was very heavy, but they had nothing to ask for." Thus wrote the great master of what he saw in the year 1860.

Such institutions had all but disappeared when our days began, though some few almshouse hospitals still exhibited the bad old system in all its foulness, infamy, and dirt. Dickens himself saw far better institutions and wrote of them. But the stories of the bad ones long lingered, lost nothing of horror in the telling and were believed in and brooded over with fear and apprehension by "God's poor toiling, suffering millions." Even thirty years ago the poor in general were suspicious and distrustful of hospitals. When a poor man was taken to a hospital he went reluctantly, and with grim forebodings of the worst. He believed he was going to exposure among strangers, to surgical and medical experiment, to coldness, to neglect, probably to cruelty, and to the traditional "black bottle," and the dissecting room should his disease prove interesting or his presence annoying.

How changed things are today. The poor man now knows that he will find in the hospital food, shelter, rest, kindly care, sympathetic attention, and the most humane and scientific treatment. He goes there as a matter of course. Most of the very sick poor ask to go to the hospital knowing it to be the very best place for them, and realizing that by going there they remove a crushing burden from their struggling families.

I trust I have made clear to you that a hospital is the most necessary and beneficent of institutions and one of the very noblest of all objects of charity. Counting out the few state and municipal institutions endowment depends chiefly on the philantrophy of private citizens, aided it may be by the wise generosity of the state. I ask you citizens of Allentown to think of this splendid institution of yours and to always see to its needs.

Fine buildings are eminently desirable, but the staff is more important still. Good surgery can be done in very poor buildings, but a palace can't make an incompetent do good surgery. A bean-plant won't grow grapes even though it is trained on an arbor. The trustees of a hospital must select the members of the staff with scrupulous care, select them purely because of fitness, and decline to be swayed by any influence personal, religious, social, or political. There is no such thing as a Friendly cancer, a Baptist strangulated hernia, an Aristocratic carbuncle, or a Republican fracture, and hence there is no need of a surgeon whose only claim is in some such name. A serviceable staff, built on scientific lines, contains a specialist for every branch. In this age there is so much to learn in each branch that the ordinary man cannot be thoroughly equipped in two or more. When a good staff is once chosen the trustees should defend it, believe in it, give full attention to its recommendations, never lightly disregard its views on technical matters, and save it from dilution by the unworthy. A medical director should be at the head of the hospital. He should manage the hospital and should be responsible to the trustees. Divided authority means failure.

As a rule, hospital staffs do contain the best available men of their respective communities, men who study, men who observe, men who report their interesting cases, men who ably, scientifically and conscientiously perform their duties; who never use the institution for self-advancement or to damage professional brothers; who never blow the bellows of puffery; who never beat the great drum to attract the attention of the galleries; men who never get mixed in identifying the trump of Fame from the Horn of

25

Plenty, and the tin whistle of Notoriety; men who seek for reputation among their brother doctors rather than the general public, and men who are in earnest. This hospital has the men as well as the buildings. Such a staff, more than the finest buildings, causes all medical men in a neighborhood to look upon a hospital with respect and to send with confidence their patients to it.

An imperative duty and one of the highest duties of the chiefs is to guide, educate, instruct, and inspire the resident physician. In Pennsylvania a man cannot obtain a certificate to practice until he has served a term as resident physician. This is a beneficent law for the protection of the public. This term in a hospital should make the recent graduate a trained physician experienced in all ordinary diseases and emergencies. Much of the future of a resident may depend upon his chief. The younger man is apt to take to the traits of the elder. Hence the serious responsibility upon that elder to be at his best in all things. The chief must take a personal interest and do his duty by the intern, otherwise the young man may start wrong and continue wrong, may become lazy, indifferent, careless, an encumbrance or a positive menace. The intern should be encouraged to ask questions and to discuss cases; he should be led, guided, saved from pitfalls; given every possible opportunity to help in operations and, when fit, to do certain operations under the direction of his chief. He must take histories and learn how to question a patient systematically and his histories should be read and revised by an experienced man. He should train his ear, his eye, his sense of touch by repeated examinations of patients. He should observe prescribing and the actions of drugs, go through a course in the laboratory, and he should study, not only read up his cases, but study systematically. Thus is a real physician made. What a great work a hospital is doing when it furnishes the community with highly qualified practical medical men. I know you do that here. Not only interns should be trained, but assistants. Every surgeon should try to train at least several young men so that should anything happen to him the natural successor is right at hand. I believe too that every hospital should afford opportunities to any physician who wishes to see some of the work. This can be done by establishing courses of clinical lectures and inviting physicians to attend. A free patient who consents to be lectured upon thus pays the hospital for its care of him. The doctors who attend the clinics receive benefit. So do the doctors who hold them. A man teaches himself by lecturing, and to do surgery in public requires careful and continuous study and training.

No hospital can do scientific work without a laboratory run by an expert and well fitted with microscopes, oil immersion lenses, blood counters, incubator, sterilizer, freezing microtome, etc. To understand most patients some laboratory study is necessary, in fact, a diagnosis may rest absolutely upon laboratory findings. You can no more run a hospital well without a good laboratory than you can run an ocean steamship correctly without consulting good chronometers. The laboratory reports must be made by one who is a trained expert. A careless or mistaken report would throw our views all wrong and act like a railroad semaphore which sets to white when it should set to red or vice versa.

If a hospital would do accurate work it must insist on full and accurate histories being taken, filed, indexed according to both the disease and the name of the patient, and accessible for immediate production, and for use in the annual report. A history may be needed in case of a law suit. It may be needed to aid one of the staff in writing a book or an article for a medical journal. A person who was once in the hospital may come in again and the history of the former trouble is then very important. A physician in private practice or a physician in another hospital may take charge of one of our former patients and we should be able to furnish him with a copy of his history when with us. Without careful histories hospital cases cannot be published for the advancement of science and the institution lags in the road of progress.

The modern trained nurse is the surgeon's right hand. But a few years ago she did not exist. Thirty years ago, when I served my term as resident physician in a huge hospital, the attempt to introduce trained nurses was just being made in Philadelphia. The nursing at Blockley was fifty-fifty—in part by trained nurses, in part by representatives of the fine old Mrs. Gamp and Mrs. Prig schools. It did not take me long to decide as to the side where my sympathies belonged.

The old-timers, as a class (although there were brilliant exceptions), were ignorant, callous, and indifferent, frequently dirty, and not unusually drunk. All they knew was what had been picked up haphazard in a sordid experience and much that they knew was not true. They were ignorant of drugs, ignorant of methods, ignorant of the very fundamentals of surgical cleanliness, practically ignorant of everything, sometimes even of humanity.

The newcomers were young ladies with high ideals and earnest purposes. They were ruled by conscience. They were educated, were being carefully taught their profession, were dainty, tender, and charming. They worked rapidly and certainly, without noise or hurry. They knew what was wanted and how to have it ready. They worked not only with their hands but also with their brains and hearts. They watched their patients through the long hours with the calm self-reliance and confidence which bore a message of hope, with the knowledge that at once detected a change for the better or for the worse, with a tenderness that helped to blunt the very arrows of anguish.

Ever since Blockley days my respect for the trained nurse and my confidence in her have increased. She is an absolutely necessary part of a hospital. You can't run a hospital without her. An institution with a training school has given bonds to have first-class nurses. I do not dare to stand here and counsel the young ladies of the training school. I no more dare to do so than I would dare, stained as I am with worldly contact, to go into a fairy garden and admonish the lilies to be fair and bid the violets to be true. But I do bow in respectful admiration to those who devote their lives to this most useful calling. The Allentown Hospital does well to house them worthily, as we see it is about to do.

But, now enough! Were I to continue much longer I fear that I would violate the eight-hour law.

The story is told of two men who were lost in a trackless wilderness. For several days they wandered aimlessly seeking escape from the dreadful solitudes. At last, when they had almost perished from hunger, thirst, hopelessness, and exhaustion, they saw before them a huge stone building surrounded by a high wall; a building with barred windows; a building of grim and somber aspect. It was a jail. One of the men cried out in fervent gratitude, "Thank God, at last we have reached civilization." A jail the symbol of civilization!

Alas, yes, it is one of many such symbols, for the tramp has come with the locomotive, the pallid hand of hunger reaches out for bread in the light of show-windows containing ransoms for princes, the death penalty is still thought necessary to protect the lives of the community, and on the very steps of church and college, of museum and library, we find those menacing human figures who threaten the very existence of society (see *Progress and Poverty*, by Henry George).

These things, of course, are not evidences of real civilization, but they go with civilization and they follow it as the shadow does the substance. A modern community appeared to Thomas Carlyle like a jar full of tamed Egyptian vipers, each one striving to get its head above its neighbor's.

The glorious chariot of Progress, drawn by the thunderfooted coursers of the Sun, casts a huge shadow, and in that shadow crawls every noisome reptile and springs every noxious plant. The dust of that chariot is composed of perished hopes and of dead ambitions, and the wheels of that chariot are as of Juggernaut, and crush out not only the weak and helpless, but some of the best and noblest among the sons of men. Hence, in a certain sense, a jail is a sign of Civilization, of its failures, its errors, its mistakes, its sorrows, its ignorance, its horrors, its shadows, and its degeneracies.

But a hospital is a far truer sign of Civilization. It is a sign of its light, its mercy, its humanity, and its boundless charity.

To the hospital doors misery is the open sesame. In the hospital necessity is the one real claim, and to the hospital all may come who are poor and suffering, Jew and Gentile, Christian and Mohammedan, black and yellow, and brown and white. The passport is not morality, not religion, not wealth, not high pretence, but suffering, simply and alone. No questions are asked as to opinion or past conduct, as to creed or politics. Help is given to all and help is to be had for various wants. Wants of the mind and wants of the body. Help is given to the moral side as well as the physical side of the nature and aid is extended on the road to easement of the toils of life.

One who would look at the philosophic side of the hospital sees many of the most vital problems of life before him. There, of course, are physical illness and mutilation, suffering and sorrow, but there also are those Sphinx's riddles which society must answer or be destroyed. There are the consequences of drunkenness; there are the hideous results of prostitution. There is illegitimacy; there is madness. There is pauperism; there is wickedness. There is Vice with her naked talons. There is Crime with her dripping fangs. The Hospital seems a barrier, feeble, it is true, only partially effective, without anything like the public interest that it deserves, but still a barrier, to the rush of the waters which would overwhelm mankind.

Each of us, trustee, doctor, nurse, must do the duty which belongs to him or her, do it bravely, do it earnestly, do it intelligently, do it conscientiously. Few of us can do much. All of us can do something. We must not falter from tire. We must not halt from pique. We must not retire because of lack of proper recognition or reward. We must remember that

> "Never yet
> Share of Truth was vainly set
>   In the world's wide fallow.
> After hands shall sow the seed,
> After hands on hill and mead,
>   Shall reap the harvests yellow."

THE PERSONAL SIDE OF PEPYS*

ALL of us are personally acquainted with Samuel Pepys, the shrewd, stirring, curious, garrulous, delightful diarist of the first ten years of the Stuart Restoration—the Sam Pepys of his contemporaries, of whom Evelyn speaks as "a very worthy, industrious and curious person."

I do not intend to tell of his official positions and notable public achievements—of his having been, as MacCaulay says he was—"the ablest man in the Admiralty"—of his distinction as President of the Royal Society—of the celebrated men with whom he associated—of the important business affairs he managed and discussed. Instead I will gather haphazard from the diary statements, anecdotes, sayings, stories which will exhibit the personal or curious side rather than the worthy and industrious sides of the author. We will thus view many of his unpraiseworthy habits, his natural liking for pretty ladies, his frequent and fragile vows, his domestic quarrels, his food and drink, the expression he used, the plays he visited, the bribes he took and gave, the clothes he wore, his methods of travel, and as much about his amatory exploits as is admissible outside of a medical lecture room.

It is these familiar things of everyday life that bring before us, living and active, the men and women of the time of Charles II. We move among the grim soldiers who fought under the formidable Oliver and the crowds who shouted with joy when the King came to his own. To read this diary is to accompany the Clerk of the Acts, who is clad in the famous plum-colored coat with the broad skirts, in his various excursions in street and on river.

For instance, on the way to Lincoln's Inn, after a morning draught (for few ate breakfast), we may take boat at the Tower Wharf and alight at the Temple Stairs—walk the muddy, carrion-

* Delivered before the Librarians of Philadelphia, February 13, 1917.

391

filled streets to Gresham College, Bishopsgate, and attend a meeting of the Royal Society—stroll out through a gate in the old London wall and breathe country air in the Strand—enter Piccadilly Road from the top of the Haymarket and watch the workmen laying the stones of the mansion of the great Lord Clarendon—attend a service in the church of St. Olave's in Hart Sreet—enter the Naval office at the corner of Crutched Friars and Seething Lane, and interview the individual referred to by Pepys as that "perfidious rogue," Sir William Penn—after having been forced to take the wall by drunken bullies swaggering down Fleet Street, partake of a heavy lunch at the Fleece in Cornhill—call in Axe Yard on a friend's wife before she is arisen because she will look pretty in bed—drop in at a cock fight in Shoe Lane—see a hanging on Tower Hill—glance up the front of Westminster Hall and note the dried heads of Bradshaw, Ireton, and the great Cromwell—at 2 P. M. set a poor man in a pit seat of the Duke's Theater in Portugal Street to hold the seat until the performance shall begin and in the meanwhile stop in at Garaway's coffee house where Radcliffe is writing prescriptions for apothecaries, or drop in at the green room of the King's Theater in Drury Lane and chat with pretty, witty Nelly (and ever after you'll "forget to quite forget her")—after returning to Portugal Street and seeing Betterton in Hamlet go to the Cock Tavern in Bow Street and drink some sac—then to a book shop in St. Paul's Churchyard to buy Hudibras—then by means of a rough, springless coach to the Flemish Ale House where we sit down to a bountiful dinner of buttered salmon, fowls, ham, a lark pie, suet pudding, distilled waters, and old ale—go to the Mitre Tavern in Wood Street, sit very late, singing, playing, smoking, drinking, expounding, arguing, story telling, and lying—carry a horn lantern or be led by a link boy through the black streets in the reeling way home—be held up and robbed by rogues with clubs at the entrance of some black alley and finally reach home and "so to bed."

The above is a typical Pepsian day not particularly, if at all, exaggerated. He went to all the places named and also many others, and did all the things mentioned and a vast number more.

It was a mad, merry, drunken, dangerous, debauched, and care-less place, that London of the Restoration—a place of plague and conflagration, of gambling and astrology, of duels and robberies, actresses and orange wenches, bravos and bullies, seditious plots and bold abductions, biting epigrams and cruel waylayings, as-signations and seductions, morning draughts and midnight revels, hatred and envy, bribery and treachery, gallantry and jealousy, wit and humor, vulgarity and obscenity, tears and laughter, high-born harlots as unrestrained as Messalina, sultanas with the reek of the gutter and the brothel still fresh upon them, mysterious priests entering secret doors, scheming politicians in hidden rooms, plotting courtiers, dissolute councillors, drunken poets, complacent bishops, ignorant and superstitious physicians, crafty and unscrupulous lawyers, corrupt and subservient judges, wealthy quacks, hypocritical preachers, mutinous sailors, undis-ciplined soldiers, and unpatriotic statesmen bought by French gold. Drunkenness, dancing, sensuality, debauchery, ribbons, silks, perfumes, jokes were in the very air. All paid worship to Folly as the Chief of the Gods.

In this Witches' Sabbath dwelt Sam Pepys.

He was the son of a tailor, though a first cousin once removed to the Earl of Sandwich. The relationship to the Earl made Pepys's fortune. To the fact that he was a tailor's son may be due that intense interest in clothes which is seen everywhere in the diary. A new suit was an event. It was carefully pondered and finally ordered. Its delivery was noted and the wearing of it of rapturous interest. It matters not what else happens to be set down in the diary, the death of potentate, the loss of a sea fight, the bill of mortality at the height of the plague, the sweep of the London fire, the arrival of a new suit of clothes is always carefully noted and the garments are carefully described. Men's clothes were very expensive and cost much more than those of women. One of his suits cost over £24 ($120) and money was 4 or 5 times as valuable then as now. May 24, 1660: "Up and made myself as fine as I could with the linning stockings on and five canons" (canons were hose tops for the boots). After thus arraying himself he, quite naturally, did go into an "extraordinary press of noble company and great mirth all day." That "merry droll" Sir Thomas Killigrew was there and told "many merry stories." The nature of the stories may be guessed. "Tom Killigrew," says Pepys, "hath a fee out of the Wardrobe for cap and bells, under the title of the King's Foole or Jester, and may with privilege revile or jeer anybody, the greatest person, without offence by the privilege of his place." He was the last official Court Jester. It is interesting to note that in 1661 he received 30 yards of velvet, 3 dozen of fringe, and 16 of damask, the entry in the Chamberlain's records being headed "Livery for Ye Jester."

Although Pepys loved to dress up it sometimes irritated him to see another very fine. For instance: "This evening came Mr. John Pickering on board, like an ass, with his feathers and a new suit." The author was fond of the term "ass." He says that Creed went from boat to boat proclaiming himself an ass. Afterward in London, with this jealousy still rankling, he wrote: "Mr. J. Pickering came in and stayed long enough to make all the world see him to be a fool."

One day he records that "I left off my great skirt suit and put on my white suit with silver lace." Another day—"put on my suit with the great skirts"—another most solemnly important record comes—viz., "This day I began to put on buckles." He then had an extremely pleasant and alcoholic time at the Half Moon Tavern. It was also a successful time as "Billingsly paid for all," yet Billingsly was a Quaker. July 1, 1660: "This day came home my fine Camlett cloak, with gold buttons, and a silk suit, which cost me much money, and I pray God to make me able to pay for it." He says this silk suit "is the first that ever I wore in my life." He never liked to pay for it, but he liked still less to pay for things for Mrs. Pepys. When Lady Sandwich decided that Mrs. Pepys should be better dressed she took that unfortunate female out, purchased a quantity of things and sent the bill to Samuel. He casts up his accounts in agony of spirit and groans out so many pounds, shillings and pence—God help me. He was inclined to take it out of Mrs. Pepys, but was afraid of Lady Sandwich.

July 13, 1660 he for the first time put on the "black Camlett coat with the silver buttons." A few days later he wore his "jackanapes coat with the silver buttons." He went toward Westminster, stopped in at Pim the tailor's, "and there found my velvet coat (the first that ever I had) done, and a velvet mantle." Pim was Lord Sandwich's tailor and a genial soul. He took Captain Feners and Pepys to "the Fountain Tavern and did give us store of wine." When Pim was out of town Pepys was worried. On one occasion Wooten the shoemaker "helped me to a pretty man, one Mr. Penny, against St. Dunstan's Church."

Things were often sent to taverns for selection. Pim's boy came to the Bull's Head "by my direction with two monteeres (caps) for me to take my choice of, and I chose the saddest color and left the other for Mr. Shepley."

On Lord's Day, February 3, 1661—"begun to go forth in my coat and sword, as the manner now among gentlemen is."

The King determined to set the fashion in clothes. He wanted to do in England as Louis XIV did in his dominions, and thought to indicate his independence of French control in great things by showing it in small things. Evelyn liked the new garment and says he had suggested a like one in his pamphlet "Tyrannus or the Mode." Evelyn describes it as "a comely dress after ye Persian fashion." Pepys naturally took great interest in the whole affair.

October 8, 1666, while on the way to Westminster Hall with Mr. Pierce, he received from Mr. Pierce much information about the Court: "The Duke of York and Duke of Albemarle do not agree. The Duke of York is wholly given up to this bitch of Denham. The Duke of Albemarle and Prince Rupert do less agree. So that we are all in pieces. The King hath yesterday in Council declared his resolution of setting a fashion for clothes, which he *will never* alter. It will be a vest, I know not well how; but it is to teach the nobility thrift and will do good."

That anything could teach the nobility, or for the matter of that the King, thrift was of course out of the question. That the

King would never alter the vest was so doubtful that "various courtiers bet him gold" that he would. The ease and freedom with which courtiers disagreed with the King seems to us amazing, many of them dared to say highly impertinent things to him. For instance, when the King said: "Ashley, I believe you are the wickedest man in my dominions," and Ashley answered: "Speaking only of subjects, perhaps I am."

October 13th, the Duke put on the famous vest and "I stood and saw him dress himself."

October 15th was a notable day with Pepys. He learned "that Lady Castlemaine is concluded to have another child"—that Mrs. Stewart "is a most excellent natural lady"—and that the King was to assume the vest. It "being a long cassocke close to the body, of black cloth and pinked with white silk under it, and a coat over it, and the legs ruffled with black ribbond like a pigeon's leg; and, on the whole, I wish the King may keep it for it is a very fine and handsome garment."

Pepys at once ordered one.

November 4th (Lord's day)—"Comes my taylor's man in the morning and brings my vest home, and a coate to wear with it, and belt, and silver-hilted sword. So I rose and dressed myself, and like myself mightily in it, and so do my wife."

In spite of the King's resolution never to abandon the vest he did so very soon because the King of France dressed his footmen in a like manner. Pepys says this "would incite a stone to be revenged." Besides the annoyance caused by this event, Pepys had another trouble the same day. "My wife and I fell out, I being displeased with her cutting away a lace handkercher sewed about her neck down to her breast almost, out of a belief, but without reason, that it is the fashion." Had he lived in the year of our Lord 1917 he would have more cause for surprise and displeasure and could have left out the word "almost."

So strange was public opinion that the abandonment of the vest was looked upon by the people as a sign that Charles had again become "the hired viceroy of France."

October 8, 1662, bought a lace band or collar called a scallop.

"A very neat one. It cost me about £3 and £3 more I have given him to buy another. I find myself much bound to go handsome, which I shall do in linen."

A few days later he was so pleased with the band "and so neat it is, that I am resolved my great expense shall be lace-bands."

One day he wore the band and other grand things and went from church to church. In one church he stood against "a black girl" (his term for a brunette) and tried to rub against her "but she did stick me with a long pin." On another occasion when all dressed up he sat in the rear end of a church. A young lady in front of him spit back and so in his face. He was first disposed to be "horrid angry," but as the offender turned around saw "she was a pretty lady," so everything was all right.

When the new velvet cloak was brought home Pepys had a rather hard day. It was the first velvet cloak that "ever I had in my life and I pray God it may not be too soon now that I begin to wear it." He found his bands "sluttishly washed" and "so ill-smoothed that I crumpled them and flung them all on the ground and was angry with Jane." He went out to the Lord Mayor's dinner and was very miserable because he had made one of the numerous vows which he never kept. He had vowed most solemnly not to drink wine. At the dinner "wine was offered and they drunk, I only drinking hypocras which do not break my vow, it being to the best of my present judgment, only a mixed compound drink, and not any wine. If I am mistaken, God forgive me! but I hope and do think I am not." We can appreciate (to use Scott's words) this piece of "bacchanalian casuistry" when we recall that hypocras was red wine or white wine mixed with sugar and spices and that Pepys knew this very well. Sir Walter says its only equal is Fielding's Newgate Chaplain who used punch instead of wine because it was a "liquor nowise spoken against in the Bible."

Another instance is how he handled a vow against going to plays, reserving the right to go to a Court play once a month. He went to the Theater Royal (Drury Lane) and saw "The Humorous Lieutenant." "My oath against going to plays do not oblige me against this house, because it was not then in being, yet believing that at the time my meaning was against all public houses, I am resolved to deny myself the liberty of two plays at Court, which are in arreare to me, for the months of March and April."

On one occasion he established a system of fines when he did wrong things. The money was to go to the home, but they got very little. Kissing, of which he was fond, was to cost a fine. On one occasion he indulged in this amusement with a pretty girl and as he pays the fine (to himself) reflects that it was worth the money.

He had so much trouble keeping his head free from dirt and lice that "I went to Mr. Jervus's, my old barber"—and tried on periwigs, "meaning to wear one."

Lice constituted the real reason for wigs. But they did not mind. They very seldom washed. On one occasion Pepys got a severe cold by wiping his toes on his stockings. Another time by taking off his hat at dinner "and sitting with the wind in my neck." Men were loath to be separated from their hats. It was worse than in Lord Clarendon's younger days for he never kept on his hat in the presence of his elders "except at dinner." Hats were worn in church, a custom to which some clergymen were beginning to object. "So to church again and heard a simple fellow—exclaiming against men wearing their hats on in the church, but I slept part of the sermon, till latter prayer and blessing and all was done." Then he went home, drank hard and was very merry.

When Pepys put on his periwig the Duke of York did not know him. When he went to church he found "that my coming in a perriwigg did not prove so strange to the world as I was afeard it would." He heard "an ordinary, lazy sermon of Mr. Mills." In the afternoon he went "to church again, where the Scott preached, and I slept most of the time."

November 13, 1663, he got his second periwig "made of my own haire, which comes to 21s. 6d. more than the worth of my own haire, so that they both come to £4, 1s. 6d., which he sayth will serve two years, but I fear it. Put on my new shagg purple gowne with gold buttons and loop lace." In a few days he found the new periwig was lousy. "To my barber's, to have my perriwigg he lately made me cleansed of its nits, which vexed me cruelly that he should put such a thing into my hands."

After the plague periwigs made of human hair became a great danger, so many of them were made from hair clipped from the heads of those dead of the plague.

September 3, 1665—"Up and put on my colored silk suit very fine and my new perriwigg, bought a good while since, but durst not wear because the plague was in Westminster when I bought it; and it is a wonder what will be the fashion after the plague is done, as to perriwiggs, for nobody will dare to buy any hair for fear of infection, that it had been cut off of the heads of people dead of the plague."

In 1655 Pepys, when twenty-three years of age, married Elizabeth St. Michel. She was a Huguenot of good birth, very poor, beautiful and fifteen years of age. Her father was very poor and visionary. He spent his years in seeking perpetual motion, devising plans to discover King Solomon's mines and backing useless devices to correct smoking chimneys. When the diary begins Pepys was twenty-eight and Mrs. Pepys was twenty. Pepys did not know the date of his marriage, neither did his wife. He said it was October 10th. The registers of St. Margaret's Church, Westminster, show it was December 1st. Neither Samuel nor Mrs. Pepys remembered the year.

Pepys tended to be a querulous and sometimes a brutal domestic tyrant, but Mrs. Pepys could hold her own in temper and language. If some of his denunciations are unprintable her responses are equally so. Quarrels were common.

February 12, 1660: "So to bed, where my wife and I had some high words." The high words were about the bad bedroom manners of Mrs. P.'s dog, "the dog which her brother gave her." Pepys threatened to throw the dog out of the bedroom window.

It will be remembered that the Merry Monarch had a number

of dogs sleep in his bedchamber. Buckingham, Rochester, and other gentlemen in attendance complained bitterly of the habits of the spaniels.

October 13th: After eating oysters at Sun Tavern he went by water home. "I was angry with my wife for her things lying about, and in my passion kicked the fine basket which I bought her in Holland, which troubled me."

September 17, 1660: "So to bed after having looked over the things my wife had bought today, with which being not well pleased, they costing too much, I went to bed in discontent."

October 24, 1660: "I took occasion to be angry with my wife before I rose about her putting up of half a crown of mine in a paper box which she had forgot where she lain it."

He often admired her and approved of her.

November 4th: The Lord's Day that Mr. Mills "did begin to nibble at the Common Prayer," "my wife seemed very pretty today, it being the first time I had given her leave to wear a black patch." Imagine a wife of today asking leave! He liked her when she had her teeth cleaned and approved of her in "the black silk gown which is now laced all over with black gimp."

Now and then things happened which caused queries in his mind.

January 10, 1661: "So to Mrs. Hunt, where I found a Frenchman, a lodger of hers, at dinner, and just as I came in was kissing my wife, which I did not like, though there could not be any hurt in it."

September 2, 1661: His wife had been abroad and bought things for herself, "and tells me that she met at the Change with Mr. Somersett, who did give her a bracelet of rings, which did a little trouble me, though I know there is no hurt yet in it, but only for fear of further acquaintance." He got decidedly jealous when he and Mrs. P. were on the way to Uncle Fenner's. "On the way meeting a French footman with feathers who was in quest of my wife, and spoke with her privately, but I could not tell what it was, only my wife promised to go to some place tomorrow morning, which do trouble my mind how to know wither it was." The French footman was the servant to the Mr. Somersett who kissed Mrs. P. at the dinner.

September 6th: "My wife holding her resolution to go this morning as she resolved yesterday, and though there could not be much hurt in it, yet my own jealousy put a hundred things into my mind which did much trouble me all day." All day he was much troubled and "unfit for business." Drank largely with Sir William Penn and others and went home. His wife was at home, "but I seemed very angry, as indeed I am, and did not all night show her any countenance, neither before nor in bed, and so slept and rose discontented." The next day he was much improved and was made happy by going to the theater and sitting by Barbara Palmer (Lady Castlemaine) "which was great content; and indeed I can never enough admire her beauty." He did admire Lady C. immensely. Once he was thrilled by seeing some of her pretty undergarments hung out to dry. Christmas Eve of 1667 he went to the Queen's Chapel, saw Lady C., "who looked prettily in her night clothes," and then went to the Rose Tavern and drank burnt wine.

December 19, 1661: He and his wife were on the way home in a coach. "On the way I took occasion to fall out with my wife very highly about ribbands being ill matched and of two colors, and to very high words, so that, like a passionate fool, I did call her a strumpet."

November 22, 1662: He and Mrs. P. "fell out cruelly" because of a difference between Mrs. P. and her maid Sarah, "to my great discontent Mrs. P. was set against the wench." Reluctantly Pepys determined to dismiss the maid, but gathered comfort from the reflection that the "change will cost some trouble to my wife." He did not act at once, however, because he considered Sarah a good servant. She did various things for him, especially combed his head. So about ten days later "my wife and I had another falling out about Sarah, against whom she has a deadly hate." He finally discharged Sarah who later got a job with Sir William Penn.

The reason of the hate came out later. She told Samuel things
26

about his wife and Mrs. P. heard of it. Samuel met the discharged servant at his brothers. She told, "out of good will to me, for she loves me dearly, that I would beware of my wife's brother, for he is begging or borrowing of her and often." "I do observe so much goodness and seriousness in the maid, that I am again and again sorry that I have parted with her—I bad her good night and did kiss her, and indeed she seemed very well-favored to me tonight as she is always." Mr. and Mrs. P. disagreed so fiercely over this matter, she tore up his love letters to her, he had to follow a time-honored custom and to bribe her into silence from bad words of which she had a plentiful vocabulary. "At last for my honor am forced to make her presently a new Moyre gown, which troubles me to part with so much money." This gift made him "mighty friends" with his wife, although in a few days he was "vexed cruelly" with her because she had a new waistcoat snatched away from her by thieves. A few days later he was angry again because a rabbit for dinner "was not half roasted." Then again in a few days, "angry words with my wife about neglecting the keeping of the house clean. I calling her a beggar and she me ——." Again he is angry with his wife because she did what is very popular in our day—"minding nothing now but the dancing master, having him come twice a day, which is folly." They had very high words and he got so abusive that he vowed to refrain from it in future and to fine himself 2s. 6d. for every time "which, if God please, I will observe." He got so jealous of Pemberton that that worthy had to stay away from the house entirely and Mrs. P. took revenge by getting very jealous of Ashwell.

January 4, 1664, he vowed again to do better. "Home and at my office till 12 at night making my solemn vows for the next year, which I trust in the Lord I shall keep, but I fear I have a little too severely bound myself. But, however, I know the worst, and shall by the blessing of God observe to perform or pay my forfeits punctually"—neither of which did he do.

Within a few weeks they had a truly frightful row because he was "not willing to have her have her gown laced." She followed him from home to the naval office where she abused him "in spiteful manner like a vixen." But there was the usual result. March 26, 1664: "My wife found her gowne come home laced—which will cost me a great deal of money, more than ever I intended, but it is but for once." It was not for once, however, for soon after the tailor brought to Mrs. P. "her other new laced gown."

A month later he suspected her "to have been abroad," although she denied it. "I pulled her by the nose. The poor wretch took it mighty ill."

December 19, 1664, they quarrelled. Samuel hit her over the left eye and she tried to bite and scratch him. The eye blackened in spite of butter, parsley and poultices, and this worried Pepys because people would observe it. Strange to say that evening the wronged lady was "in a very good temper to me."

The discovery that the kitchen accounts were 7s. short caused a tremendous row, although that very evening he cast up his accounts "and find myself worth £1270, for which the Lord God be praised."

Light colored locks caused another row. She put them on: "It makes her look pretty, but, not being natural, vexes me and I will not have her wear them."

Although Pepys strongly objected to his wife having any admirers, he had torrid affairs almost indiscriminately, affairs of sufficient gravity to have put him in the divorce court many times over. His wife was highly suspicious and eventually proved it on him.

He found a resource at times in sending Mrs. P. into the country at Bramptom. She developed the evil habit of appearing in town unexpectedly to find out his courses. "It is only to see what I do and why I come not home; and she is in the right that I would have more of Mrs. Knipp's company."

She was very rude to Mrs. Pierce and Mrs. Knipp. Although Mr. P. was vexed, he was also guilty and afraid of exposure, so he said "no words to offend" Mrs. P. when she reproached the two ladies as wenches. She heard of his "going to plays and carrying people abroad every day in her absence" and got into "a melancholy, frosty humor." He was in a miserable state of apprehension and wondered fearfully how much she knew and records "I cannot help but the storm will break out, I think, in a little time."

Lord's Day, October 25, 1668, Deb was combing his head. "My wife coming suddenly up did find me embracing the girl." Anxious to lie out of it and as he was not certain how much of the affair she had really seen, he determined to let her do all the talking until he found out. She had seen and it was "the greatest sorrow to me that ever I knew in this world." Not the embracing but the getting caught. He expressed a similar view about people who were arrested for going to conventicles: "I would to God they would either conform or be more wise and not be catched." He solemnly promised Mrs. P. fair usage in future. The girl remained in spite of Mrs. P.'s wishes, for Samuel says "I love the girl."

Mrs. P. day after day had rearing, tearing hysteria, and finally Samuel agreed to discharge Deb and did so, as "I am apt to believe she is a cunning girl and a slut." The family then have the first tranquil rest for 20 nights. Two or three days later this reformed gentleman went home and was "pretty pleasant and at mighty ease" in his mind because he had determined to meet Deb outside without Mrs. P. knowing anything about it. The next day he hunted up Mrs. Willets and, to his delight, found her. "And so home, and there told my wife a fair tale, God knows, how I spent the whole day." But she found out about it and called "me all the false, rotten rogues in the world." "I did awhile deny," but finally confessed. She would only "be pacified upon condition that I would give it under my hand never to see or speak with Deb while I live, as I did before with Pierce and Knipp, and which I did also, God knows, promise for Deb too, but I have the confidence to deny it to the perjury of myself." She pulled his hair, scratched him, threatened to slit the girl's nose, and menaced the distinguished naval official with a red hot tongs. This matter cost him £30 a year which income he was obliged to pay his wife. Ever after, when unquiet at night, Mrs. P. became "mighty peevish" and insisted that his restlessness was due entirely "to evil thoughts in his dreams." The matter never was entirely settled. She was always charging him with some offense or other. In nearly the past pages of the diary we learn that she engaged a good looking maid, but expressed great doubt about doing it because she was so pretty. Now hear Mr. Pepys: "But I did assure her of my resolutions to have nothing to do with her maids, but in myself I was glad to have the content to have a handsome one to look upon."

Samuel would have been the despair of a modern prohibitionist. He drank everything from bottled beer to brandy and from ale to malaga wine. When a student at Cambridge he was reported for having been "scandalously overserved with drink" and he continued often in his life to be scandalously overserved. I count up 124 taverns he frequented. He loved the liquor and good fellowship of the tavern and was prone to be merry in good company on all possible occasions. In these taverns he was told the most extraordinary lies by sea captains and other apostles of the truth. He believed them all implicitly and carefully set them down. His morning draught was an invariable ceremony. It was the custom of the time and was taken instead of breakfast. P. rarely ate breakfast, although on one occasion he breakfasted nobly on radishes. He was frequently drunk, not unusually very drunk. It was that well-trained and long-experienced bacchanalian artist, Sir William Penn, who taught him the value of liquor the morning after, the hair of the dog that bit him. On one occasion he tried to fix his own father with Margate ale. On another occasion he reeled home and vomited in his bedroom. The maid came in to hold the basin, "Lord, it was a pretty sight to see her running around in her smock." During the plague he sought to avert infection by carrying a bottle of brandy with him and sipping it from time to time. He was always resolving and vowing to stop and fining himself for not stopping.

January 18, 1661: Will Joyce came to Pepys' house drunk and in "a vaporing humor." Although Mr. Pepys liked liquor himself he was censorious to others who used it. In the same way he objected to Sir William Penn being drunk as "a disparagement to the office." Joyce's condition and conduct "did vex me cruelly." So he went out to the Grayhound Tavern in Tower Street where Mr. Hollier "did advise me above all things, both as to the stone and the decay of my memory (of which I now complain to him) to avoid drinking." Samuel resolved to leave off if he could.

Precisely three weeks later he met Dick Scobell "and there I drank a great deal with him, and so home and to bed betimes my head aching."

A month later drank all the afternoon and "set to it" until "it was very late." Alderman Sir William Wale, who was fuddled and quarrelsome, took him home in his coach "almost overcome with drink." He says the evening was "a great content and joy to him" because he had been received among such high company. On many occasions he records headache and sick stomach due to drink. One day, being full of liquor, he lay down for an afternoon nap, but overslept. "Slept until the four o'clock gun the next morning waked me, which I mistook for 8 at night and rising . . . mistook the sun rising for the sun setting Sunday night."

April 2, 1661, he went to the Dolphin and had a drinking bout with Sir William Penn, Sir William Batten, and Mr. Delebar. "Strange how these men, who at other times are all wise men, do now, in their drink, betwitt and reproach one another with their former conditions, and their actions as in public concernments, till I was ashamed to see it." Next day his head ached violently.

On Coronation night, met some gallant sparks at Mr. Thornbury's. They all drank the "King's health over and over again till one of the gentlemen fell down stark drunk, and there lay spewing and I went to my Lord's pretty well. But no sooner a-bed with Mr. Shepley but my head began to hum, and I to vomit, and if ever I was foxed it was now—when I waked I found myself wet with my spewing." Thus did the day end with joy everywhere.

A few weeks later he and Sir William Penn sat in the leads, talked, sang, ate botargo (dried mullet's roes) and drank "great drafts of claret." He went to bed in the moonshine, "very near fuddled" and the next morning had his usual headache. And so on time after time, sometimes going into black glooms of remorse, always swearing off and always going at it again with the greatest enthusiasm at the first opportunity of a dinner with some pretty ladies or a merry party in an ale house.

We have already noted some of his flirtations. He always had several running at once. He liked to look at women, stand by them, dance with them, kiss them, and would, if given the slightest opportunity, cross the borders of propriety as speedily and certainly as the Germans crossed the Belgian line. He tended strongly to the vulgar and low and some of his exploits are unrelatable. He would have an affair with a cook, a waiting maid, an actress, the wife of a friend, in fact, with any one acquiescent or even tolerant. The real meaning of love he did not know, although he knew jealousy and suffered cruelly from it.

He greatly admired Nell Gwynne and "did kiss her." It is interesting to note the different views taken of Nell by the serious Evelyn and by the eager and flirtatious Pepys. P. calls her "pretty, witty Nelly." Evelyn speaks of "an impudent —— by the name of Eleanor Gwynne." He loved to hear about and look upon Frances Stewart (whose figure is still to be seen as Britannia on British coins)—Frances Jennings (who dressed up as an orange girl and was caught in the escapade)—the Countess of Castlemaine—and all of the soiled doves of that befouled Court. On one occasion a lady showed him her nether extremity and he solemnly records "and it is monstrous fine."

He liked pretty Rebecca Allen who slyly flattered him. "Who seemed to be desirous of my favors and would in all things show me respects." He succeeded in kissing her to his great content. He was infatuated with Mrs. Knepp, the pretty actress "of the King's Theater, the most excellent, and mad humored thing and sings the noblest that ever I heard in my life." Her husband Pepys envied and hated and called a brute and a horse jockey— "an ill, melancholy, jealous-looking fellow." A short time after he met her he was very free with her in a coach, and refers to her as "my dear Mrs. Knepp." He grew to call her Bab Allen after a

Scotch song of hers, Barbary Allen, and greatly enjoyed kissing
her. She mightily pleased him by singing his song "Beauty Retire," "which she sings and makes go most rarely, and a very fine
song it seems to be." She learned to sing it "bravely" and "makes
me proud of myself." He finds her the "pleasantest company in
the world" and reflexts that "musique and women I cannot but
give way to, whatever my business is." On one occasion in the
theater "the jade came to him all undressed." He used to buy
her presents and give her money, as much as five guineas at a time.
He liked her maid Betty and always kissed her when she brought
a message.

Mrs. P. soon took notice and raised furious gales about her
"in spite of my having been so innocent." Mrs. P. did not believe
in this innocence, and the affair made her recreant spouse promise
under his hand and seal never to see Mrs. Knepp again.

He also loved Mrs. Pierce, wife of Dr. James Pierce. She was
very pretty and had a fine complexion. Mrs. P. joined her with
Knepp in the index expurgatorius of her household. Samuel also
had to vow under his hand and seal as to her.

We have not time to tell of the maid Mary Mercer (whom P.
used to kiss and with whom he was free), of pretty little Betty
Nichel (whose hand he held when he broke his vow and went to
the play), of Rebecca Allen, of Nell Payne, of Mrs. Burrows—of
Mrs. Dinah and the others. We have told of Deb Willets. Surely
a goodly number of inamoratas in ten years for a married gentleman who took vows.

Pepys loved the theater. It was a great expense to him, took
him from his work in the afternoon, caused him to spend much
for dinners to actresses and others and led him to stay out late
with the natural consequences of domestic suspicion and ill temper.

His views upon Shakespeare's plays are interesting—September 29, 1662—"To the King's Theater, where we saw *Mid-
summer Night's Dream*, which I had never seen before, nor shall
ever again, for it is the most insipid ridiculous play that ever I
saw in my life." "*The Taming of a Shrew* hath some very good
pieces in it, but generally is a mean play." *Macbeth*, "a most excel-

lent play for variety." *Othello* he once esteemed "a mighty good play, but having so lately read *The Adventures of Five Hours* it seems a mean thing."

The Tempest "hath no great wit, but yet good above ordinary plays."

Romeo and Juliet "is a play of itself the worst that ever I heard in my life."

Hamlet—"mightily pleased with," but more with Betterton's acting than with the play.

Twelfth Night—considered the play a "Burthen" and took no pleasure at all in it. He was troubled for having gone at all because he had very recently sworn to his wife that he would never in future go to a play without her. We have seen how he kept that promise.

Henry IV did not please him.

What struck him most about *Henry V* was that the actors wore new vests and that they came "into my back and neck, which did much trouble me."

Henry VIII—"Saw the so-much cried up play of *Henry the Eighth* which, though I went with resolution to like it, is so simple a thing made up of a great many patches, that, besides the shows and processions in it, there is nothing in the work, good or well done."

Merry Wives of Windsor—"I went to the new Theater, there saw the *Merry Wives of Windsor* acted. The humors of the country gentleman and the French doctor very well done, but the rest very poorly, and Sir J. Falstaff as bad as any." Another time it did not please him at all.

He was very fond of eating and records on most days what food he had. He knew good food and objected to pretences. For instance: "The venison pasty was palpable mutton, which was not handsome." His narrative abounds with references to rare, fat venison, venison pasty, braun, sack posset, jowl of ling, lark pie, breast of mutton, buttered salmon, eggs, peas porridge, herrings, mullet's roes, anchovies, turkeys, chickens, and all sorts of edibles.

They were large eaters in those days. Here is a home dinner in his house: Marrow bones, leg of mutton, loin of veal, dish of fowls, three pullets, two dozen larks in one dish, a great tart, a veal's tongue, a dish of anchovies, a dish of prawns, cheese. They were very merry at this dinner. Mr. Joyce drank very hard.

Mrs. Pierce became so gallant as to put "the two young women quite out of courage." A few hours later Pepys felt the pangs of hunger and "he ate a bit" before going to bed.

Once, when guest at a meal, they discussed Marriot, the great eater, so "that I was ashamed to eat what I would have done." For six persons he got up the following dinner:

"I had a pretty dinner for them, viz.: a brace of stewed carps, six roasted chickens, and a jowl of salmon, hot, for the first course; a tanzy and two veals tongues, and cheese the second; and was very merry all the afternoon."

He was fond of music, played various instruments, sang I know not how well, set songs to music and played cards, billiards, and bowls.

He knew William Penn, the founder of this Commonwealth when he came to London from Oxford. He invited young William and sister Peggy with Mrs. Pepys to the theater to see the *Spanish Curate*, by Beaumont and Fletcher. When he had invited them William and P. "walked, and to the Stationers and looked over some pictures and maps for my house." William and Peggy went to Pepys' house to dinner. "After we had eat a barrel of oysters we went by coach to the play." After the play they went to Pepys' home. "They sat with us till late at night at cards very merry, but the jest was Mr. W. Penn had left his sword in the coach, and so my boy and he run out after the coach and by very great chance did at the Exchange meet with the coach and got his sword again."

The Admiral grew discontented and worried about something he kept hidden. One day he came to Pepys "much troubled upon letters came last night. Showed me one of Doctor Owen's to his son, whereby it appears his son is much perverted in opinion by him; which I now perceive is one thing that hath put Sir William so long off the hooks."

The Admiral determined that such foolishness should cease, sent William to Paris to get the proper ideas about men and things. He came back apparently reformed and wearing pantaloons. He visited Mrs. Pepys while Samuel was out and Mrs. P. reported him as "a most modish person, grown, she says, a fine gentleman."

He drank liquor, played cards, attended theaters, and was a changed man. In fact, he was such a very modish gentleman that his visits to Mrs. Pepys excited Samuel's jealousy. "I was troubled to find my wife, but in a necessary compliment, expecting Mr. Penn to see her, who had been there and as by her people denied, which, he having been three times, she thought not fit he should be any more. But yet even this did raise my jealousy presently and much vex me. However, he did not come, which pleased me." A few days later, when Pepys returned home, he found Mr. Penn visiting Mrs. P. Samuel had an appointment which took him out "and against my will left them together." In a little while he sent for them to come out and sup with him, which they wisely did. "We supped nobly and very merry." Penn continued to call at intervals. He was a very merry talker, "Talking of his travels and French humors."

In spite of the Admiral's apparent success in causing his son to become modish the subject relapsed sadly.

December 29, 1667: "Mr. William Penn, who is lately come over from Ireland, is a Quaker again, or some very melancholy thing; that he cares for no company, nor comes into any; which is a pleasant thing, after his being abroad so long, and his father such a hypocritical rogue, and at this time an atheist."

In 1668 William Penn published a book, *Truth Exalted*. Pepys read it. "A ridiculous nonsensical book set out by Will Penn for the Quakers; but so full of nothing but nonsense that I was ashamed to read in it."

A short time later his second book was published. This caused his confinement in the Tower. "Pelling hath got me W. Penn's book against the Trinity. I find it so well writ as, I think, it is too good for him ever to have writ it; and it is a serious sort of book, and not fit for everybody to read."

This is the last we hear of the great Quaker.

Pepys used Sir William Penn, but grew to hate him and refers to him as a perfidious rogue, a devilish plunderer and the falsest man ever born of woman. He was careful not to let Sir William Penn know his feeling, because he was afraid of him and wanted to use him.

"At noon had Sir William Penn (who I hate with all my heart for his base treacherous tricks, but yet I think it not policy to declare it yet) and his son William to my house to dinner." P. gave them venison roasted and baked and umbles baked in a pie. "We were merry as I could be in that company, and the more because I would not seem otherwise to Sir W. Penn, he being within a day or two to go for Ireland."

Pepys would put up with a great deal for policy. For instance, when his own uncle misbehaved so infamously to Mrs. P. he never said a word about it.

He was a various and peculiar man. He must be judged as a man of his age and not as a man of ours. He was not entirely honest, but as honest as most of his contemporaries and more honest than many of them. He made promises with mental reservations, broke them when it suited him, and justified the want of reliability by the most curious casuistry. His vows went to pieces from a whiff of desire like the fluff of a dandelion at a breath. They were as fragile as houses of cards. He dealt in equivocations, treachery, and actual lies. He took money and presents to do favors and gave them for favors. He was full of mean suspicions of most men and often his suspicions were justifiable. He hated with a hearty vigor. He was jealous of the fortunate, bullying and often cruel to the unsuccessful, and cringing to his superiors. According to Thackeray's definition of a snob he was a genuine snob, "meanly admiring mean things," literally groveling before the great and recording with delight every atom of respect accorded and recognition vouched him.

He feared all who might harm him and conciliated them by all hypocritical ways. He was jealous of and brutal to his wife, as when he became suspicious of William Penn and others and when he blacked her eye. When she put on false hair he raised a tremendous row: "swearing by God several times and bending my fist that I would not endure it." He had a high and quick temper, was very violent when in a rage, and beat his servants fiercely. He was most apprehensive of public opinion. He was ashamed of his father and he did not want to walk with his friend, Mr. Pechell, because of his red nose, "though otherwise a good-natured man." When he beat his wife or a servant, his greatest anxiety was as to what the neighbors would think of it. When caught red-handed in various things his conscience troubled him. He went through the plague with calm courage, saving himself from infection by carrying brandy and taking frequent sips. He saw the fire and during it buried his money, his wine, and his Parmesan cheese. He saw the King touch for the Evil: "an ugly office and a simple one." He was very credulous, believing all travelers' tales and being led to believe money was buried in the Tower, which he dug for, to use his own words, "like a fool." He did not believe in witchcraft (in spite of reading Glauvil), was doubtful about astrology, but did believe in charms and kept written-down charms to arrest cramp, to stop bleeding, etc. He believed in certain omens, particularly that a high wind portended the death of a great person. He was a time-server and readily changed sides. He had been a Puritan, but easily became a Stuart office holder. One of the fears of his life was that someone would remember and tell things he had said about the Royal family while it was in exile. He was a most useful public servant, and did great things for the navy, laying the foundation of his fortune during the time he was Secretary of the Admiralty.

He was of notable service to the Royal Society, tried to stimulate scientific research, and was interested in dissection, transfusion of blood, the effect of cold in preserving meat, the powers of the burning glass, and a multitude of other things. In all of these things he showed something of an understanding of the value of practical applications, a spirit which was to reach its highest point in our own Franklin.

He loved money and frequently cast up his accounts. When the balance was favorable, he cried "praise be to God." When it was unfavorable, he wailed "God help me." He was seldom liberal from generosity, but sometimes for show or family duty. He refused to lend money to his own father. He spent freely on himself, but complained bitterly over what Mrs. Pepys cost him. Once he casts up clothing expenses. They show £55 for him, £12 for her. His chief expenses were dress, books, drink, theaters, dinners, and women. His camelott coat cost him £24. Mrs. Knepp and others cost him much money.

He sometimes pretended to liberality, as when Lady Sandwich gave him a haunch of venison. When he found it was spoiled he gave it to his mother. He was the embodiment of pompous vanity and cherished every word of praise from whoever it came. Sly women observed this as a sure road to his affections and his purse.

He was a great eater and drinker, smoked a pipe, drank coffee and chocolate (which latter beverage he sometimes took as a morning draught), and regarded tea as a medicine good for cold and defluctions. He regularly attended church, as a rule, going twice on Sunday. He always speaks about the sermon, a "good sermon," a "lazy sermon," etc. Frequently he gives the text and sketches the discourse. When the sermon did not suit him, which was often, he went to sleep or read or diverted himself with girls. On one occasion he nearly read through the book of *Tobit*. On another he held a pretty girl's hand.

Though calm through the plague he was afraid all night after punishing his boy for fear the strippling might do him harm.

He frequently sets down remedies for diseases and observed that you could cure a horse of an attack of blind-staggers by blowing tobacco smoke in his nose. His interest in medicine may have arisen from his having been successfully cut for stone a short time before his diary was begun. Every year, on the anniversary of that event, he held a feast; the stone being placed in a dish on the center of the table.

He was susceptible and lascivious. His flirtations were numerous, were often coarse, were frequently with kitchen maids, and were conducted in taverns, coaches, bedrooms, parlors, churches, his empty house in Axe Yard, and in the house in which he dwelt with his family. All the world is said to love a lover. It does not love Pepys in this capacity, although, at times, it can't help sympathizing with him. His views upon marriage became very cynical. He saw a wedding on a Christmas Day. "Strange to see what delight we married people have to see these poor fools decoyed into our condition, every man and woman gazing smiling at them."

He was a scholar and a student, bought good literature, and knew it. He was an excellent musician. Was one of the most garrulous of mortals and one of the most selfish, for he took the lace from his wife's best petticoat for his own coat. He feared war and showed an apprehension we can all understand: "So that the warr is begun: God give a good end to it." He had not a grain of humor in his nature, but this diary is full of what Lowell calls unconscious humor. Lowell considers that one of the best examples of this is Pepys's solemn account of the Mayor of Dover giving King Charles a Bible as he landed. The King said: "It was the very thing that he loved above all things in the world." Another instance is the affair with Mr. Barlow, the former Clerk of the Acts. Pepys was to get the job and had to buy Barlow off. Pepys met Barlow, "an old consumptive man, and fairly conditioned," and agreed to pay him £50 a year if the salary stood as it was and £100 if it were increased to a certain amount. Barlow lived about five years.

"February 9, 1665: Mr. Barlow is dead; for which, God knows my heart, I could be as sorry as is possible for one to be for a stranger, by whose death he gets £100 per annum, he being a worthy, honest man; but after having considered that when I come to consider the providence of God by this means unexpectedly to give me £100 a year more in my estate, I have cause to bless God, and do it from the bottom of my heart."

Samuel gravely approved the King's proclamation against blasphemy, drunkenness, and debauchery.

So much for Pepys the man.

I repeat that he shows us the lousy, noisy, merry, amorous, drunken London of the Restoration.

We walk with him in those streets which were a panorama of amusing spectacles and interesting scenes. The driveways filled with wagons, pack-horses, laden mules, and hackney coaches. The walks thronged with pedestrians and porters and all but blocked with sedan chairs. All day and most of the night songs, cries of itinerant merchants, blasphemy, music, drunken shouts, and sounds of quarrels and combats.

Chairmen, rudely forcing a way through crowds, being set upon for pushing, and fighting furiously to avenge a blow or an insulting epithet. Hack drivers, eliminating from their natures just such masterpieces of unstudied profanity as erupt from taxi drivers today. Venders of most imaginable articles, shrieking of the superior quality and unheard-of cheapness of their goods— fish, lavender, fruit, sausages, buns, vinegar, and many other things. Tooth drawers crying their skill. Crowds gathered about quacks, each one of which exploits a miraculous cure-all; multitudes elbowing for place to see a man eat fire. Harpers, fiddlers, vocal artists, tight-rope dancers. Such are the scenes he shows us.

He leads us into taverns and coffee houses marked by great, carved, painted overhead signs, and introduces us to acquaintances of all ranks and characters. Has us eat with them, drink with them, and smoke with them, and listen to stories of king, courtiers and politicians, literary men, scientists, lawyers, soldiers, sailors, Quakers, preachers, merchants, farmers, actors, actresses, bawds, and mistresses. Takes us to churches, theaters, wrestling matches, bear baitings, cock fights, billiard games, green rooms, and private houses. Shows us the inner workings of the naval office and a fleet in being. And, finally, drives us to the Court, introduces us to Clarendon, Buckingham, Rochester, Churchill, Lady

Castlemaine, Moll Davis, the Duke of York, and the Merry Monarch, himself.

Such scenes we can visit and such persons meet in the company of Samuel Pepys.

Finally, and in his oft-repeated words: "Good night and so to bed."

27

SUICIDE*

WHEREVER civilization is, there suicide occurs, and wherever civilization is advancing, deaths from suicide are increasing in number, absolutely and relatively to population. This is true in "countries different in race, religion, and number of inhabitants."† Suicide is rare among savage races and among them is only sought because of hunger, fear of torture, the horror of slavery, or religious fanaticism, but as a savage people becomes civilized suicides occur from other motives and become much more frequent. The rate of increase among civilized nations is remarkably regular.

Years ago Buckle said that "after making allowance for the impossibility of collecting complete evidence, we are able to predict within a very small limit of error, the number of voluntary deaths for each ensuing period: supposing, of course, that the social circumstances do not undergo any marked change."‡ By "change in social circumstances" we mean widespread financial disaster, speculative frenzies, waves of gloomy or highly emotional religion, fierce political turmoil, war, famine, and other disturbing conditions. Buckle maintains that suicide is "merely the product of the general condition of society" (*Ibid.*). The regularity of the increase of suicide can only be explained as "an effect of that universal and complex influence to which we give the name of civilization."§

Lecky says that suicide is "peculiarly characteristic of those nations which rank highest in intellectual development and in general civilization. In one or two countries strong religious feeling has counteracted this tendency: but the comparison of town and country, of different countries, of different provinces of the

---

* Read before the American Philosophical Society, October 7, 1910.
† *Suicide*, by Henry Morselli.
‡ *Civilization in England*, by Henry Thomas Buckle.
§ Morselli, *Ibid.*

418

same country, and of different periods of history, prove conclusively its reality."*

In all civilized countries suicide increases and at a rate beyond the rate of increase of population.

It seems certain that the numerous common motives of suicide are born of civilization, that suicide results from civilization, is one of the shadows cast by the chariot of Progress, and is a social symptom as truly as insanity, epilepsy, dipsomania, and sexual perversion.

Statistical tables do not give the real number of suicides. There are always more than are reported. All of our conclusions are founded upon underestimates. Many cases reported as death from accident should be tabulated as death by suicide. Buckle says: "Even the best evidence respecting suicide must always be very imperfect," and self-murder is very "obscure in regard to proof" (*Ibid.*). Suicide is usually done in secret. Dramatic public suicides sometimes occur, but are rare. When a dead body has been found it is often impossible to determine whether the death was suicidal or resulted from murder or accident. We are apt to assume that hanging must be suicidal, and yet accidental hanging has occurred, and homicidal hanging is not unknown, as in the case of Gouffe in France, and the Vienna case of a tailor who hung his five children.†

It is usually impossible to determine if a person found drowned died by accident or design. A coroner's jury is apt to practice what Lecky calls "charitable perjury," and to find in such a case that the death was accidental if murder can be ruled out.

In the Ninth Annual Report of the United States Census the area where registration is accurate shows that in 1908, 5848 died by drowning and only 1171 (20 per cent) of these are reported as suicides. These figures refer to only about half of our population. Some suicides are subtly planned, so as to mislead and deceive investigators.

This is commonly the case when death is sought in order that

* *History of European Morals.*
† Draper's *Legal Medicine.*

a life insurance shall be paid to the beneficiary. Actions at law are common in such cases.* Some of those cases have been most puzzling, strange, and obscure, and some of them highly dramatic.

When a man of wealth, prominent position, or high social standing commits suicide he is apt to try to make the death appear accidental. Sometimes he plans so that it may be thought that murder has been done. Such men, if sane, would avoid posthumous condemnation, fear a blot on the family name, and shrink from disgracing the surviving relatives. The attitude of the church and of public opinion toward suicide usually causes the surviving relatives of the victim of self-slaughter to shield themselves from supposed vicarious disgrace by perverting or concealing facts. If an impossible woman drives her husband to suicide she naturally tries to hide from the world the fact that he killed himself to get away from her. It is certain that many deaths recorded as deaths from accident are really deaths from suicide and that the figures of suicide given in tables are far below the figures which really belong there.

In the figures we are about to quote we use the Ninth Annual Report of the Bureau of the Census of the United States.

The figures are taken from "the registration area," an area in which there are satisfactory systems of registration. This area includes "seventeen states, the District of Columbia, and seventy-four registration cities in states not yet possessing satisfactory systems of state registration. The aggregate estimated population represented is 45,028,767, which is 51.8 per cent of the total estimated population of the country."

In reaching totals for the entire continental United States we are justified in doubling many of our figures.

In the registration area in 1908 there were 691,574 deaths and 8332 of these were known suicides. In other words, 1.2 per cent of all deaths were due to suicide. This is 18.5 per 100,000 of population, as against 6.7 homicidal, and 91.2 accidental. In 1907 there were 6745 suicides (16.2 per 100,000 of population).

* Tidy's *Legal Medicine. Stratagems and Conspiracies to Defraud Life Insurance Companies*, by John B. Lewis, M. D., and Charles C. Brombaugh, A. M., M. D.

In 1904 there were 4912 suicides (14.8 per 100,000 of population). So we see that in four years suicide increased from 14.8 to 18.5 per 100,000 of population.

In 1908, in the registration area, there were 2058 more deaths from suicide than from diabetes; 2755 more than from scarlet fever; 3721 more than from measles; 7223 more than from malaria; 5900 more than from syphilis; 5945 more than from paresis; 5061 more than from puerperal sepsis; 334 more than from smallpox, rabies, exophthalmic goiter, Addison's disease, leukemia, tetanus, hernia, locomotor ataxia, pericarditis, scurvy, gonorrhea, pellagra, and malignant pustule combined. There were nearly one-fifth as many deaths from suicide as from Bright's disease, just about one-fourth as many as from cancer, and over one-tenth as many as from all forms of tuberculosis. The deaths from suicide exactly equalled in number the deaths from appendicitis, alcoholism, ovarian tumor, carbuncle, actinomycosis, and glanders combined.

Even these figures indicate the appalling incidence of suicide and its ominous increase and these figures are all underestimates and must be practically doubled to express the entire continental United States.

SUICIDE IN URBAN AND RURAL COMMUNITIES

Our cities grow more rapidly than the country. There is a strong drift of population toward the cities. In cities material progress touches its highest level, and poverty its lowest depths. In them are slums, reeking tenements, stunted children, criminals, pretenders, impostors, hypocrites, new women, idiots, monsters, tramps, misers, plutocrats, lunatics, epileptics, hordes with social aspirations, degenerates, drunkards, armies of the lost, and paupers. In cities suicide is far more common than in rural communities. All writers agree upon this. Suicide is more common in country communities near cities than in country communities far away from great centers of population.

I do not pretend to affirm that the tendency to suicide bears a *direct* ratio to the *size* of a city. It does not. Much of the influence depends on the mental and moral atmosphere of the city. In France "the frequency of suicide in relation to population is chiefly governed by the degree of proximity to Paris. The same is true of the capitals of the other European countries, each one of which rays out an influence in favor of suicide which circles in ever-widening waves until its force is ultimately spent. It would seem, therefore, that the capital cities act as great moral pest-centers, whose evil influence extends to the remotest confines of their respective lands, and is most felt the nearer they are approached from these confines."*

In the registration area of the United States in 1908 the rate of suicide in rural districts was 14.4, and in urban communities 21.1 per 100,000 of population. In 1904 it was for rural communities 10.1 and for urban communities 16.7 per 100,000 of population.

St. Louis has a suicide rate of 31.8 per 100,000 of population; Chicago 22.8; Washington 20.8; Greater New York 23; Manhattan (a part of Greater New York) 34.7; Pittsburg 20.8; Boston 21.4; Baltimore 17.4; New Orleans 27.5; Cleveland 18.9, and Philadelphia 17.3. Philadelphia has the lowest suicide rate of all of these great cities. This fact is significant of things creditable to our city. The figures for Harrisburg are amazing for a small town, viz., 29.5. If the moral atmosphere of a city is an influential factor in the suicide rate, as has been asserted, Harrisburg should investigate and act. Perhaps the proximity of the Legislature has an effect.

Cities grow in population at a much greater rate than the country. There is a drift toward the cities and it is in the cities that suicide is most common per fixed figure of population and increases at the greatest rate.

This drift to the cities began long ago. Bishop Hugh Latimer, in the reign of Henry VIII, said: "Men have taken to whoring in towns instead of shooting in fields." The disasters springing from this drift are enough to modify the views of the most optimistic. In cities material progess is at its highest level. Material progress is supposed to be the great good. All schools teach it.

---

* *Suicide*, by James J. O'Dea, M. D.

All legislation favors it. At its base is the doctrine of discontent, for one entirely contented does not progress. Force rules the world still and resignation under calamity is not a virtue which would aid one in securing an important job at the hands of a captain of industry. And with material progress comes inevitably an increase of suicide and of insanity, elements thought to be full of menace to the future of the race. It seems a law of nature that the race must pay a penalty for development, and while some develop others must degenerate, hence insanity and suicide must increase as civilization and material progress advance.

In cities civilization is most highly developed, in them are the greatest wealth and the deepest poverty, the most active progress, and the blackest misery, and in them the keen-edged strife of competition is ever keenest and fiercest.

In them sudden depressions of business throw multitudes out of employment and make them want for the bare necessities of life. As Lecky says, "Civilization makes many of what once were superfluities, necessaries of life, so that their loss inflicts a pang long after their possession has ceased to be a pleasure."*

Multitudes pour into the cities not only from the country, but from foreign lands. They come to seek for the remedy of Cortez. Cortez told the natives in Mexico, "I have a malady of the heart and gold helpeth it." The search for gold as the only object of desire is pure narrow selfishness free from a trace of altruism, it generates suspicion, falseness, and insanity, is truly antisocial, and, as Maudsley says, tends to breed degeneracy of some sort either in that generation or the next.

We all know how commonly children of narrow-minded, suspicious, ignorant, successful money makers are the victims of degeneracy. Idiocy, sexual perversion, eccentricity, vice, crime, absence of moral sense, epilepsy, and insanity are common in such a stock. So long as it is taught and believed that the ledger is the gospel, the check book the divine command, and the dollar mark the luring curve of flawless beauty, these things will be true. The fathers "eat sour grapes" and the "children's teeth are

* *History of European Morals.*

set on edge," and the fathers are often our wealthiest and most influential citizens.

The town dweller is prone to become a restless, anxious, suspicious, self-conscious egoist, one who struggles for existence and is wearied by the strain of competition, his life and often his heredity make him neurotic, unstable, hypochondriacal, brooding, and self-conscious. He often feels upon him a sense of injustice, wrong and outrage. He writhes under the stings of restrained desires and the yoke of a life-long hypocrisy. His nervous system is unstable, his stomach and liver incompetent, his kidneys irritated.

Anxiety and harassment injure body and mind. His mind is over-stimulated and his body is over-driven. He is apt to spur himself to efforts beyond his powers, is cast down by numerous disappointments, tortured by countless irritations, depressed by failures, and usually disenchanted by success. He feels the sting of envy and the coldness of ingratitude, humiliation, and neglect, and responsibility sits heavily upon him. He may go to alcohol for relief and then the curse is truly on him. Restlessness is almost inevitable, ennui results from restlessness, people seek society to gratify vanity and banish ennui and always fail to find the happiness they seek. Is it any wonder that philosophies like those of Schopenhauer and his follower Hartmann arise, crude and indistinct in most minds, clear and definite in some. Schopenhauer believed that no one is or can be happy, and that all the things for which men labor even when obtained are only the worthless possessions of the moment.

Multitudes of town-dwellers live in reeking tenements set in sunless alleys, tenements dark, damp and ill ventilated, without privacy and with no sense of home, where murder, insanity, prostitution, crime, shameless vice, anarchy and ferocity are bred and cultured as truly as is tuberculosis. There seems to be no help for such people. Certain it is that they "find no ease" "in our pale Christ and tangled trinities." They constitute a poison produced by civilization and they threaten to destroy the civilization that creates them.

Country people as a class live better, are healthier and are more content than town-dwellers. They are less emotional, less ambitious, more stolid, less distrustful, less self-conscious, and possessed of more stable and less excitable nervous systems. They are satisfied with less and seldom eat out their hearts because they have not more. They are free from a multitude of temptations, excitements, exertions and desires, which beset, dominate, and often torture the town-dweller. The very ambitious and neurotic in the country are apt to go to the cities. Towns breed in their inhabitants a special neurotic temperament which might well be called the *town temperament* and which specially tends to suicide. Mr. Lecky, in speaking of civilization says: "It also, by softening the character, renders it peculiarly sensitive to pain, and it brings with it a long train of antipathies, passions, and diseased imaginations, which rarely or never cross the thoughts or torture the nerves of the simple peasant. The advance of religious scepticism and the realization of religious discipline have weakened and sometimes destroyed the horror of suicide; and the habits of self-assertion, the eager and restless ambitions which political liberty, intellectual activity, and manufacturing enterprise, all in their different ways, conspire to foster, while they are the very principles and conditions of the progress of our age, render the virtue of content in all its forms extremely rare, and are peculiarly unpropitious to the formation of that spirit of humble and submissive resignation which alone can mitigate the agony of hopeless suffering."*

That suicide should be most common in cities is only what we should expect. That it should increase faster in cities than in the country is only what is occurring in all conditions expressive of degeneracy or ill adaptation to the necessities of environment. Country life today is more nearly natural than city life. City life is distinctly unnatural and unnatural life deforms some to fit its behests and maims or kills all who cannot or will not adjust themselves to it.

Heredity, syphilis, alcoholism, and worry are the great creators

* *History of European Morals.*

of degeneracy and suicide is one of the ways by which civilization wipes out voluntary or involuntary obstructionists to her unhappy plan. By destroying them she often prevents the procreation of a degenerate stock and at least frees the world of one who is a clog and a cost and may at any time become a positive danger.

SEX

In Europe and the United States suicide is certainly more common among men than among women. Morselli estimates the proportion as one woman to three or four men, "as in crime it is also one to four or five."* In Spain female suicide is particularly high. Morselli attributes this to the fierce passions of the Spanish women, but this view seems to lose in probability when we note that female suicide is also extremely common in Hungary and in Scotland. Perhaps, however, these last two citations do not overthrow the opinion of the Milan authority, because some parts of Scotland have the highest level of illegitimate births in the world and illegitimate births may be regarded as the straws which show which way the sexual wind blows. In India suicide is more common in women than in men, but there are special reasons for this and in any case India cannot be used in such a statistical study to set off European and American conclusions. In India women are extremely ignorant and degraded, they obtain slight consideration and are of the lowest social rank and further, and most particularly, suicide among widows is extremely common, as a survival of the old custom of suttee.

In 1908, in the registration area in the United States, there occurred 6429 male suicides and 1903 female suicides, and in that area female population exceeds male population.

The great preponderance of suicide among men seems strange in light of woman's weak and unstable nervous system as compared to man. Theoretically it would seem that suicide should be more common in women than in men. Woman is more emotional, more unstable, more cowardly, more suspicious, narrower, more sensitive than man and she has less self-control. In other

* *Suicide*, by Henry Morselli.

words, woman's nature is such that she will go insane or commit suicide from slighter causes than a man. But she is not the victim of so many or of such powerful causes. Her nervous system will not stand the blows a man's gets, but the blows are neither so frequent nor so violent. The intrinsic causes are most powerful in women, the extrinsic causes in man. Then man is much more prone to alcoholism, a powerful cause, and to sexual excess, a baleful influence. Man is the bread winner, he has to struggle for existence, to fight the battles, to bear the chief strain, to carry the burden of financial anxiety. He is more prone to self-analysis, to misanthropy, to that savage indignation which cursed the life of Swift. Again, woman has, to a much higher degree than man, capacity for self-sacrifice and resignation, that is, she has in everything but in matters involving the affections. Disappointment is not so violent and disastrous to woman as to man.

If we regard all suicide as cowardice, lack of courage must be looked upon as a common cause, and women (speaking generally) have less courage than men. That fear is a more potent cause of suicide among girls than among boys is shown by figures quoted by Havelock Ellis.* In Prussia 19 per cent of the boys who commit suicide do it through fear of punishment, but 49 per cent of the girls do it for this reason. But many people who fear something or would avoid something and who think of suicide as a means of release from intolerable conditions are afraid of the pain of the act or afraid of death, and they do not commit self-slaughter *because* they are cowards. So we see that fear may cause suicide and cowardice may save from it and the lack of courage of the sex prevents many female suicides.

Again, women are more religious than men and more impressed by the condemnatory attitude of the church, an attitude not drawn from the Bible, for nowhere does that book specifically forbid suicide as does the Koran. Women are more conventional than men, public opinion is violently adverse to suicide, and public opinion influences women more than men. What saves woman from a multitude of causes is the passive part she plays, a fortu-

* *Man and Woman.*

nate rôle when we consider her weaknesses and predispositions. Of late there has arisen a disposition to bring women into the forum to combat with men while the home takes care of itself. Those possessed of this disposition repudiate anatomy, spurn physiology, and disregard religion, history, and common sense. Woman is not competent in man's work, she is inefficient, she loses at least twice as much time from sickness and she breaks down under sudden strains of overwork or difficulty. When she works as a man she must put aside not only many charms and prejudices, but womanly things in general, and among the things she must put aside are healthy babies, the home, and the rearing of children, and God Almighty constructed her bodily to bear children and mentally to rear them. Such women may have children, but the job is usually very ill done. She cannot do properly what she was built to do. Seguin says: "As soon as women assumed the anxieties pertaining to both sexes they gave birth to children whose like had hardly been met with thirty years ago; insane before their brain could have been deranged from their own exertions; insane, likely by a reflex action of the nervous exhaustion of their mother." If woman invades man's callings she will pay a a dreadful penalty in insanity, suicide, and in the delivery of her progeny, and she will wreck the chief hope of civilization, the clean, decent, happy home. If she works as a man she will be treated as a man and will be subjected as is a man to a multitude of irritations, depressions, and worries from which she is now free. A woman's real profession is matrimony and she often makes a bad failure even in her natural profession. To make a success of this will require all her ability and energy, tact, and self-sacrifice. She had best leave man's affairs to man. The blatant and militant suffragette (a gynaegoge Doctor Ireland calls her) is well along on the highway of degeneration.

Maudsley says, "In proportion as women invade those departments of work which men have hitherto appropriated they will expose themselves more and more to those extrinsic causes of derangement, and it is a grave question whether they will not find themselves overpowered by the joint action of the weight

from without and the weakness within." This applies strongly
to intellectual occupations. Herbert Spencer said mental powers
highly developed "in a woman are in some measure abnormal,
and involve a physiologic cost which her feminine organization
will not bear without injury more or less profound."

In the cities the rate of female suicide approaches toward the
rate of male suicide, or else, the two rates approach each other.*

It is impossible to get figures as to the actual growth of suicide
among women who work as compared with those who do not
work. We do know that out of 100 laundresses that die 0.7 per
cent die of suicide (and laundering is essentially a female occupation); of female telegraphers that die 5.6 per cent die of suicide;
of stenographers, 3.6 per cent; and of cigarmakers, 4.4 per cent.
But the rate even among cigarmakers, high as it is, is less than
among male cigarmarkers (6.1 per cent). In statistics regarding
suicide among females in different occupations the figures are
often so small as to give no reliable averages. We will learn
statistically about this matter when we can study what happens
to numbers of female lawyers, doctors, dog-catchers, barkeepers,
preachers, brokers, manufacturers, conductors, barbers, politicians, liquor dealers, shoemakers, policemen, laborers, firemen,
sailors, and soldiers. If women have their way there must be
female soldiers. Those who would enjoy all the privileges of
citizenship must be prepared to serve the state at need.

Female suicide is most common at a menstrual period, as are
acts of criminal violence and attacks of insanity. This has been
commented on by Esquinol, Moreau of Tours, Krugelstein, and
others. Menstruation has a marked psychic effect on most women.
During the period they are usually capricious, depressed, ill-
tempered, jealous, and emotional. Self-control is at the lowest
level and "outbursts of self-confession" are liable to occur.† A
woman psychically affected by menstruation is ill-fitted for any
work requiring effort, skill, concentration, judgment, or courtesy
to the public.

* *Suicide*, by James J. O'Dea, M. D.
† Havelock Ellis, *Man and Woman.*

"It seems very probable that the superstitions regarding the evil influences exercised by women at their periods on the food, etc., they prepare may be supported by an actual decreased success in such operations at this time, due merely to a physiologic decrease in energy and skill."*

There is one age period in which female suicides outnumber male suicides, that is from fifteen to nineteen. In this period the census for 1908 shows that 162 males and 186 females killed themselves. From twenty to twenty-four there were 531 men and 271 women. From ten to fourteen years of age there were 15 boys and 8 girls who killed themselves. The large rate of female suicide from fifteen to nineteen years is due to the onset of menstruation, to sexual desires, excitements, or repression, and to fear of the consequences of illicit sexual relations. Many suicides result from pregnancy or from bringing illegitimate offspring into the world.

Whereas statistics show that fewer women than men kill themselves, statistics do not show and cannot show how many people want to kill themselves but cannot get up the courage, and how many try, but fail.

Many more women than men shrink from the act because of cowardice. Many more women than men fail to successfully carry out the act. Some fail intentionally, the whole procedure being a well-acted drama to secure sympathy, to punish some one, or to gain notoriety. Many fail because of mere bungling incompetence, doing even this thing partly and incompletely, as they do so many other things inefficiently. To them an old maxim does not apply, viz., "If you want a thing well done do it yourself."

Sex influences the method of suicide. Woman, as compared to man, has a strong predilection for drowning, and a considerable leaning to poison. She does not care particularly for hanging. She seldom uses firearms. Even when she wants to die she seems afraid of firearms and she seldom understands how to use them. A man prefers hanging or the use of firearms. Women almost

* Clouston, *Mental Diseases.*

never jump in front of trains, men often do. Women are more apt than men to jump from heights. If a woman takes poison she is not nearly so careful as is a man to select a painless one. "Woman manifests everywhere the characteristic of her psychical individuality by the preeminence she holds in deaths by drowning. The greatest difference between the two sexes is always in the use of firearms, because in every country woman has little tendency to make use of violent means, and thus it is that hanging also is chosen by her much less often than by men. Domestic habits alone account for the somewhat high average of suicides by voluntary falls and poisoning."*

Occupation

Years ago Doctor Hall said that the tendency to suicide is greater among those who work indoors. He cited as open-air trades, masons, carpenters, and butchers, and showed that there is much less suicide among them than among tailors, shoemakers, and bakers. In his figures the suicide relation of the former class to the latter is as 1 to 5.6 per cent.†

In this country the outdoor occupations named by Doctor Hall show for the most part a lower suicide rate than the selected indoor occupations, but it is nothing like the proportion of 1 to 5.6. We find from the last United States Census that of the death rate among bakers, 4 per cent was from suicide; among tailors, 4.2 per cent; but shoemakers showed 2.3 per cent. The figures for masons are 2.4 per cent, carpenters 3.2 per cent, and butchers 3.4 per cent. We may conclude that outdoor workers as a class are less liable to suicide than indoor workers.

Millers show a rate of 0.9 per cent, miners of 1.6, sailors (merchant service) 1.9, and steam railroad men 1.7, blacksmiths 2.8, laborers 2.4, farmers 2.1, and truckmen 2.9, cabinetmakers show a rate of 4.3, domestic servants 4.2, male teachers 5, apothecaries 5, confectioners 4, and jewelers 4.9. Some of the

* *Suicide*, by Henry Morselli.
† *Suicide*, by James J. O'Dea, M. D.

figures are contradictory, as the low rate among shoemakers. But many circumstances enter into particular cases and the most we can say is that outdoor work is more healthy than indoor work.

In the United States records the highest suicide rate is found among men of the army, navy, and marine corps. Seven and two-tenths per cent of all deaths are due to suicide, a truly dreadful showing. Sailors, other than naval men, show a rate of only 1.9 per cent, about one-fourth of the naval rate. The determination of the cause of this condition rests with the government authorities. It cannot all be due to homesickness, as merchant sailors go as far and stay as long. It is not hardship, the men are well fed and splendidly cared for. It may be something in the discipline, but surely rigid discipline is imperatively necessary. Whatever the cause may be it should be found, and, if possible, eliminated.

Next to soldiers and United States sailors the highest suicide rate is among cigarmakers (6.1 per cent), apothecaries, commercial travelers, servants, liquor dealers and barkeepers, cloakmakers, jewelers, brewers and distillers, teachers, artists, architects, bankers and brokers, actors, cabinetmakers, collectors, barbers, bakers, confectioners, leather workers, and tailors.

The lowest suicide rate is among clergymen and millers, 1.9 per cent. Next to clergymen come leather makers, stonecutters, miners, steam railroad men, physicians and surgeons (2 per cent), laborers (2.4 per cent), compositors and printers (2.9 per cent), hatmakers (2.1 per cent), and iron workers (2.9 per cent).

One might speculate for an indefinite time on these curious figures without reaching any certain explanation. We might say that the low rate among clergymen is due to religious conviction, but I have known millers who swore freely and had no symptoms of religion, and yet millers have the same low rate as the clergy. We wonder why leather makers have one of the lowest rates and leather workers one of the highest. How is it that miners, of whose pitiable condition we hear much, resort so seldom to suicide? Why driving a hack, cutting stone, or practicing medicine seem

to free a man from many impulsions to suicide. We can guess
why the rate is high among bankers and brokers, artists, actors,
apothecaries, barkeepers, commercial travelers, and teachers. The
high rate among lawyers (3.5 per cent) admits of several inter-
pretations, one of which is remorse. We are at a loss to explain
the high rate among barbers, collectors, editors, and auctioneers.

It is not specified that any undertaker killed himself. We
are not to judge from this that undertaking is a light-hearted
business, which gives immunity to suicide (although Dickens
thought them merry souls when off duty).

Further, sextons show a high rate. So probably undertakers
are hidden under the general heading of "other callings." Naturally the occupation sometimes influences the method chosen.
For instance, one who has access to poison, is apt to take poison.
O'Dea says: "A tinsmith committed suicide by swallowing muri-
atic acid, a substance in common use in his trade. A picture-
frame maker ended his days by a dose of sulphuric acid, a fluid
in frequent use in his particular craft." O'Dea then gives two
striking examples: "One was the suicide of a blaster who blew
himself to atoms with the gunpowder he was to have used for
blasting rock. The other was that of a young coal worker, Prussian
born, who, during mid-day recess, when his companion workmen
were dining, plunged into a seething furnace, and perished after
a moment of what must have been dreadful agony."

AGE

Suicide occurs at all ages. The United States Census for
1908 reports 8322 suicides in the registration area (6429 males
and 1903 females). One was over ninety-five years, 7 were from
ninety to ninety-five years, 21 were from eighty-five to ninety years,
62 were from eighty to eighty-five years, 925 were from thirty-five
to forty years. In all periods except from fifteen to twenty
male suicides greatly outnumber female suicides. In this period
162 males and 186 females killed themselves. In this period
puberty begins. It comes on more suddenly in the female than
in the male, hence is more dangerous to mental stability. In this

28

period females often suffer from suppressed natural desires and some are the victims of dissipation, but most female suicides in this period are connected with the fear of pregnancy or the results of pregnancy.

Accurate conclusions as to the influence of age upon the suicidal tendency can only be reached by comparing the number of suicides at a given age with the number of people of that age living. I have no new figures thus derived and must rely on the accepted figures of authorities.

Suicide is most frequent among men of from forty to fifty years of age. Among women it is most frequent from fifteen to twenty-five years. In women after twenty-five the suicide rate decreases except for a rise during the climacteric. In men the rate regularly increases after twenty-five. Child suicide is markedly increasing, though not as rapidly as adult suicide. The United States census shows that in 1908 there were reported 15 male and 8 female suicides between the ages of ten and fifteen. I do not know what relation these figures bear to the number of people of those ages living. Proval asserts the increase of suicide in youth. He reports that in 1880 there were 55 suicides under sixteen years of age, whereas in 1892 there were 87.* Child suicide often results from very inadequate motives. It may be due to insanity and in children insanity is frequently unrecognized. It may be due to fear of punishment, to anger, or to a sense of injustice, but it is often due to a sudden uncontrollable impulse. Injustice is apt to drive a child into melancholy brooding and self-consciousness, and a child in this condition may commit suicide because of self-pity or in order to make others sorry. How love of self often leads a boy to act when he has been punished is shown by Mark Twain in his story of *Tom Sawyer*. Tom grew sulky because he had been punished. He "exalted his woes." Tom "pictured himself as lying sick unto death and his aunt bending over him beseeching one little forgiving word." He seemed to see "himself brought home from the river, dead, with his curls all wet and his sore heart at rest. How she would throw herself upon him,

* *Le Crime et le Suicide.*

and how her tears would fall like rain." Twain says it was a luxury to Tom to *pet* his sorrow that he wished "he could only be drowned, all at once and unconsciously, without undergoing the uncomfortable routine devised by nature." Tom, being an entirely normal boy, did not drown himself, but went home to bed. An abnormal boy might have committed suicide. Children, especially, as puberty approaches, are prone to day-dreams and musings which may be associated with mental depression, and melancholy may result from a cross word, a threat, an old-fashioned sermon, and many other things. The sorrows and griefs of childhood are very real and intense. Fortunately they are usually soon forgotten, were it otherwise child suicide would be far commoner than it is. The normal condition of a normal child is happiness. Habitual depression in a child is morbid and ominous. Children have committed suicide in order to go to the heaven which had been pictured to them in such an alluring way that they naturally wanted to get there as soon as possible. Harriet Martineau when a child tried to kill herself from this motive. Gloomy religious teaching is a cause of child suicide. It familiarizes him with the thought of death, frightens him with the perils of life, and fills him with morbid ideas. No child should think of death at all and no child should ever be permitted to hear an expounder who holds out very little hope of salvation to those who move about in this totally depraved world. A false educational system is generally believed to be the great cause of child suicide. Hall cites as supposed school influences "overpleasures, anxieties, and mental strain," but is doubtful as to the school's responsibility for suicide.* Certain it is that examinations are a serious strain. At least three-fourths of children lose weight during examinations.† Certain it is that a proper education might save many from crime, insanity and suicide in later life, by stimulating self-control, awakening interest in many things, strengthening reason and judgment, memory and observation; founding proper and attainable ideals, and punishing with almost old time severity lapses from decency, truth, and honor. *Just* punishment can save many from

* *Adolescence,* by G. Stanley Hall.   † Hall, *Ibid.*

insanity, crime, suicide, and futile lives. Unjust punishment is
an infamy and a danger. In our schools we try to strengthen the
memory alone. We fill a child's mind with isolated and unrelated
facts. We educate all up to the level of a few and fill the world
with unhappy failures, who are crushed because they must labor
to live. They might have been contented working men instead
of idle grumblers, grievances, obstructionists, or destructionists,
and most of them would have been had they been given the education they needed. The practical destruction of the apprentice
system is a deplorable thing.

Child suicide is most common in cities, and in precocious
children. Precocity is more often a sign of degeneration than of
strength. Precocious children attain a high level soon, but are
eventually passed and left far behind in most cases by the common
place plodders. Spoiled children are particularly apt to commit
suicide. A spoiled child is the embodiment of pure selfishness.
He has no conception of sympathy, generosity, fair-dealing, truth,
bravery, or decency. He seeks only for his own gratification and
if balked in attaining it he either broods in ugly sulkiness or rages
in furious anger. A spoiled child represents the aggregate of the
stupidities, weaknesses, and selfish tendencies of the parents. All
his appetites and bad tendencies riot unchecked. He is a curse
to himself and others, and yet the parents guard and cultivate all
his evil instincts. Such parents are enemies to society and to the
child they ruin.

The real amount of child suicide is uncertain. Parents usually
make every effort to conceal the facts because they fear public
censure. These parental efforts are probably often successful.

During the period of adolescence (from fifteen to twenty-five)
there is a great increase of suicide and in this period female suicide
is most common. At one time or another during adolescence most
people think about death and suicide with more or less yearning.
In this period hereditary weaknesses, the results of a stupid system of education and the consequences of parental shortcomings,
are apt to crop out. In this period love, jealousy, and ambition
come into existence, and envy becomes more insistent and of

darker hue. Egotism and vanity are prominent in the character and self-love is easily touched and hurt. Sexual ideas fill the mind, and perhaps sexual acts occupy some of the time. Imitation is a common tendency (hence the influence of published accounts of suicide or of the suicide of a relative or friend). Sombre religious teaching makes many brood on death. Every great revival entails an increase of suicide and insanity. Cowardly natures shrink from the worldly contests which they are driven to make. The work and worry of life have begun and are probably most distasteful. Large desires are confronted by colossal impediments. Many lose their illusions on finding life is not as they dreamt it would be. In a number dissipation and troubles springing from dissipation play a part. The necessity of restraining natural desires puts a burden on the mind and necessitates the development to a high degree of hypocrisy. The nature narrows. The generous impulses contract. The stream of life no longer holds the image of the stars. Only the strength and natural hope of youth keeps suicide from being far more common.

During maturity suicide is most common in men. It is at this period that exciting causes are most numerous, the effects of youthful excesses are telling, resisting power is wearing out, life tire is gathering strength, and hereditary tendencies fight their way to control. In this period failures in business, in projects, in ambitions are most common and despair is often the dark heritage of youthful hope.

In the aged suicide is frequent and, as is noted in children, often results from trivial motives. The aged are apt to be selfish, egotistical, vain, pessimistic, and extremely sensitive. Even a man of over ninety-five (as our figures show), may not be willing to wait for the inevitable to arrive naturally.

RELATION TO INSANITY

Are all suicides insane? It is a popular belief that they are, but it is an error. Most of them are insane. Suicide is a symptom of some form of insanity, a possibility in many. Sometimes it is the first symptom noted. Many suicides are on the border line, but some are undoubtedly sane. A man who kills himself may make a mistake, but a mistake does not prove insanity. Sometimes those who regard a mistake as insanity fail in particular instances to prove that there was a mistake. That is often a matter of opinion. The victim of a loathsome incurable disease does not of necessity make a mistake in committing suicide. One damned to a life of racking pain obtains ease by self-slaughter. A gentleman on the brink of disgrace, a trusted official facing discovery and the penitentiary, may well argue that the act is wise. Suicide may be from high motives as when Sforza committed suicide because he feared torture might make him betray his companions. Sidney Carton in Dickens's *Tale of Two Cities* committed suicide when he went to the guillotine to save Evrémonde for the girl he loved. A soldier who blows up a mine which will destroy him with the others, a sailor who to save a ship, closes a compartment and drowns within it, does the same. Perhaps, however, a distinction should be made between suicide for an altruistic and suicide from a selfish motive. But some suicides are certainly sane. Some men go through years of life fearing exposure or disgrace and ready with a plan of suicide should exposure come. At the present time some such men are living in every great city. Exposure may never come, for many have weathered such storms, or death from another cause may end the drama. In either case the world knows nothing of the thoughts of suicide. The man whom we sit next to at a banquet, who is the model of propriety and self-restraint, and who entertains us with jest and story, may have at home a revolver ready loaded for ghastly work or in his pocket a bottle of poison, the last resource in the expected emergency. Such a man is not insane.

When the idea of suicide is new to the sane mind it causes perturbation and horror. When it has been long lodged it may cease to irritate, like an encapsulated bullet. The man with a *town-dweller's* temperament often has a vague suicidal tendency hidden in the depths of his mind, and it always comes into the cognizance of consciousness in times of humiliation, trouble, and worry.

Many people on the borderline of insanity are in danger of suicide. In some forms of lunacy suicide becomes a desperate craving.

Because people often talk about suicide is not a sign they are apt to commit it. Neither is it a sign, as some assert, that they will not commit it. Some neurotic people who never intend to try it babble about it constantly. But some who talk of it perhaps for years, suddenly do it. Some who never mention it surprise all their friends by doing it. A carefully prepared dramatic suicide is apt to be an insane act. At least it is instigated by a morbid vanity which loves notoriety. In this age of the world a philosophic suicide, done without mental depression, without the idea of escaping trouble, pain or disgrace, seldom occurs. This sort of suicide was common among Grecian sages and Roman thinkers. They killed themselves calmly when simply done with life. Perhaps now and then, by a sort of atavistic reversion, such a suicide happens today.

I wish that time permitted me to consider some of the following points:

The greater frequency of suicide in spring and summer. The large number of cases during and after sudden hot spells. The popularity of Monday as a suicide day, and of the early morning hours as a suicide time. The effect of race and the enormous excess of suicide among pure and mixed Teutonic races. The effect of habitation. The effect of example as shown by the number of suicides that always follow the publication of the account of a horrible and dramatic one. (Such newspaper reports should not be published. The paper of today which lies upon my desk reports on its front page and at length three suicides.) Such suicides exhibit the effect of a sort of contagion. Suicide epidemics. Suicide facts. Suicide clubs. The motives for and methods of suicide. The prevention of suicidal tendency in the race and in individuals. But I cannot speak of these things. Were I to try this drowsy paper would swell into a somnolent book.

I would add two thoughts:

First: When civilization reaches a higher level in some dim future century, will we recognize that some suicides are reasonable, natural, and justifiable. Will we then have a suicide tribunal, as Sir Thomas More devised for his Utopia. In Utopia the priests and magistrates are to permit or actually direct those afflicted with incurable disease to commit suicide.

I do not advocate this any more than Doctor Osler really advocated chloroforming people over sixty years of age. I only wonder if it will be.

Second: Is not suicide perhaps an obscure part of the plan of evolution by which multitudes of weaklings are removed, weaklings who clog the wheels of progress and who procreate degenerate children. Suppose the 16,000 people who killed themselves last year in the United States had been kept alive. They would now be making trouble in many communities and numerous families, and either out-of-doors breeding degenerate descendants or kept unhappy in asylums at great cost.

Alcoholism and suicide destroy degenerate stocks, wipe out weaklings, and in the long run may be said to tend to the evolution of the race. If this be true, we may well cry with Tennyson:

> "Are God and Nature then at strife,
> That Nature lends such evil dreams,
> So careful of the type she seems,
> So careless of the single life."